Dangerous Australian Animals

By Struan K. Sutherland:

Family Guide to Dangerous Animals and Plants of Australia

Venomous Creatures of Australia

Australian Animal Toxins: the Creatures, their Toxins and Care of the Poisoned Patient

Take Care! Poisonous Australian Animals

Hydroponics for Everyone

A Venomous Life

Cautionary tales
with first aid and
management

DANGEROUS
Australian Animals

Struan K.
Sutherland
MD, DSc, FRCPA, FRACP
and
Guy Nolch
BSc (Hons)

First published in Australia in 2000 by
Hyland House Publishing Pty Ltd
50 Pin Oak Crescent
Flemington, Vic. 3031

National Library of Australia
Cataloguing-in-publication data:

Sutherland, S. K. 1936–.
Dangerous Australian animals.

Bibliography.
Includes index.
ISBN 1 86447 076 3

1. Dangerous animals – Australia.
2. Bites and stings. 3. First aid in
illness and injury. I. Nolch, Guy,
1967–. II. Title.

616.0252

Design by Rob Cowpe Design
Printed by Everbest Printing Co., China

Acknowledgments

It is a pleasure to record that requested
information or advice was, without
exception, never refused and always
willingly forwarded by clinicians,
research scientists, herpetologists, marine
biologists, photographers, etc., as well as
members of the general public. Whenever possible such assistance has been
duly recorded in the text. However, the
brevity of the acknowledgment often
does injustice to the considerable efforts
that many kind people have made to
provide information.

We appreciate the generosity and debt
owed to those listed below:
Lyn Abra, Dr Chris Acott, Dr Phil
Alderslade, Professor Paul Alewood,
Professor James Angus, Dr Brian Baldo,
Chris Banks, Belinda Bonham, Allen
Broad, Professor Kevin Broady,
Professor Joseph Burnett, Dr Inese
Busmanis, Professor Vic Callanan,
Rosemary Capper, Dr Amanda Caswell,
Dr Hal Cogger, Neville Coleman, Alan
Coulter, Dr Jeanette Covacevich,
Dr John Coventry, Professor Bart
Currie, Marjory Davey, Marc Dorse,
Vernon Draffin, Dr Alan Duncan,
Dr Carl Edmonds, Dr Robert Endean,
Dr Peter Fenner, Professor Malcolm
Fisher, Keith Gillett, Graeme Gow,
Dr Mike Gray, Professor John Harris,
Rodney Harris, Dr Robert Hartwick,
Professor Harold Heatwole, Dr Douglas
Howarth, Professor Merlin Howden,
Dr Bernie Hudson, Kathy Hutton,
Professor George Jelinek, Susie
Kennewell, Rudie Kuiter, Dr Richard
Lewis, Dr Col Limpus, Dr Paul Masci,
Professor Dietrich Mebs, Professor
Sherman Minton, Peter Mirtschin,
Marge Overs, Mary Papadopoulos,
Professor John Pearn, Dr Robert
Premier, Dr Robert Raven, Dr Jacquie
Rifkin, Dr Ron Southcott, Dr Bernie
Stone, Charles Tanner, Dr David
Theakston, Professor Tom Torda,
Professor Mike Tyler, Sony Varma,
Dr Ken Walker, Dr Bryan Walpole,
Professor David Warrell, John and
Robyn Weigel, Dr Julian White, Dr Ian
Whyte, Professor John Williamson,
Carolyn Wiltshire, Eric Worrell.

Special mention should be made of
the help and support received from
Professor James Tibballs and our friends
at the Australian Venom Research Unit:
Drs Ken Winkel, Gabrielle Hawdon,
Anna Young and Ms Vanessa Tresidder.

Our final thanks are to Kathryn Ryan
for her early encouragement, and to
Michael Schoo, Nerissa Greenfield,
Kylie Matthews and Rob Cowpe for
producing what we hope will be a useful and well-received product.

Photo Credits

The authors and publisher wish
to thank the following people
and organisations for permission
to reproduce their photographs
in this book:

Chris Banks
Platypus and spur, page 181

P. Brown & R. Dunn
Dugite, page 78

CSIRO Entomology
Bull ant, page 130
Dust mites, page 143
Fleas, page 139
March fly, page 146
Mite, page 151

**Michael Cufer, Ocean Earth
Images**
Fortescue, page 28
Sea snake, page 43

Neville Coleman
Bluebottle, page 4
Scorpion fish, page 29
Sea urchin, page 46
Sponge, page 51
Surgeon fish, page 30
Turtle, page 65

Bruce Cowell
Cane toad, page 163
Leech, page 175

**Kevin Deacon, Ocean Earth
Images**
Bearded ghoul, page 27
Catfish, page 21
Crocodile, page 166
Crown of thorns, page 34
Dingo, page 170
Gurnard perch, page 28
Old wife, page 29
Port Jackson shark, page 41
Sea blubber, page 17
Shark, page 48

Vern Draffin
Australian native wasp, page 154
Bee, page 140
Bird-eating spider, page 126
Blue-ringed octopus, page 39
Brown house spider, page 123
Centipede, page 136
Leaf-curling spider, page 128
Mulga snake, page 80
Orb weaving spider, page 128
Red-back spider, page 114
Scorpion, page 116
Stonefish, page 25
Sydney funnel-web spider, pages
   118, 119
Taipan, page 94
Tree-dwelling funnel-web spider,
   page 121

Graeme Gow
Stephen's banded snake, page 107

Keith Gillett
Box jellyfish, page 6
Butterfly cod, page 19

Chiropsalmus, page 10
Cone shell, page 31
Puffer fish, page 60

Dr Robert Hartwick
Flathead, page 27
Irukandji, page 13

John C. Wombey
Frog, page 172

**Warren Jones, Ocean Earth
Images**
Stingray, page 23

**Ken Kates, Ocean Earth
Images**
Glaucus feeding on jellyfish, page
   37

Susie Kennewell
Mouse spider, page 111

Dr John Knight
Scombroid poisoning, page 62

Rudi Kuiter
Goblin fish, page 28

Raymond Mascord
Huntsman spider, page 127
White-tailed spider, page 124

Peter Mirtschin
Bandy-bandy or ringed snake,
   page 102
Broad-headed snake, page 104
Brown tree snake, page 105
Collett's snake, page 70
Common brown snake, page 72
Death adder, page 76

Pale-headed snake, page 107
Red-bellied black snake, page 82
Rough-scaled snake, page 85
Small-eyed snake, page 87
Yellow-faced whip snake, page
   108

Dr D. Moorhouse
Paralysis tick, page 109

Queensland Museum
Cassowary, page 179
Crabs, page 55

Queensland Surf Rescue
Jimble, page 15

Dr Robert Raven
Black window spider, page 123

Dr Ron Southcott
Caterpillar, page 133
Fiddleback spider, page 126

P. Spradbury
European wasp, page 156

Struan K. Sutherland
Bullrout, page 160
Jumping spider, page 127
Whiplash rove beetle, page 158
Wolf spider, page 129

Charles Tanner
Copperhead snake, page 74
Black tiger snake, page 99
Gwardar, page 101

John Weigel
Small-scaled snake, page 90
Tiger snake, page 96

Contents

Spiders and Other Arachnids

Necrotising spiders

Other Australian spiders

Insects and Other Arthropods

Other Creatures

First Aid

Introduction

A knowledge of the appearance, distribution and behaviour of our dangerous Australian wildlife, combined with good sense, should ensure the safety of even the most adventurous person. *Dangerous Australian Animals* is an up-to-date and practical guide to the acquisition of this knowledge. Although it should be stressed that most of the 'accidents' described in this book are preventable, accidents do happen. The first-aid measures described in this book could be life-saving: not only scouts should 'be prepared'!

The medical management has been kept to the essential information required to treat human and animal victims, and the use of technical terms has been limited so that the general reader would not be put off. A small glossary has also been provided to ensure the text is user-friendly.

Dangerous Australian Animals has its origins in a series of articles which appeared in the early 1990s under the title 'Creature Feature' in *Australian Doctor* and—in abbreviated form—in *The Veterinarian* as the 'The Ouch Column'. As they appeared to meet a need for palatable, easy-to-use information by a wide range of readers, they were brought up-to-date and expanded to include more creatures and information on first-aid and medical management.

We wish the reader a venom-free life.

STRUAN SUTHERLAND
GUY NOLCH

MARINE CREATURES

Avoiding marine stings, bites and injuries

The last thing a holiday-maker wants is to become a news item after an encounter with a sea creature. Unfortunately, this happens all too often. Most of those who need stonefish or box jellyfish antivenom are tourists. Only rarely is the injured person engaged in their normal occupation, such as fishing or diving. This discrepancy can be attributed to tourists' ignorance of marine creatures and what it takes to upset them. As a result, severe injuries and even death occur each summer due to contact with our venomous marine life.

Shark attack

There are a few simple rules that swimmers, surfers and divers should observe to reduce the chance of shark attack. Do not swim in areas where sharks are known to be common. Avoid swimming alone, especially at dusk or after dark when feeding sharks are likely to be closer to the shore. If possible, use only beaches where netting is in place. Only swim at beaches where there are lifeguards present—getting into difficulties in the water is far more likely than shark attack.

Do not swim when people are fishing, either from boats or the beach. If large numbers of fish are present, or those present are acting strangely, leave the water immediately. Never swim or wade in the open sea with a dog. Swimmers should not urinate in the water or swim if they have bleeding wounds. Although there is no evidence that menstruating women are at special risk, caution is advisable. Finally, it may be cowardly but swim in the midst of a crowd rather than at its periphery.

Many of the idyllic resorts in the Indo-Pacific region are also idyllic for various venomous marine creatures. Unfortunately, some of these remote places—even some of the very posh destinations—do not have even basic medical facilities, let alone antivenoms. Maimed tourists regularly limp out of international terminals in Australia with terrible tales of how their holiday was ruined. This can be avoided by taking some simple precautions:

- Take care as to what you pick up.

- Treat all fish as though they will spike and injure you.

- Don't go barefoot in tropical waters, especially near reefs. Always wear protective footwear and gloves when exploring tropical reefs.

- Avoid walking in murky water or in the sea at night.

- If the locals warn that stinging jellyfish are around, keep out of the water.

- Avoid jumping out of a boat, except on dry land.

- If stingrays are around and you must walk through their territory, shuffle along slowly, probing ahead with a pole. Use an oar if necessary.

- Don't bring spiky-looking fish onto a crowded boat.

MARINE CREATURES
JELLYFISH

Bluebottle

Thousands of surfers at Sydney beaches were treated yesterday for stings by bluebottles. Large numbers of bluebottles, some with stingers more than 6 ft long, were reported for the third successive day ... children seemed to be crying and yelling all day ... at Manly, lifesavers closed the beach when they sighted a mass of bluebottles drifting towards the shore ...

This newspaper item appeared on 9 January 1967, but it could well have been 1867 or be reported again in 2067. Like sharks, bluebottles are not particularly popular with swimmers. Fortunately, no deaths have been reported in Australian waters following bluebottle stings, but some deaths have occurred in the United States.

The Australian *Physalia,* or bluebottle, is similar but smaller than the Atlantic species, which is often called the Portuguese man-o-war. Recently a second, larger Australian species has been described.

The bluebottle is found from time to time in all Australian waters and in all hot and temperate waters throughout the world.

Technically, the bluebottle is not a true jellyfish. It is, in fact, a collection of at least four types of individual animals that have banded together to sail across the oceans of the world. They do this most successfully by specialisation. One develops into a gas-filled float that keeps the group on the surface. This float measures 2–13 cm in length and has a little gland that produces carbon monoxide and other gases to fill the float.

Some other members of the touring group have long tentacles for catching plankton and hauling them up to other members that perform the digestion. The fourth kind of creature quietly and discreetly carries out reproduction.

The floating *Physalia* colony may range in number from a handful to 1000. As described above, each group is highly specialised and does not survive long if separated. All the tentacles, and parts of the float, are a bright blue colour.

The bluebottle is a good sailor. It consists of two mirror image types that allow it to sail to the left or the right, respectively, at 45° to the wind. In very still conditions it appears to be unstable and sometimes rolls over. The purpose of this may be to keep the float moistened. The tentacles, which consist of a bunch of short-frilled ones and a long trailing or fishing tentacle, collectively act as a sea anchor. The fishing tentacle may be as long as 10 m and is responsible for injuries to humans. It has stinging capsules grouped in bean-like packets. When someone is stung, a row of bean or button-shaped lesions can usually be seen where there has been contact with the patches of nematocysts. When the stinging capsules discharge they inject a high molecular weight toxin that has been found to have both haemolytic and lethal effects.

In October 1991 a clinically more troublesome species of *Physalia* dumped itself in large numbers on the beaches of northern Queensland. They were larger than the common Australian bluebottle and had float lengths up to 15 cm. They had up to five thick fishing tentacles that were dark blue in colour and up to 10 long thin pale coloured tentacles. Over previous decades there had been anecdotal sightings of these larger species in Australian waters. Experts consider that it is very closely related to the Atlantic species *Physalia physalis*, which can have a float up to 25 cm long and a multiple thick mane of tentacles that has been reported to reach a length of 30 m. The experts who found this large bluebottle support earlier suggestions that our common bluebottle be referred to as *Physalia utriculus* and the larger specimens be referred to as *Physalia physalis*.

A bluebottle sting causes immediate pain and red lines, with scattered, discrete, papular weals developing rapidly. Typically, the injury resembles a linear 'string of beans', the centre of which is blanched and surrounded by erythaema. Vesicles may develop but in most Australian cases all sign of injury has faded within 24 hours. The local pain may last up to 2 hours and may spread through the whole limb or around the trunk when body stings have occurred. Sometimes movement of the injured limb increases the severity of the pain. It is uncommon after bluebottle stings to have significant general effects, but headache, vomiting, abdominal pain, nausea, shortness of breath and collapse have all been reported.

First aid

Rescue the victim from the water if necessary and wash off any adherent tentacles by dousing with sea water. Apply cold packs or ice/water mixtures to the injured area for a minimum of 15–20 minutes to reduce skin pain. Should the sting be severe, medical aid should be sought.

Recent Australian experience with *Physalia physalis* has found that its stings differ from *Physalia utriculus* in some ways. The severe skin pain produced by this creature is only slowly relieved by the use of cold packs. Its tentacles appear more adherent and are harder to rinse off with sea water. The rescuer may receive some stinging on his/her fingers when pulling the tentacles off.

Some people stung by *Physalia physalis* suffered a mild Irukandji-like syndrome (see page 12). Symptoms, which lasted 1–2 hours, included limb muscle cramps, restlessness and chest pain, the latter due to intercostal myalgia.

Severe cases may require treatment for the intense pain and possible shock. Airways, breathing and circulation should be closely monitored. Although the injury is easily diagnosed by the experienced eye, if there is doubt it is useful to know that skin scrapings will usually demonstrate the presence of undischarged or discharged nematocysts, which for *Physalia* are character-istically spherical.

A significant allergy may develop following a bluebottle sting. People who suffer from this allergy should take special care to avoid being stung again as near fatal reactions have followed a second sting. Tests are under development at the Australian Venom Research Unit to diagnose such allergies.

If you have ever been stung by a bluebottle, the following tale will make you wince. A diver near Panama surfaced directly under a large *Physalia* and was immediately stung. It was estimated that the creature was some 25 cm long and its tentacles hung down more than 6 m. For hours he was delirious with pain and developed massive blistering lesions over his shoulders. It was considered he was lucky to survive and that a child or frail person would have succumbed. A virtually identical sequence of events resulted in the death of a SCUBA diver off North Carolina in 1988.

MARINE CREATURES—JELLYFISH

Box jellyfish

The young woman was unlucky, but she was also lucky. She stepped into the sea off The Strand in Townsville and into the path of a large box jellyfish. Three metres of tentacles made contact and the excruciating pain was instantaneous. Fortunately help was at hand. Windsurfing a few metres away was Prof. John Williamson, an expert on the treatment of jellyfish stings. He helped her out of the water and, within 90 seconds of the stinging, the adhering tentacles were doused with 2 litres of vinegar. The vinegar-inactivated tentacles were quickly removed and, still suffering intense pain, the victim was transported to hospital, accompanied by Prof. Williamson. He administered box jellyfish antivenom 35 minutes after the stinging. Prof. Williamson described the response as dramatic. He noted that 90 seconds after the injection there was an unmistakable diminution in the severity of the skin lesions and the pain began to abate. Five minutes later the patient said that the severity of the pain had diminished by 90 per cent. As they watched, the severe redness around the stung areas faded. The patient made an uneventful recovery and the residual scarring and pigmentation was minimal.

Other victims have not been so fortunate. The box jellyfish (*Chironex fleckeri*) is the most dangerous jellyfish in the world. Since 1900 more than 80 people are known to have met sudden and painful deaths after contact with the box jellyfish in the subtropical waters of Australia. Many were young people who died within minutes of being stung.

Surprisingly, the creature responsible for these deaths was not identified until 1956, when Dr Ron Southcott named it *Chironex fleckeri* in honour of Dr Hugo Flecker, who for many years had investigated serious marine stings in Queensland waters. It's hard to imagine why it took so long for this potentially lethal creature to be found and identified. One explanation is that if someone has been painfully or even fatally stung by something, it might be considered a foolish act to march into the sea to look for the culprit. Besides, this jellyfish is awfully hard to see.

The term 'sea wasp' is an alternative but bad name for the box jellyfish. A lot of people think that the sea wasp is some sort of flying creature. Sometimes a March fly has caused panic!

There is not yet complete information about the distribution of the box jellyfish in the Indo-Pacific region. In Australian waters it is found from as far south as Gladstone in Queensland and possibly as far west as Broome. At times the

DISTRIBUTION

creature may be found in a vast area around the northern parts of Australia.

The box jellyfish has a pale blue cubic or box-shaped bell that may grow to 25 cm in diameter and a height of 20 cm, roughly the size of a 2 gallon laundry bucket. It may weigh more than 6 kg and is semi-transparent, being composed of about 95 per cent water. There are four pedalia (or fleshy arms) from which up to 15 tentacles are attached. Each of these tentacles may be as long as 3 metres and on each side of these tentacles there are some 12,000 stinging capsules per square millimetre.

The jellyfish is a highly advanced species. Its well developed nervous system is superior to that of most other jellyfish and it has eye spots that attract it towards light. It propels itself along by ejecting water from its body cavity. It can even change direction by varying the position of the cavity opening. The usual rate of movement is less

than 1 knot but, if alarmed, it can turn rapidly and sprint at up to 2 knots. The tentacles do not help its propulsion but stream along behind.

The natural history of this important jellyfish has been skilfully researched by Dr Bob Hartwick of James Cook University, Townsville. He has discovered infantile polyps and juveniles upstream in tidal creeks, and the occasional adult box jelly-fish have been found as far as 2 km upstream. It has not been proven yet, but it is quite possible that the creature breeds in sheltered tidal streams and not in deeper waters, as was once thought. The box jellyfish is not found around coral reefs or in the open ocean. There are plenty of other dangers to avoid near coral reefs!

The classic box jellyfish season occurs during December and January. However, it is clear now that severe stings may occur at other times of the year, particularly around Darwin where there

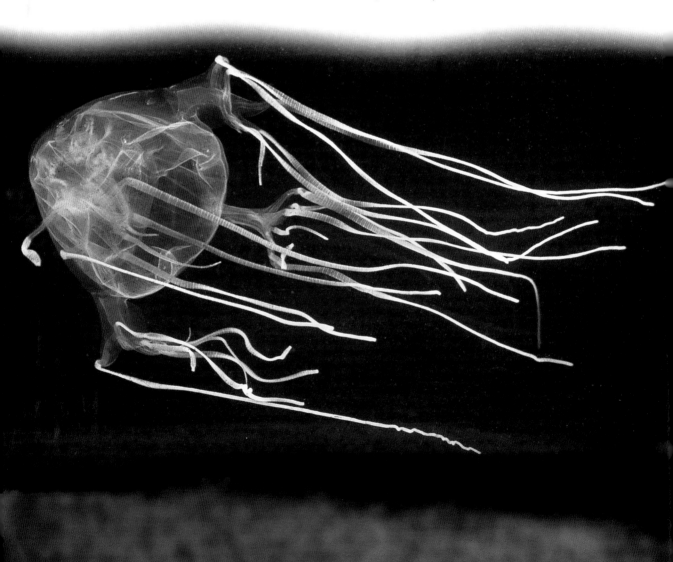

have been severe stingings in June. On days that are hot and overcast but calm, the box jellyfish may move around in shallow water pursuing prey, such as small prawns. Their invasion of a popular swimming spot may go unnoticed until some luckless swimmer brushes against the tentacles.

Venom apparatus

Although there is no venom apparatus on the bell of the creature, the tentacles have millions of spring-loaded capsules or nematocysts. These are discharged with great force, and a penetrating thread soaked with fluid toxins literally screws itself deep into the skin of any creature it touches. The threads, which are about 0.2 mm long, have no problem reaching into the dermis of the human skin on most parts of the body.

The penetration of millions of threads, many through the cavity of capillaries and other vessels, results in a massive absorption of venom, to some extent intravenously. When a prawn or fish is stung by the box jellyfish, its death appears instantaneous. There is no struggle that might damage the jellyfish while its prey is drawn into its bell for digestion.

The stimulus for the explosive release of the threads includes physical and chemical contact. The use of vinegar to stop nematocysts discharging is discussed under first aid.

The box jellyfish has a second type of capsule that produces a gluey substance on the tentacles. This helps the tentacle to stick to the victim.

Venom

The venom has at least three separate activities:
- the dermatonecrotic component, which causes rapid skin death;
- a high molecular weight toxin that is largely responsible for cardiovascular collapse and respiratory failure; and
- a third venom component that produces mild haemolysis and associated elevation of serum potassium, which possibly contributes to dysrhythmia.

The late Dr Jack Barnes was a general practitioner in Cairns who devoted a great deal of time and money to investigating the box jellyfish. It is likely that his outstanding research into both jellyfish and jellyfish stings saved many lives. He devised a way of 'milking' freshly cut-off box jellyfish tentacles by laying them on a membrane and stimulating them with an electric current. This guaranteed a supply of potent venom that led to the release of an effective antivenom by Commonwealth Serum Laboratories (CSL) in 1970. This antivenom is raised in sheep.

Human envenomation

The victim rarely sees the box jellyfish until he or she has been stung; even then it may not be seen. Dr Barnes found the best way to spot them was from a boat when he was wearing polarised glasses. Children swimming or wading in shallow water are the most common victims. Most deaths involve children because of their smaller body weight and possibly the greater time they spend swimming.

After contact, the tentacles are easily torn off; they resemble earthworms of a grey, pink or bluish hue as they adhere to the skin. Stings from very small specimens cannot penetrate adult skin, although those with a bell 5–7 cm in diameter can cause localised pain lasting for hours. Larger creatures with a bell wider than 15 cm can cause devastating injuries.

The effects of the sting were well described in 1960 by Dr Barnes:

> During the first 15 minutes, pain increases in mounting waves despite removal of the tentacle. The victim may scream and become irrational. Areas of contact are linear and multiple, showing as purple or brown lines often compared to the marks made by a whip. A pattern of transverse bars is usually visible. Wealing is prompt and massive. Oedema, erythaema and vesiculation soon follow and, when these subside (after some 10 days), patches of full thickness necrosis are revealed. Healing is by granulation and cicatrisation, taking a month or more and leaving permanent scars, perhaps with pigment changes.

Dr Barnes observed that many stings are minor, but death is probable if the total length of the weals on a victim is greater than 6–7 metres. He recorded that death could occur within minutes of

Avoiding stings

People should never swim in tropical waters when the locals warn that box jellyfish are about. In fact, it is wise never to go swimming alone in tropical waters. During the jellyfish season it is best to swim only in netted areas or to use wetsuits or stinger-resistant lycra costumes. These are made of pantyhose-like material and prevent the tentacles from sticking to one's skin. If they can't stick, they can't sting.

Lifesavers play an important role in monitoring beaches for safety, and in northern Queensland they almost invariably have vinegar available. Many ambulance officers have been trained in the intramuscular administration of the antivenom. Although the preferred route is intra-venous, ambulance officers have saved many lives by on-the-spot intramuscular injection of antivenom. Sadly, deaths still occur, usually of children who are stung in areas remote from medical care.

the stinging, sometimes before the victim reached the shore.

In severe cases, consciousness is lost, perhaps mercifully, within seconds of the injury. The diagnosis is usually clear-cut. The skin is heavily marked, usually in a criss-cross fashion with trans-versely barred weals that may be 8–10 mm wide. Lesions produced by another related highly dangerous jellyfish, *Chiropsalmus quadrigatus*, are narrower and the effects are milder (see page 9). There is invariably a tentacle remaining for identification but, failing this, skin scrapings will disclose characteristically shaped nematocysts.

First aid

Assist the victim out of the water and, as soon as possible, flood the adhering tentacles with house-hold vinegar for at least 30 seconds. If breathing or circulation is difficult, begin resuscitation immediately. Prof. John Williamson advises that such resuscitation should be done aggressively, optimistically and, unless spontaneous recovery

occurs, it should not be abandoned until the patient reaches a hospital.

Research has shown that alcohol should NOT be poured on the adhering tentacles because it stimulates them to discharge their stinging capsules. Although it was recommended in the past, all the experts now condemn its use and recommend the use of vinegar.

In severe stings involving the limbs, Prof. Williamson's advice is not to waste time removing the tentacles after they have been rendered harmless by vinegar, but to apply pressure–immobilisation bandages (see page 186) over the stung area immediately. The bandages should then be dowsed with vinegar.

If vinegar is not available, all that one can do is carefully to pick off the bulk of the tentacles and apply firm bandaging, which should be soaked with vinegar at the first opportunity. While the rescuer is also likely to be stung when removing the tentacles, the hands are relatively thick-skinned and are unlikely to be stung severely enough to cause any systemic effects.

It is important to note that vinegar will not give relief from pain and in fact may worsen it. The important role of vinegar is to prevent further discharge of the stinging capsules.

Medical management

Antivenom may save the patient's life, markedly reduce pain, and decrease the degree of local tissue

Immunisation against box jellyfish venom

Twenty-five years ago CSL investigated the possibility of a vaccine to immunise lifesavers and others at risk against this jellyfish. It was possible to produce a vaccine but it could cause reactions that were not acceptable. Furthermore, immunised individuals would require regular injections to maintain some degree of immunity. Another factor was that, unlike tetanus, the body does not have time to produce an immune response and may be overwhelmed by sudden massive envenomation.

damage and scarring. When possible it should be given intravenously with an initial dose of three ampoules. The dose for children is the same, if not more, than for an adult.

In addition to standard resuscitation methods, the seriously stung patient will require very close monitoring of myocardial function. In the past, the use of verapamil has been advocated, but recent research suggests this may be contraindicated. The patient who has regained consciousness and is stable will require continuous pain relief for some time. This is best achieved by further antivenom infusion and/or narcotic intravenous infusions. Ice packs and lignocaine applications are not effective analgesics. There is little evidence that topical steroids reduce scarring.

MARINE CREATURES—JELLYFISH

Chiropsalmus

In February 1994, a party of worried Japanese visited CSL's head office in Melbourne. They were all from Okinawa and were seeking advice on the treatment and prevention of horrific stings by a little known jellyfish. The jellyfish involved, *Chiropsalmus quadrigatus*, has no common name, but is second only to the box jellyfish (*Chironex fleckeri*) as a danger to humans.

The Okinawans certainly had something to worry about. This jellyfish had killed young children and the photographs of near fatalities were horrible. Arrangements were made to supply box jellyfish antivenom, but a wider problem for Okinawa's tourism-dependent economy was evident. The peak season when visitors from Japan's main islands liked venturing into the water coincided with the arrival in large numbers of *Chiropsalmus*. The return of maimed tourists was offsetting the tourist authority's best efforts. Something had to be done about it.

C. quadrigatus is the most common species of *Chiropsalmus* found in northern Australian waters. To date it has mainly been found between Cooktown and Innisfail on Queensland's east coast. When further studies have been carried out, its range in Australian waters will probably be discovered to be far less limited.

Although rarely found to date, other dangerous species such as *C. quadrumanus* have been collected in Australian waters occasionally. Species of *Chiropsalmus* are believed to cause up to 50 deaths annually in the Philippines.

Chiropsalmus recently caused the sudden death of a 4-year-old child off a beach in the Gulf of Mexico. He was swimming in the water at 2 pm when he began screaming and was carried out by his mother. Jellyfish tentacles were wrapped around his left arm. These were removed and a meat tenderiser was placed on the affected area. (Note: this is not considered effective first aid.) Paramedics performed chest compressions.

DISTRIBUTION

When he reached the Emergency Department of a hospital 40 minutes later, he was cyanotic and limp with fixed dilated pupils. There was no spontaneous respiratory movement nor could cardiac activity be detected. Cardiopulmonary resuscitation was continued and he was intubated. A chest X-ray showed massive pulmonary oedema. Resuscitation was unsuccessful and he was declared dead at 3.21 pm. Skin scrapings taken identified the jellyfish as *C. quadrumanus*. (The box jellyfish is not found in the Gulf of Mexico.)

Although the possibility of a viral myocarditis could not be ruled out, the post mortem findings were compatible with acute cardiac arrhythmia with congestive heart failure following envenomation by a jellyfish. This sad case demonstrates

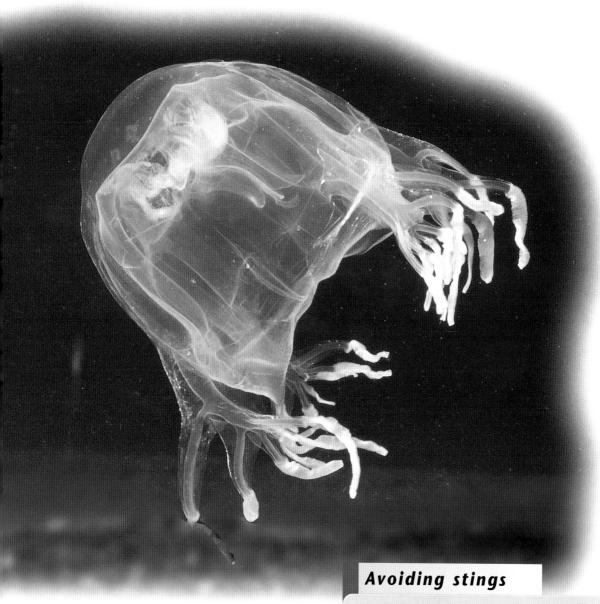

the speed at which an irreversible situation may be reached if effective first aid, adequate resuscitation and antivenom are not used.

Chiropsalmus looks fairly similar to the box jellyfish, which has certainly overshadowed it in the medical and popular press. A mature *C. quadrigatus* is smaller than a box jellyfish, its bell rarely exceeding 70 mm in width. Certain features of the bell allow the expert to distinguish it from the box jellyfish. Its gonads are finger-like compared with the box jellyfish's grape-shaped gonads. For the non-expert, the two jellyfish may usually be distinguished because

Avoiding stings

In northern Australian waters people should only swim when the local surf lifesaving authorities consider it safe to do so. People should never swim alone in remote waters, especially in the summer months.

If 'stinger-free' enclosures are available, these should always be used. The wearing of 'stinger-resistant' lycra suits gives sound protection from jellyfish stings and has become almost routine in certain areas in Queensland.

Remember, most dangerous jellyfish are almost impossible to see when you are swimming.

of the size of the specimen and/or by inspection of the tentacles. *C. quadrigatus* rarely has more than nine tentacles attached to each of its four pedaliums (or fleshy arms) and its tentacles are yellower, shorter and much finer than those of the box jellyfish. (The box jellyfish may have up to 15 tentacles streaming out from each pedalium.)

Chiropsalmus are not as robust as the box jellyfish and are slower swimmers, but otherwise have similar habits. When seeking shrimps, which are their favourite food, they swim near the surface. They may be found in shallow water when conditions are calm. When there is turbulence they will disappear, possibly to deeper waters. Little is known of their natural history, but when more information becomes available it may be possible to control or reduce their population in recreational areas. (The Japanese party that visited in 1994 included engineers who were planning to install an extensive netting system to render certain beaches stinger-free.)

Dr Jack Barnes found that *Chiropsalmus* populations tended to be more uniform within a particular swarm, whereas very large and small box jellyfish would often co-exist in the same area.

Although neither the box jellyfish nor *Chiropsalmus* have stinging capsules on their bells, they both have myriads of stinging capsules on their tentacles. For both types of jellyfish, the smaller the specimen the less likely it is that discharging capsules will penetrate adult human skin of normal thickness. As far as total armament is concerned, a large box jellyfish far outweighs *Chiropsalmus*.

Dr Barnes could not electrically 'milk' *Chiropsalmus* tentacles as he had done with the box jellyfish tentacles (see page 7) as they were far more fragile. However, workers have studied whole tentacle extracts and found they had similar lethal dermatonecrotic and haemolytic activities to the milked venom or whole tentacle extracts of box jellyfish. The *Chiropsalmus* venom extracts were less potent than box jellyfish venom, but the components were present in the same proportion and the mode of death in experimental animals was virtually identical.

Human envenomation

Sudden severe pain and shock may occur after contact with the tentacles. Fortunately, the illness is usually mild compared with box jellyfish stings. In the literature there are few authenticated descriptions of stings by *Chiropsalmus* and the more severe ones may well have been attributed to box jellyfish. After *Chiropsalmus* stings, swelling and redness may develop immediately and tissue breakdown may occur. Unlike box jellyfish stings, pigmentation and scarring has usually faded by 8 weeks.

The only way a positive diagnosis can be made is by capturing the offending jellyfish as it is difficult to distinguish injury by this jellyfish from that following mild injury by a box jellyfish. Its preservation in alcohol or formalin may allow later expert identification. However, skin scrapings from the affected area may only reveal nematocysts similar to those from either jellyfish.

First aid

The injured person should be rescued from the water and the stung area flooded with domestic vinegar to inactivate adhering tentacles (as for the box jellyfish). If vinegar is not available, adhering tentacles should be lifted off using a dry towel or tweezers, but not rubbed off. Keep the patient still and apply cardiopulmonary resuscitation if necessary.

Medical management

This is the same as for box jellyfish stings. Box jellyfish antivenom has been shown experimentally to effectively neutralise *C. quadrigatus* venom. To date, no report of its actual use in treating *Chiropsalmus* envenomations has reached CSL. Apart from its other activities, the antivenom has been shown to dramatically relieve pain caused by box jellyfish stings. It may well do so in the case of severe *Chiropsalmus* stings. The pain from milder stings may be reduced by the application of ice/ water packs after the application of vinegar to inactivate the tentacles. Vinegar itself will not relieve pain. More severe pain may warrant the administration of opiate analgesics. Topical or parenteral steroids are of dubious value.

On certain parts of the Queensland coast, ambulance officers have been trained to give intramuscular injections of box jellyfish anti-venom. Although the intravenous route is preferred, there is little doubt that this on-the-spot administration of antivenom has reduced suffering and probably saved lives.

MARINE CREATURES—JELLYFISH

Irukandji

In December 1961, Dr Jack Barnes, using SCUBA gear, lay waiting on the seabed near Cairns hoping his research on the time and place where most Irukandji stings had occurred would yield results.

Suddenly he saw something quite odd. A small fish was moving in a peculiar way near the surface of the water. Closer examination showed it had been captured by a tiny, transparent jellyfish. With a sweep of his net, Dr Barnes captured a specimen of what was to be named *Carukia barnesi*. Shortly afterwards he put the jellyfish on his arm and, somewhat to his satisfaction (if not discomfort), he proved the little creature was responsible for the sometimes near-fatal Irukandji syndrome.

For many years people around Cairns had suffered from the Irukandji syndrome. The disease was named after an Aboriginal tribe that had once inhabited the area. This sting was different to other types of marine stings because, although the affected area was moderately painful at the time of the sting, some time later the victims experienced highly distressing effects that required considerable medical skill to control.

The Irukandji occurs in the subtropical waters of Australia from Dampier in the west to Mackay in the east. Unlike the box jellyfish (which stays close to shore), it is an open-water jellyfish. With a body only 2 cm wide and 2.5 cm long, it is surprising that a jellyfish so small can produce such severe effects. It has four tentacles that vary in length from several centimetres to 65 cm. Its body is almost transparent in water: only the tentacles can be faintly seen. There are clumps of stinging capsules (nematocysts) appearing as little red dots that cover the body and are packed more tightly in small bands on the tentacles.

The syndrome usually follows a minor or insignificant sting, generally occurring near the surface of the water. The injury is very faint and may not actually be visible. The systemic effects develop some 30 minutes or more after contact with the creature. Severe pain, which has been described as 'boring', starts low in the back area. Cramping muscle pains soon follow, particularly in the abdomen, thighs and upper arms. These spasms come in waves almost like labour pains, and are described by the victims as excruciating. They may last for many hours.

DISTRIBUTION

If all this wasn't enough for the poor victim, there are the additional and severe effects of various degrees of catecholamine excess, especially high blood pressure. In very extreme cases, hypertension may reach 260/130 mm Hg. Other effects are nausea and vomiting, severe headache, extreme anxiety and restlessness, hyperventilation and nearly always a marked tachycardia. Sweating frequently occurs and may be profuse, but sometimes it has a peculiar localised distribution well away from the sting site. It has been established that acute pulmonary oedema may be part of the Irukandji syndrome.

The Australian Venom Research Unit is investigating this creature's venom, and an antivenom is the ultimate goal. Research to date has been limited because there is a shortage of specimens: they are difficult to find and so small! The venom promises to be extremely interesting.

First aid

Domestic vinegar should be poured over the stung area and then a vinegar-soaked pack applied to it. All victims should be hospitalised.

It is always handy to make a skin scraping from the area of a suspected jellyfish sting. Experts can often identify the type of creature involved by examination of the undischarged nematocysts.

Medical management

In most cases the main medical problem is the severe pain. Generally this will only respond to high doses of intravenous narcotics. Usually 50 mg of pethidine is given immediately intravenously and the same drug infused at the rate of 30 mg per hour. The excessive catecholamine release may be controlled by the alpha-adrenergic blocker phentolamine. A dose of 10 mg should be given and repeated until symptoms are controlled. Pulmonary oedema may require oxygen, sublingual nitrates, diuretics and possibly intubation.

Dr Peter Fenner, who has treated many cases, believes there is an urgent need to develop an antivenom. Hopefully in time this specific treatment will become available.

Differential diagnosis

Clinicians unfamiliar with the Irukandji syndrome may fall into diagnosis pitfalls. For example, sometimes children have been taken to hospital complaining of abdominal pain due to this jellyfish and, rather than receiving pain relief, they have been treated for food poisoning. Barnes has described how two children so inflicted were denied pain relief and were subjected to gastric lavage. He lists a number of surgical emergencies that can be mistaken for the effects of the venom, including ruptured spleen, ruptured ectopic pregnancy and acute appendicitis. He states that some patients only escaped laparotomy because of unavoidable delays in transit.

On one occasion a seaman on an interstate vessel swam in the ship's pool and subsequently developed

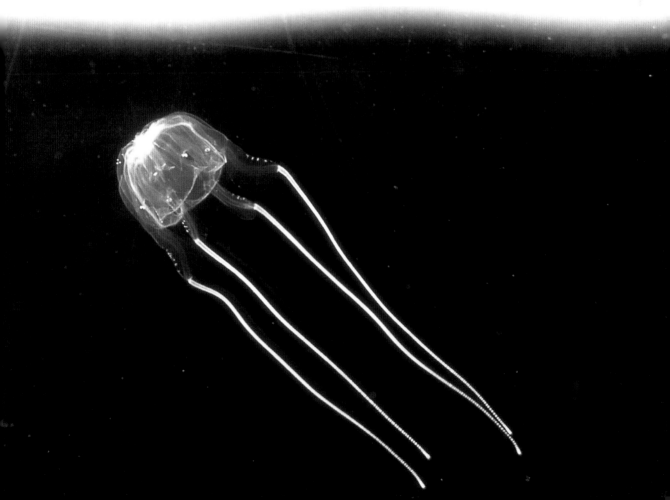

what was thought to be a serious back injury. The captain radioed for medical assistance and the doctor contacted fortunately diagnosed the Irukandji syndrome. The ship's pool contained recently pumped sea water taken off Thursday Island, and the sailor had been stung prior to the onset of his backache.

Avoiding stings by this jellyfish may be difficult. Using wetsuits and swimming in stinger-resistant enclosures is the best advice. It is wise to take advantage of local knowledge regarding seasonal incidence and swim in a chlorinated pool if stings have occurred recently in the nearby sea.

MARINE CREATURES—JELLYFISH

Jimble

To the horror of the marine biologist, the schoolboy helping her reached out and picked up the jellyfish before she could warn him. When the little animal's delicate tentacles flopped onto his bare arm, he yelped with terrible pain. She later wrote a report of the stinging in which she said that the residual injury resembled a burn, observing: 'Luckily this type of jellyfish is rarely encountered'. This latter statement, made about 50 years ago, would be challenged by many swimmers or anglers today. The jimble is now known to be quite common and in some areas may reach plague proportions. It is certainly a creature that divers know not to touch.

The jimble (*Carybdea rastonii*) was first discovered in St Vincent Gulf in South Australia, but has been found in all Australian waters. It is also widely distributed in the Pacific Ocean as far north as Japan and in Hawaii to the east, where it is sometimes known as the sea wasp.

This jellyfish is far less dangerous than the box jellyfish (*Chironex fleckeri*), which is also known as the sea wasp. The jimble has other names as well, such as the small box jellyfish, the mona, and the lantern medusa. It is a small creature with a translucent body that is usually not more than 2 cm across. It has four delicate tentacles that may stretch out some 5–30 cm in length. These tentacles become more dense when contracted and in this state may be easier to see than the almost invisible bell.

Jimbles tend to congregate in swarms and gen-erally rise to the warmer surface of the sea in the early morning and at dusk. They may be seen occasionally on the surface at other times of the day when the sky is very overcast. The creature swims along quite actively in an oblique fashion and often breaks the surface of the water to produce small ripples. They are fascinating to watch from the safety of a boat or jetty when 50 or so do this with some degree of synchronisation. It's not the sort of ballet in which a human with soft, tender skin should take part.

DISTRIBUTION

Jimbles are particularly common in certain areas of Australia. For example, in south-western Australia they are often found in Geographe Bay, at Rottnest Island and near Perth's beaches. Jimbles occur in large numbers in South Australian waters and their distribution depends largely on the intensity of light. At night they may be attracted to lights, much to the annoyance of people fishing.

The submerged jimble is almost impossible to see. While its bell is transparent, the four tentacles—which are pink, light purple or cream—are more easily detected. The only evidence of the jimble's presence may be the shadows created by the transparent bell on the sand in shallow water.

The jimble is quite an active swimmer with a good appetite, and often relatively large fish can be observed within its stomach. The strangely positioned dead fish may be more easily seen than the jellyfish!

The tentacles are covered with oval-shaped stinging capsules averaging 16 x 28 µm. The discharge of these capsules can cause the instantaneous death of its prey.

Japanese workers have done a great deal of work with toxic extracts of this jellyfish's tentacles and have found they are potent constrictors of smooth muscle using a number of different mechanisms. They cause prostaglandin and noradrenaline release, and stimulate calcium movement across membranes, thus enhancing other pharmacological effects. The tentacles have also been shown to contain a potent aggregator of platelets. There is nothing bland about the pharmacological cocktail this creature injects.

Its stings produce immediate pain and the lesions are almost invariably linear. They are usually four in number and range from 10 to 20 cm in length. The pain in most cases is of moderate severity and will last up to 2 hours. Some victims, especially children, become very distressed. Weals 3–12 mm wide quickly develop and are surrounded by a flare extending out about 4 cm.

Some stings produce variably sized blisters. The swelling generally settles down over the next few days and usually some pigmentary changes are apparent for the next 14 days or so. The discharging nematocysts easily penetrate most adult human skin but usually not the thick skin of the adult human palm. The distress and injury caused by jimble stings is generally considered more severe than that caused by the Portuguese man-o-war (*Physalia*) (see page 3), and permanent scarring may occur.

The Japanese have researched the effects of the jimble's tentacles on humans as well as its pharmacological activities. An experiment was done with 25 volunteers, each of whom had two tentacles, freshly removed from living specimens, applied to their forearms.

All the volunteers complained of severe pain lasting from 10 minutes to 8 hours. Erythaema and weals appeared within 3–4 minutes and enlarged for 15–20 minutes. This erythaema took 1–3 days to subside in all but two of the volunteers.

A week or so after the application, 15 of the

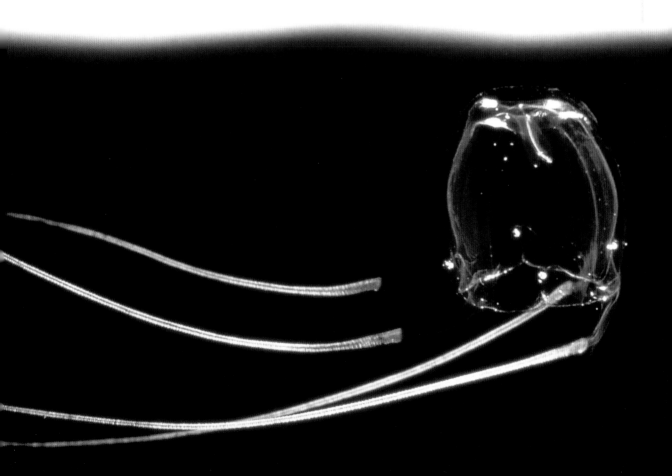

volunteers suffered itchy papulo-vesicular lesions. These lesions subsided after 1 week, leaving slight pigmentation. Biopsies from the volunteers showed these secondary reactions were compatible with dermatitis.

Such experiments are ill conceived because some jellyfish victims develop an allergy and may suffer quite severe local or general reactions upon being re-stung, not only by the particular jellyfish involved but sometimes by quite different species. People who have become allergic to jellyfish stings should take great care to avoid further stings as fatal reactions have followed a later contact.

First aid

Remove the person from the water and wash off any adhering tentacles by dousing with sea water. As with the other box-shaped jellyfish, domestic vinegar should be poured all over the stung area and any remaining tentacles. Alcohol should not be used for this purpose as it will cause the firing of any undischarged nematocysts. The application of vinegar will not provide pain relief and ice/water packs or local anaesthetic ointment may be used for this purpose. If lesions are extensive, local application of steroids and/or antibiotics may be warranted.

If injury involves the eye, it is wise to consult an eye specialist. Local anaesthetic drops should be used and eye injuries may require topical application of antibiotics and steroids for several days.

Immunological responses may be seen with these and other jellyfish stings. Sometimes the area involved may flare up 7–10 days after the sting has occurred in a pattern similar to the earlier sting. This will usually subside rapidly. This local cellular response is usually treated with topical steroids.

Finally, remember that jimbles rejoice in the peace and tranquillity of quiet bays. In the middle of the day they may collect near the bottom to shelter from the bright sunlight. The creatures may be having a siesta, but if you walk through them you'll find that their tentacles are not.

MARINE CREATURES—JELLYFISH

Other Jellyfish

Little mauve stinger

The little mauve stinger (*Pelagia noctiluca*) inhabits most oceans of the world, ranging from tropical zones to quite cold areas. Sometimes it is found in huge swarms in the open sea extending from the surface to depths of 200 m. It occurs in all seas around Australia.

DISTRIBUTION

The jellyfish is multi-coloured and has eight spaghetti-like tentacles. The bell of a mature specimen has a diameter of some 3 cm but may occasionally be as wide as 12 cm. The upper surface of the bell has a number of warts that contain nematocysts, as do the tentacles that all arise from the bell edge.

This creature is not known to have caused human fatalities but is often a great nuisance to swimmers. Immediate pain, which may be distressing, can follow contact with the creature and irregularly shaped weals resembling urticaria may develop. Severe cases have suffered from dyspnoea.

First aid

Remove the person from the water, wash off any adhering tentacles with sea water and apply ice/water packs to relieve the symptoms.

Sea blubber or hairy stinger

The sea blubber or hairy stinger (*Cyanea capillata*) is widely distributed in the Indo-Pacific region and is found in all Australian coastal waters. There are several species of the genus *Cyanea*, and they are generally known as hairy jellyfish. Some have highly descriptive common names such as hairy stinger, sea nettle, hairy jelly and lion's mane.

DISTRIBUTION

These jellyfish have bells that are flattened like a plate with the edge turned inwards. In Australian waters the bell may be more than 30 cm across; however, specimens in the cold Antarctic may be as wide as 2.3 m. These are the largest jellyfish in the world. On the underside of the creature's bell are eight V-shaped clusters from which many delicate hairy tentacles trail downwards. Descriptions of this jellyfish range from 'a repulsive big slimy jellyfish' to bearing a 'general resemblance to a

mop hiding under a dinner-plate'. The tentacles can easily be detached from the creature but are still capable of inflicting a painful sting when floating free.

Contact with the tentacles may produce a burning sensation that develops into severe pain. A fine, stippled, linear weal bordered by a narrow flair may appear. Usually the pain and swelling subside after 15 minutes or so, leaving a bright red streak that may remain for several days. This long-lasting streak aids the diagnosis. In some severe cases, nausea, abdominal pain, profuse sweating, muscle cramps and respiratory distress may occur. As with other jellyfish, eye injuries have occurred after contact with either the tentacles or shed nematocysts. Allergic reactions have also been reported.

First aid

See first aid for bluebottle stings, page 3.

Blubber

The blubber (*Catostylus mosaicus*) is a common jellyfish that causes minor irritation. It has been described as 'a mushroom wearing frilly underwear'.

It is the most frequently found large jellyfish down the eastern coast of Australia. At times it abounds in the Brisbane River, Sydney Harbour and Port Philip Bay. The bell grows to a diameter of 35 cm and is usually milky-white or bluish. It has characteristic cross-shaped digestive organs that can easily be seen looking down on the bell. Severe stings have been attributed to this creature.

First aid

As for bluebottle stings (see page 5).

Morbakka

The morbakka or 'fire jelly' is possibly a species of *Tamoya*.

In 1985 Dr Ron Southcott proposed the name 'morbakka' for a type of box jellyfish often found in Moreton Bay. The name was derived from 'Moreton Bay carybdeid medusa'.

Superficially the morbakka looks like a small box jellyfish (see page 5), and hence the public concern when it was found as far south as Moreton Bay.

Dr Peter Fenner, who has studied the jellyfish, states that it is found as far north as Port Douglas and describes a typical northern specimen with a transparent bell of diameter 13 cm and height 18 cm. The four thick tentacles are mauve and could extend 60 cm. The tentacles have multiple transverse bars similar to *Chironex* but much larger.

People stung by this jellyfish have developed weals, with severe burning pain lasting some 24 hours. One victim developed a cough and back pain that remained for 24 hours. By the third day the skin lesion had become papulovesicular and remained so for 1 week.

Dr Fenner carried out experimental stingings with this jellyfish and demonstrated that skin scrapings could be diagnostic and that the tentacles were inactivated by vinegar. No fatalities have been attributed to this jellyfish to date but it certainly warrants further investigation.

First aid

As for box jellyfish stings (see page 5).

Sea nettle

This is a widely distributed, medium-sized jellyfish that causes serious injuries in many parts of the world, especially along the Atlantic coast of the United States of America. The species found in Australian waters grows to about 6 cm across the bell, with multiple tentacles growing to 15 cm. Contact may produce painful linear weals, and a rash may last many weeks. In severe cases an illness similar to the Irukandji syndrome may develop.

First aid

As for Irukandji stings (see page 12).

MARINE CREATURES

STINGING FISH

Butterfly cod

The diver was 38-years-old and in peak physical condition. He was at a depth of 5 metres when his right hand accidentally made contact with a butterfly cod. Two of its many spines penetrated his middle and ring fingers and he was suffering severe pain when he reached the shore a few minutes later. Ten minutes after the stinging he was seen by a doctor. He was stuporous and in a state of severe shock.

Both of his affected fingers had swelled to double their normal size and his forearm and arm were also swollen. His blood pressure was not recordable and his pulse rate was only 10 beats per minute. He received adrenaline intravenously, and repeated doses were required over the next 2 hours to maintain his blood pressure. After this time, his pulse rate and blood pressure had normalised and he was fully conscious.

The pain slowly subsided but the swelling persisted and it was a month before his fingers had returned to their normal size. The skin of both fingers sloughed off. No permanent effects were noted.

The butterfly cod (*Pterois volitans*) has a variety of alternative names, such as lion fish, fire cod, zebra fish and red fire fish. There are many other species

DISTRIBUTION

of *Pterois*, and these also
have many common
names. (Note that
another stinging
fish, *Enoplosus
armatus*, is also
known as the
zebra fish, but
usually is called the
old wife; this one is
far less dangerous
(see page 29).)

The butterfly cod is
widely distributed
through the Indo-
Pacific region and
the Red Sea. In
Australian waters it
is found as far
south as Perth and
Sydney.

Butterfly cod are
a beautifully coloured
fish and may grow as long
as 42 cm and weigh up to 1 kg.
They abound in shallow water around coral reefs
and rocks. They are inquisitive creatures and
frequently approach divers, often in pairs. Hidden
among their feather-like fins are 13 dorsal, three
anal and two pelvic venomous spines. If threatened they may advance with an array of needle-
sharp spines directed toward the aggressor. This
behaviour, and the fact that the inexperienced
diver may not allow for the refraction of light in
water, often leads to stings.

In the open water butterfly cod float about in a
most leisurely manner and make an easy target for
spear fishers (although this is illegal in national
marine parks). In their death throes they have
sometimes wreaked revenge by sliding down the
shaft of the spear and embedding themselves in
the hand of the hunter.

The creature's spines are long and finely pointed.
They are almost straight except at the base and tip,
where they incline towards the tail. Venom-
producing tissue is situated under the brightly
coloured integumentary sheath of the spine. This
sheath is ruptured when the spine penetrates the
victim's flesh, and venom diffuses into the

punctured wound. There is no venom duct and
envenomation relies on mechanical pressure.

Little research has been carried out on the
venom. In some respects it is similar to stonefish
venom in that it contains high molecular weight
toxic proteins that experimentally can cause severe
cardiovascular effects.

Some workers in the United States have
discovered a very labile low molecular weight
toxin that could only be extracted from spines
excised from living (anaesthetised!) fish. When
this toxin was added to a tank of tropical fish they
started gasping immediately, darkened in colour
and swam erratically. Paralysis and death followed
unless they were removed and placed in fresh seawater. This toxin may only be released in defence,
as tropical fish normally co-exist in aquarium
displays with butterfly cod.

The unpleasant effects that may be produced by
this venom are second in severity only to stonefish
stings. Fatalities are believed to have followed
multiple stings.

Even when these fish have been dead for some
hours, penetration by their spines can produce
severe envenomation.

In recent years, butterfly cod have become available in some parts of Australia as aquarium fish. As a result, injuries from their stinging spines are more common and, unfortunately, often the buying public is not warned that contact with the spines may cause painful injury. If you see them for sale in aquarium tanks without due warning, dob in the shop owner.

First aid and medical management of fish stings

Any projecting spines should be carefully removed. Bleeding is usually not significant, but apply firm pressure if it is. The need to relieve pain is the main problem, and this may generally be achieved by bathing the injured region in warm but not scalding water. If necessary, boat engine cooling water can be used. The pain often returns quite dramatically in the early stages when heat therapy is ceased.

Local anaesthetics are sometimes indicated and in severe cases a regional nerve block or systemic opiates may be greatly welcomed by the distressed victim. The pressure–immobilisation technique of first aid should NOT be used because it may increase local pain and tissue damage. The wound should be washed well with fresh water as soon as possible. The injured area is potentially contaminated and many marine bacteria are resistant to common antibiotics. Doxycycline is the drug of first choice. In significant injuries it is important that good drainage is ensured and an X-ray examination may be necessary. Tetanus prophylaxis should be updated as required. Often, unless the injured region is rested for a number of days, recurrence of swelling and discomfort occurs and healing may be delayed.

A warning: Dr Carl Edmonds, a specialist in diving medicine, warns of the danger of combining local anaesthetic and bathing in hot water. He reported the case of an Australian fisherman who, after immersing his anaesthetised finger in very hot water, lost the top of his finger. As Dr Edmonds recorded, the anaesthetic worked very well—he did not feel his finger cooking!

MARINE CREATURES—STINGING FISH

Catfish

In 1882, Paul William was net fishing at Sydney's Darling Harbour, which at that time abounded with succulent fish. When pulling in a net, part of his hand made contact with a catfish. According to a report published at the time: 'This gave him great pain, and soon commenced to inflame, in consequence of which he had his arm amputated to save his life. He lived long afterwards and was useful and cheerful when out with fishing parties.' These days such an outcome after a catfish sting is unlikely, but the case illustrates the immediate effects and possible complications of such an encounter.

There are more than 1000 species of catfish in the world. Most of these are found in freshwater habitats. Their size varies greatly: certain European catfish may measure 4 metres long and weigh 275 kg, while the minute Amazonian catfish is so tiny it occasionally penetrates the human urethra and often can only be removed by surgery. Apart from piranhas and other creatures, catfish are another very good reason why tourists should avoid paddling in the Amazon River.

About 30 species of catfish are found in Australia. All are considered venomous and all can deliver painful stings. They have a variety of common names, which can be confusing. In Western

DISTRIBUTION

Australia, for example, catfish are often called 'cobblers', but this is also the name for a different species of stinging fish found in both Victoria and South Australia.

Catfish were given their name because the long sensory barbels protruding from their lips are like cats' whiskers. These fleshy sense organs are harmless, but their presence should be a warning that the fish is dangerous. Since the tail of most of these creatures is similar to an eel, some are called eel-tailed catfish. Catfish have no true scales and the skin is usually thick and slimy.

Catfish are bottom feeders and are more active at night. Most species live in freshwater, but some survive in the most brackish of water. They abound in estuaries, rivers and mud flats and are frequently hooked or caught in fishing nets. Although their flesh is good to eat, they are often rejected because of their appearance or sliminess, or because they have injured the person who caught them.

Many people are stung by the striped catfish (*Plotosus lineatus*). Although it has not caused fatalities in Australia, it has done so overseas. The larger the specimen, the more severe the envenomation. Sometimes catfish cruise together in a large shapeless mass, and observers may think there is some large, but unidentifiable, marine creature swimming slowly along. The catfish may swim packed so closely that individual fish cannot be identified. The Australian naturalist, P. C. Roughley, compared the movement of such a shoal to a sluggishly animated ball as it rolls along over a reef. Another writer described how they travelled in black spherical 'pods' that slowly revolved at the surface. At times their numbers are so dense that the bottom is completely carpeted. In an aquarium they pack together in a most gregarious fashion.

The striped catfish has a black body and white longitudinal banding, but when killed it changes from a gleaming black to a dull brown.

Another common catfish is the white-lipped catfish (*Paraplotosus albilabris*), which looks similar but lacks the white stripes. This is also dark but sometimes has white spots and white lips. It grows to a highly dangerous 1.4 metres in length and is common in coastal and northern waters.

Fishers in New South Wales and southern Queensland often encounter the long-tailed catfish (*Euristhmus lepturus*). This creature is a uniform brown-grey or copper colour and may grow as long as 40 cm. Like a number of other catfish, it is particularly fancied by pied cormorants or shags.

Prevention of injuries

The only safe way to grasp a catfish is by its tail, but because catfish can move quickly even this is not recommended. E. M. Grant, the author of what has come to be the fisherman's bible, says catfish are one of the few groups of Australian fishes that cannot be safely handled, even when a cloth is wrapped about the hand or fish. Few anglers or trawler deckhands 'can subdue a squirming slippery bodied catfish eel without being spiked'. He concludes that should it be necessary to tackle a catfish at close quarters, 'it should be pinned through the head to a bait board with a sharp pointed knife or similar instrument and sent overboard with all care ... even a dead catfish eel can sting.'

Catfish have particularly long venomous dorsal spines and two lateral or pectoral spines. It can erect these spines suddenly and with great violence. The spines are extremely fine-pointed and strong and have no difficulty penetrating deeply into the skin. If someone tries to hold a catfish it will almost certainly injure their hand with at least one spine.

Each spine has two thin venom glands that run the length of the spine. As the spine penetrates the victim, the thin membrane over the gland ruptures and forces venom into the wound.

The venom of striped catfish is toxic to a wide range of animals. A toxin called plototoxin has been isolated and is relatively more stable than most other fish venoms. This may explain why stings from catfish that have been dead for hours can still produce severe pain. Plototoxin has a number of actions, including neurotoxic and haemolytic properties. A variety of other toxins have been isolated from catfish venom glands and their skin secretions. The effects of these substances range from increasing capillary permeability to lysis of erythrocytes.

Once stung, a person will experience instantaneous pain, the severity of which is often far greater than might be expected for the size of the injury. The pain usually subsides after about 2 hours, but it may last 24 hours. The wounded area may blanch but later become red or cyanotic. Gross swelling sometimes occurs and regional lymph nodes are usually tender. Injuries due to the striped catfish may take weeks to heal.

First aid

See first aid for butterfly cod, page 18.

The best management for severe cases of catfish sting is prompt local infiltration with anaesthetic, followed by a regional nerve block and at least 24 hours of hospitalisation. Dr Hanns Pacy, who has treated a number of cases, found that opiates failed to give satisfactory pain relief.

MARINE CREATURES—STINGING FISH

Stingray

In northern Queensland in the early 1990s, a large stingray leapt out of the water right in front of a fast moving pleasure craft. The creature glanced off all three passengers on one side of the boat before falling back into the sea. One passenger, a 12-year-old boy, had a stingray barb embedded in his left knee and a small puncture wound through his left nipple. Six days later the poor lad collapsed and died suddenly following the rupture of

damaged heart muscle. He had appeared to be quite well.

In 1945 an army sergeant was swimming happily inside the sea baths at St Kilda when he suddenly waved his arms and disappeared. He partially

DISTRIBUTION

Avoiding stingray stings

Stingrays are difficult to see because they often bury themselves almost completely in sand or mud. It is best to shuffle your feet along when wading to avoid treading on the creature and also to encourage it to move off. It is a good idea to probe ahead with a long stick. Diving boots may give little protection from stings. You should not swim along the sea bed because the length of your body is then exposed to a possible sting.

surfaced a minute or so later and then sank again. When rescued a small wound was found on the front of his chest. He died soon after and, at post mortem, a penetrating wound to his heart was found that was compatible with a stingray injury.

Fortunately deaths caused by stingrays are uncommon, but stingray stings themselves are not rare. Indeed one doctor on Morton Island, east of Brisbane, has treated more than 100 cases of minor stingray envenomations in recent years.

There are 22 species of stingrays found around the coast of Australia. They are the largest of our venomous fish, but clinically the physical damage done by the stinging barb is usually a bigger problem than the effects of the venom.

The size of the stingray varies enormously with the species. The black or thorn-tail stingray (*Dasyatis thetidis*) is the largest stingray in the world and can grow to 2 metres wide and 4.2 metres long. The common stingray or round stingray (*Uroluphus testaceus*) is found all around the Australian coast and is relatively small, reaching only about 80 cm in length. It is probably the most common cause of stingray injury.

Stingrays are basically gentle creatures and divers can find them a joy to watch. They swim with extraordinary grace and appear far bigger in the water than they actually are.

Stingrays have a variety of stinging spines attached to their tail. The spines, which are shed

each year, are associated with venom-producing tissue. There is no venom duct and the tissue lines each side of the spine. Little is known about the various stingray venoms. They tend to lose their potency quickly, especially if exposed to heat.

Stingrays feed on the seabed and may lie there motionless until the unfortunate human either treads on them or swims low over them. If the stingray is touched, particularly towards its rear, the response is a sudden thrust of its tail forward and downward, which drives the spine into the victim. At penetration, the delicate skin over the spine is broken and venom and tissue may enter the wound. Further injury may occur when the spine is withdrawn, and additional venom and tissue may be left behind.

Most stings are inflicted on the lower limb. There may be a penetrating wound and/or deep lacerations. Usually the wound bleeds quite freely and becomes a pale bluish-white. Pain may not be severe immediately, but often increases over the next hour and may cause general distress. In rare cases there may be general effects related to the venom, such as muscle cramps, cardiac arrhythmia, vomiting, salivation and/or convulsions. Overall, the most common problem is distress due to local pain.

However, the injury must be considered potentially serious if the torso has been penetrated by a spine.

First aid and medical management

See first aid for butterfly cod, page 18. Ensure that the patient's tetanus prophylaxis is current as deaths from tetanus have followed stingray injuries.

MARINE CREATURES—STINGING FISH

Stonefish

The stonefish sitting in the sand in shallow water was having a quiet think when it noticed two weird creatures. They were the feet of an approaching tourist. It braced itself as one soft white footsie came down firmly on its venomous spines.

The tourist's screams of pain carried hundreds of metres and his helicopter rescue made it into all the papers. The stonefish merely moved a few feet away and its damaged spines soon healed. From time to time he saw other similar creatures pass by, but at the time of writing had not been trodden upon again.

Stonefish are the most venomous stinging fish in the world and, except in the eyes of other stonefish, are also among the ugliest fish.

There are two species of stonefish (genus *Synanceia*): the reef stonefish (*S. verrucosa*) and the far more common estuarine stonefish (*S. trachynis*). Stonefish inhabit the entire Indo-Pacific region.

They are found along two-thirds of Australia's coast, from near Brisbane to some 500 km north of Perth.

DISTRIBUTION

Stonefish were given their name because they resemble an encrusted rock or piece of old coral. Their camouflage is near perfect, especially when encrusted with marine growth. Experts often have difficulty locating them, and the inexperienced has almost no chance—except by being stung!

A native name for the stonefish is nohu, which means 'the waiting one'. This is because the stonefish normally sits quite still for hours, but a dramatic flurry of activity occurs when a nice little fish passes near its large upturned mouth. Within a fraction of a second, the prey is snapped up and the stonefish resumes its waiting posture.

Stonefish are very heavily built and may grow to nearly 50 cm long. One wag has likened it to a politician: it is fat, has a large mouth, sits around doing nothing all day and can prove pretty venomous if you try to move it!.

The dreadful venom apparatus of this creature is used only for defence and does not aid in the capture of its prey. It has 13 dorsal spines, each of which has paired venom glands. The spines are quite strong and taper to very fine points. There is a groove on each side of the spine in which the long thin venom glands are attached.

When disturbed, the spines become erect and the front three, which are the largest, stand near vertical. The needle-sharp tip of the spine is bared at this stage. If a human foot, for example, is pressed down on the spine, it penetrates the foot, not only squirting liquid venom deep into the tissue but forcing the venom gland tissue deep into the wound under great pressure.

Each spine can deliver 6 mg of venom. The venom causes extreme local pain and tissue damage. It can also disturb muscle function, including the heart. Fortunately, an effective antivenom was developed in 1959 by Dr Saul Wiener at CSL. This was the world's first marine antivenom. To be stung by a stonefish when the antivenom is not available can be a dreadful experience.

Even minor stonefish stings are excrutiating. Pain is instantaneous and rapidly increases. Swelling occurs locally and may be extensive. The pain is so severe that the victim may become irrational. The more stings and the deeper they have penetrated, the worse are the signs and symptoms. Occasionally some muscle weakness and paralysis develops in the affected limb and some degree of shock may occur. Although no deaths have been recorded in Australian waters, they have been reported elsewhere. The victims have reportedly suffered terrible agony before becoming unconscious and expiring.

First aid

After the victim has been taken out of the water, pain relief is the first requirement. For lesser stings this may be achieved by bathing the stung area in warm to hot water (never scalding). Sometimes

Avoiding stings

Each year at least 30 stonefish stings in Australia's northern states receive antivenom. Most of the victims are male, and for many years all the injuries reported have occurred on the hands or feet. The circumstances of the stinging never cease to surprise. In 1992 a man caught a stonefish and brought it ashore with great care. He dug a hole, intending to bury it, but was badly stung when he accidentally dropped it on his foot.

Stonefish are pretty tough. Provided they are kept slightly moist, they can live for a day or so out of water. Thus there are three simple rules to avoid stings:

- Never touch prickly looking fish with bare hands.
- Never jump out of a boat into shallow tropical water.
- Never walk around tropical reefs in bare feet—use sand shoes or divers' boots.

the cooling water from an inboard or outboard motor has proved useful. However, with more severe stings, pain relief may only be obtained by the use of antivenom and potent opiate drugs such as pethidine or morphine.

The pressure–immobilisation type of first aid should NOT be used in cases of stonefish stings.

Any attempt to retard the movement of venom from the stung area will only enhance local pain and tissue damage.

This first aid is for stonefish only. For first aid and management of all other stinging fish, see page 18.

Medical management

Antivenom is recommended for all except the most minor of cases. The dose of antivenom depends upon how many spines have penetrated the skin. As a general rule, two spine penetrations require one ampoule of antivenom. The antivenom is usually given intramuscularly and should not be injected into the area of the sting.

The injection of local anaesthetic into the track of the sting or the surrounding area is a useful practice even though the relief may only be temporary. The use of a regional block should be considered when multiple stings have occurred and the patient is severely distressed. A regional block using bupivacaine has the advantage of giving lasting relief and also allowing surgical exploration of the injuries. Potassium permanganate ('Condy's crystals') should never be used; apart from being ineffective, it will increase local tissue damage. Emetine hydrochloride (65 mg/mL) has been used to give some relief from pain in the past, but there are very few commercial sources of this drug.

Apart from the actions of its venom, stonefish stings cause wounds that are easily infected and may contain foreign bodies.

MARINE CREATURES—STINGING FISH

Other Stinging Fish

There are many types of fish whose defensive spines can cause human injury. Venom of some sort is often introduced by the spines, and thus the pain experienced is often greater than one would expect from the physical injury inflicted.

Any reader who has ever been fishing is bound to have been stung at some time, even if only by the humble flathead. Every weekend thousands of inexperienced or unlucky anglers are stung by fish and many seek medical attention.

Bearded ghoul

There are a number of species of these very spiky, odd–looking fish (*Inimicus caledonicus*). An appropriate name for one is the demon stinger. They are particularly common in northern waters of Australia where they have attacked underwater photographers at times.

DISTRIBUTION

The bearded ghoul grows to about 30 cm and has a yellow-brown belly. Overall, it is black or brown above, with its sides bearing dark brown freckles. It has 17 extremely long spines on its back. The potential injuries from these spines is possibly second only to that of those inflicted by the stonefish. As with many stinging fish, its venom has never been researched.

Prawn fishermen find them a great nuisance as they may cause awful injuries when they get mixed up with the catch, which must be sorted out some-times in semi-darkness or in rough conditions. One crewman so stung suffered 12 hours of hell. The pain was immediate, and the injured thumb became rapidly swollen and blue-grey in colour. Fifteen minutes later he was sweating profusely, and his whole limb was stiff. He was delirious 20 minutes after the sting and threw himself about the cabin in fearful pain. The crew did their best to restrain him for more than 30 minutes. During this time he was screaming and complaining of pains around his chest and neck. Later, some relief was obtained by bathing his hand with hot water, but the pain immediately returned as soon as the water cooled somewhat.

People who have suffered stings from this fish may become so tired that they sleep for several days after the acute episode.

Flathead

These are probably one of the most common causes of pain and distress among amateur anglers. In Australian waters there are about 40 species that live in a variety of habitats, ranging from estuaries and bays to the continental

DISTRIBUTION

shelf. They are usually 30–60 cm long but some, like the dusky flathead (*Platycephalidae fuscus*), which is found in all states, may grow to as long as 1.3 metres and weigh 14 kg.

G. P. Whitley's *Handbook of Australian Fishes* states that this particular flathead has a great ability to bite through lines with its sharp teeth, and notes that experienced anglers use wire tracers to avoid this.

Flatheads are bottom-dwelling fish and like to bury themselves in the sand with only their eyes exposed. Apart from the dorsal spines, the head of many flatheads is often armed with large spines believed to be associated with venomous glandular tissue. To grasp a wriggling flathead with a bare hand guarantees the penetration of the needle-like spines.

Fortescue

There are several species of the genus *Centropogon*, and these little horrors can ruin a day's fishing. *C. australis*, known as the wasp fish or southern fortescue, is common in the estuaries of the eastern parts of Australia. It does

DISTRIBUTION

not grow longer than 15 cm. The marbled fortescue (*C. marmoratus*) is particularly common in Moreton Bay in Queensland, and is smaller, barely reaching 11 cm in length. Both these fish have 16 venomous dorsal spines and other poisonous spines, which suggest that the origin of the name fortescue may be in 'forty skewers'.

Both species are often caught in nets. Even tiny specimens can cause painful stings. They are a danger to uninformed skindivers who may be tempted to catch them because they are very common and slow-moving.

Goblin fish

This nasty little fish is also known as the saddle-head. It is found in all waters west of Adelaide all the way to Carnarvon. A mature goblin fish (*Glyptauchen panduratus*) may measure 25 cm and is most oddly shaped. It

DISTRIBUTION

has 17 closely webbed, highly venomous dorsal spines. As with many other stinging fish, the pain produced by these spines is out of proportion to the size of the injury. Minor scratches can produce severe pain and shock, and collapse may follow multiple penetrations. Nothing is known about the venom.

Gurnard perch or gurnard scorpion fish

This very tasty fish (*Neosebastes pandus*) has a distribution similar to the cobbler. They are usually bright red and are caught when feeding in shallow water around rocky reefs. Because of their large mouths they have other

DISTRIBUTION

names such as 'swallow-all' or 'mouth almighty'.

The appearance of a bright red spiky fish on the end of a fishing line warrants extreme caution. Some people will not allow them to be brought on board. Others, because of their fine eating, cautiously prize them.

The stress from the sting by this fish contributed to the death, 1 hour later, of an elderly man in Western Australia. On Flinders Island in 1980 a man was accidently stung by a very dead (refrigerated) specimen and suffered gross swelling and pain that spread up his arm. Complications developed that were not thought to be due to infection, and he subsequently died.

Old wife

This pretty, striped fish (*Enoplosus armatus*) is also known as the zebra fish. Its name, old wife, is attributed to the creature's habit of grinding its teeth and grumbling. No doubt this sexist nomenclature is due for some attention.

DISTRIBUTION

The fish is widely distributed around the whole of the Australian coast. Although frequently seen by divers, it is rarely hooked as it swims around jetties and wharves. It grows as long as 25 cm, and

its brown or black markings give it its zebra-like appearance. The back of its anal and nearby rays are bright red and its tail is pink. The creature is usually found in pairs or large groups, which separate suddenly when disturbed. It feeds on reeds or sea grass meadows to a depth of 40 metres. With its little mouth it also nibbles on shellfish and worms. This is why it is rarely hooked—not because it is a smart fish!

On the back of the creature are finely pointed venomous spines that can easily penetrate the human skin. Although the injuries are usually mild, sometimes severe pain may extend over the whole of the stung limb. In some instances the patient develops vomiting and a splitting headache. Great care should be taken to avoid handling this creature when it is netted or speared.

South Australian cobbler or scorpion fish

This fish has a far wider distribution than its name suggests. It is found all the way from the Darwin region, moving anti-clockwise around Australia and Tasmania to near Sydney. In Western Australia there is some confusion because catfish are sometimes called cobblers. In some places soldier fish is the common name.

DISTRIBUTION

Most experienced anglers have a very healthy

respect for the cobbler (*Gymnapiste marmoratus*). It is a solid, bottom-living fish that is active mainly at night and may grow to a length of 23 cm. Its spines number 13 dorsal, three anal, one pectoral and two on each side of its head. All these spines can produce venomous stings.

The venom of this fish is one of the few from common stinging fish that has been investigated. It has a wide variety of actions, ranging from blocking the action potential in nerves to disturbing the function of skeletal, smooth and possibly cardiac muscle. It is toxic to mice in relatively high doses, but this may reflect the lability of the venom. Excruciating pain may be caused by the spines of *G. marmoratus*. Severe stings may be associated with vomiting, sweating and even collapse (and swearing!).

People pulling in their fishing nets at night in southern waters are at particular risk. It is possible that the severe pain and shock produced by this fish contributed to the death of a 59-year-old fisherman who was found slumped over the engine cowling, with the net half pulled in and the fish in his hand. Some people appear to have developed a degree of immunity to stings by this fish and hardly notice a sting that would reduce a novice to a whimpering heap of misery.

Surgeon fish

There are a number of surgeon fish (genus *Acanthirodea*), and they have common names such as doctor fish, the tang and the spinetail. They are found in the warmer waters of Australia, ranging from northern New South Wales around the northern coast to near Perth.

DISTRIBUTION

They are called surgeon fish because they have a razor-sharp, lancet-shaped spine on each side of the tail. These spines become erect for fighting or defence, and multiple lacerations can be inflicted when the creature lashes its tail around while being handled. Surgeon fish have injured fishermen and occasionally attacked swimmers when the swimmer and the fish were in a confined area.

One of the best known surgeon fish is *A. dussumieri*, which may weigh 2 kg and be 55 cm long. Another common one is *A. triostegus*. Characteristically, it is pale cream with six vertical brown stripes, the first of which runs through its eye, while the last partially covers the tail base. The fish are quite pretty to look at, from a distance!

The deep lacerations produced by these spines are extremely painful, but the presence of a venom has yet to be proved. Those that have suffered pain for hours or even days have little doubt they have been envenomed.

Bleeding may be a special problem after injuries by this fish, and firm pressure should be quickly applied to the lacerated area.

Apart from causing injury, surgeon fish may occasionally carry the toxin that produces ciguatera (see page 53).

First aid

For first aid for stinging fish on pages 26–30, see butterfly cod, page 18.

Prevention

Treat all fish as potential stingers until they have been filleted. To date no one has been stung by a Fish Finger.

MARINE CREATURES
OTHER MARINE CREATURES

Cone Shells

It was a beautiful day, and the 32-year-old man was wading at low tide in the shallow end of the tropical lagoon. He picked up an interesting shellfish. It was partially covered with slimy algae, which he scraped off with his pocket knife. He had hardly started scraping when he felt a sharp sting in the palm of his hand, which immediately developed a burning sensation. He turned the shell over and saw part of the inhabitant withdrawing itself into the shell, taking with it at the same time a fine sharp needle that it seemed to swallow as it disappeared into its shell.

The mark on his hand was almost invisible. The burning sensation faded and his hand, and soon his whole arm, became numb. A feeling of light-headedness developed and he wisely returned to the shore and went home. Had he not done so he may well have drowned while still in the water because within an hour he could not move his limbs or sit up. Nine hours after the stinging he was brought to medical care, at which time he still had marked general weakness in all limbs. This resolved over the next few days.

DISTRIBUTION

The shellfish he had disturbed was an 8.5 cm specimen of the geographical cone shell (*Conus geographus*). He was luckier than a young man stung by the same species on Hayman Island in 1935. This man made the same mistake of annoying a cone shell by scraping its house with a knife and died 5 hours later. The official report of his death observed that 'the victim was, prior to the injury, in perfect physical condition and in training for football'. The conus shell was also in perfect physical condition.

More than 70 species of cone shells are found in the warmer waters of Australia. Many others are found in the Indo-Pacific region. Some cone shells are rare and extremely valuable, such as *C. gloriamanis*, which has never been found in Australia. (The story is told that someone lifted up a rock and found two perfect specimens and the value of other collections fell by 50 per cent.)

Cone shells that may be dangerous to people are found only in the sub-tropical and tropical waters. Specimens found in cooler waters are unlikely to cause even minor injuries to people.

Cone shells are so called because their shape is conical or cylindrical. Most species have characteristic colours and markings and can be easily identified. Five are considered dangerous to humans and *C. geographus* and *C. textile* are known to have caused deaths. The former must be considered the more dangerous.

These predatory snails have an unusual anatomy with the stomach situated above its foot, thus the name 'gastropod'. Some of the overseas specimens may be as long as 23 cm, but most Australian specimens are seldom longer than 10 cm.

Cone shellfish prefer shallow waters, inhabiting tidal reefs and generally hiding in sand or under rocks during the day. At night they crawl about busily looking for food, which they capture in the clever fashion described below. They choose a variety of prey, but the most dangerous ones tend to eat fish. *C. textile* is the exception as it fancies other gastropods.

C. geographus is a particularly agile creature. It produces a strong mucous thread, almost like a spider's silk, that allows it to descend down reef edges to catch fish and other prey. This technique can also aid escape.

When the conus shellfish goes fishing it uses a pretty sophisticated method. The venom gland expels a viscous venom that pools in the floor of the creature's mouth. The animal has a radula sac containing as many as 20 little teeth or harpoons in various stages of development. The mature harpoon, which may be as long as 1 cm in some species, is made of hard chitinous material and has several barbs. Immediately before use, the harpoon is slipped into the venom pool and then propelled to the tip of the creature's proboscis. When the creature's beady little eye has focused on the nearby victim, the firmly gripped tooth is pushed forward,

Avoiding cone shell stings

If these shells must be handled, thick gloves are mandatory and the shells should be held by the broad end, preferably posteriorly. A pair of tongs would be a good idea. Experts advise that if the proboscis is extending from the pointed end, it is best to drop the shell immediately. As some people have found out, live shells should never be carried in pockets, nor should they be left where children can touch them. Most stings have occurred when the collector is attempting to clean the shell of a freshly captured creature. One tourist scooped up a specimen in a net and safely transported it back to his hotel room. All was well until he decided to clean it up with soap and a scrubbing brush!

Best to leave cone shells alone.

and the exposed tip driven into the victim. Contraction of the pharynx forces venom down the central cavity of the harpoon to emerge near its tip.

Normally the prey is rapidly paralysed and the mouth then expands enormously so that prey, almost the same size as the actual shellfish, can be engulfed. Some large victims are partially digested before continuing down the alimentary tract.

The harpoon is not re-used. The cone can protrude the proboscis and its projecting harpoon from the narrow end of its shell and around to nearly the other end. This suggests that it is rarely safe to hold a cone shell by the broad end of the shell, as some people advise.

The venoms of cone shells have been subject to a considerable degree of research. Investigators agree that these creatures are very clever biochemists. They produce a variety of so-called conotoxins, most of which are small peptides comprising 5–35 amino acids. One group produces paralysis in a curare-like fashion by inhibiting acetylcholine receptors at the neuromuscular junction. Another type causes paralysis by targeting the voltage-sensitive sodium channels of muscles. Some conotoxins bind to calcium channels and cause hypotension. Any of these can rapidly bring the prey to a standstill.

Considerable interest has been shown in these toxins by the pharmaceutical industry. Many have been synthesised and are under investigation as possible anaesthetic agents or for the treatment of hypertension. They have also proven to be wonderful tools for pharmacological research.

Now back to the human victim. Usually a sharp pain is felt and the area around the sting may blanch or become cyanotic. The pain may be of a burning nature but sometimes is severe and likened to a wasp sting. It may be excruciating. The region usually becomes numb and local swelling is evident. General symptoms may rapidly develop after stings by a highly venomous cone. Vision, speech, swallowing and hearing may be disturbed, and lack of coordination and weakness of voluntary muscles soon follows. Patients often feel dizzy or nauseous, but gastrointestinal symptoms are usually absent. A distressing generalised pruritus has been described. In severe stings, especially by *C. geographus*, death may follow paralysis of the respiratory musculature. Less serious cases may take from a few hours to several weeks to recover. During convalescence the patients are weak and the slightest exertion may exhaust them.

First aid

Immediately apply the pressure–immobilisation type of first aid (see page 186). Once these first aid measures have been properly applied, if possible they should not be removed until resuscitation facilities have been reached. If necessary, assist respiration (see cardiopulmonery resuscitation on page 189).

Medical management

Assisted or controlled ventilation will be urgently required in severe cases. If ventilation is adequate and other vital functions are maintained, full recovery should occur in time provided that a severe hypoxic episode has been avoided. In one severe poisoning, 4 hours of assisted ventilation was required and it was noted that reflexes and muscle power returned in the order in which they had been lost.

No antivenom is available for the treatment of any conus stings. It is possible that anti-cholinesterase (edrophonium) drugs might be of some assistance in reversing the paralysis. The initial dose recommended would be 10 mg (less for a child), which should be given slowly by the intravenous route.

The lesion made by the sting is a potentially contaminated wound and the infection may require antibiotic treatment. The swelling usually subsides with rest and elevation. Tetanus prophylaxis should be updated. It is possible that all or part of the harpoon may remain embedded, but this has not been recorded.

MARINE CREATURES—OTHER MARINE CREATURES

Crown of thorns starfish

PLAGUE OF CROWN OF THORNS THREATENS GREAT BARRIER REEF

DISTRIBUTION

Such headlines regularly appear but this creature has another claim to fame. There are only two venomous starfish found in the world and the largest and most important, the crown of thorns, is very common in Australia's northern waters. The effects of contact with this starfish can be horrific to both the victim and onlookers.

The crown of thorns (*Acanthaster planci*), also known as the sea star or venomous starfish, is found on coral reefs throughout the Indo-Pacific region.

Whereas most starfish have around five arms or rays, this spiky brute usually has 13–17 arms of 10–12 cm length. The dorsal surface of the blue-coloured arms are covered with extremely sharp spines 6 cm or more in length. The spines are bright red or orange at the tips and they become a greyish-blue towards their bases. The size and colour of the arms can some-times vary over a 12 hour period. These starfish normally blend with coral and remain relatively immobile, but when

required, they can move with surprising speed and grace.

Starfish are echinoderms (from the Greek meaning 'hedgehog skin'). There are 200 known species. There is nothing 'fish-like' about them but their anatomy is quite fascinating. There is neither a front nor a rear end, and they are radially symmetrical. The skeleton is immediately under the skin and is made flexible by interlinking plates. This allows the arms to bend and twist, but not as quickly as proper joints would allow.

The starfish propels itself along by means of a remarkable hydraulic pressure mechanism that is known as a water vascular system. This is unique to echinoderms. Water enters the creature through minute openings on its surface and is drawn by ciliary action down into a rigid canal and then to the arms via side branches. The side branches deliver the water to many tubed feet, which end in small suckers. Contraction of muscles and a system of little valves extend the elastic tubed feet so that they press onto the sea bed. When the water is forced out, the tubed foot contracts and pulls the animal forward. The effect of many such expansions and contractions allows steady progress. Starfish do not have to move very fast because their normal prey includes coral, clams and oysters, which do not move at all.

This hydraulic system comes into its own when a starfish wants to feed on a live clam or oyster. If you have ever tried to open an oyster with your bare hands you will admire the method the starfish uses. It plonks itself on top of the clam in a hunched-up posi-tion and some of the suckers of its tubed feet attach to the two shells. The starfish begins to pull and the clam, already alarmed, closes more tightly. The starfish maintains a constant pulling action by using rows of its sucker feet in relays. After some time, the large muscles of the shellfish are exhausted and the starfish can then turn its stomach inside out and proceed to digest the shellfish.

By extruding its stomach through a vent on the underside of its body, a starfish does most of its digestion externally. It needs very little intestine and the text books say its anus is very small and is used very little, if at all. The nervous system is very simple and consists of a ring of nervous tissue around its mouth to which there are links to sensory cells over the surface of the creature.

Starfish have either two ovaries or testes in each arm. These open directly to the sea through small pores in the angles of the arms. As with many marine animals, fertilisation occurs after the eggs are shed into the sea water. The larva is bilaterally symmetrical and uses cilia to swim freely. It soon settles down and attaches itself temporarily to some solid base, where it develops into the adult starfish. It goes through remarkable contortions before the adult form appears with its radial symmetry.

Incidentally, some oyster growers whose oyster beds had been plagued by starfish removed the pests, chopped them in half and threw them back into the sea. As each half is capable of developing into a new starfish, this effectively doubled the population!

The crown of thorns starfish feeds on live coral and it releases digestive juices that dissolve the coral polyps. These are sucked back into the body of the animal, leaving the coral white and bare. A mature adult starfish may be nearly 50 cm in diameter at the age of 5 years and can systematically destroy a square metre or so of coral in half a day.

In 1962, vast numbers of starfish were found on the Great Barrier Reef, especially around Green Island. Since then a number of outbreaks have alarmed marine scientists. Despite more than 30 years of research, the cause of these population explosions is not certain, but some scientists believe that the phenomenon is a natural one. Certainly the over-collection of the giant triton (*Charonia tritonis*), which is a natural predator of the juvenile starfish, must have had some effect. However, it is the sudden fluctuation in the starfish numbers that has the scientists flummoxed. The fact that the female may spawn up to 20 million unfertilised eggs each year in mid-summer does not benefit the ecology of corals.

The spines of the crown of thorns starfish are composed of magnesium calcite, and being porous,

Avoiding stings

Stout shoes should always be worn in this creature's habitats. It should never be picked up unless strong gloves are worn as it is almost impossible to pick them off a submerged reef with bare hands without being spiked. These creatures may remain dangerous even when they have been washed up dead on a beach. Penetration of the spines produces pain way out of proportion to the physical injury.

are light but relatively strong. They are articulated at their base and, apart from their fine tips, have cutting edges that allow them to penetrate wet-suits and other protective clothing. Each spine is covered by an outer cuticle under which are layers of venom-producing glandular cells.

Research has shown that extracts of the spines contain a variety of active components that cause haemolysis and increase capillary permeability and platelet activation. Japanese workers have isolated a protein of molecular weight 20,000 Daltons that they consider to be the main toxin.

Reports of stings go back as far as 1705, and reviewers of the literature draw several conclusions. One is that the injuries are most frequently to the hands or feet of the individuals. Another is that the reactions of victims varies, but multiple stingings always produce serious effects. The venom's effects appear far more severe when larger starfish are involved.

Penetration of the skin produces immediate and severe pain. Even a shallow injury can prove extremely painful and discomfort may last for hours. The pain is often described as burning and throbbing. Sometimes profuse bleeding occurs. As with some sea urchin stings, a black or bluish pigmentation may be left at the site of the injury. If forceful contact has been made with these spines, they may snap and remain embedded. The wound may turn bluish, surrounded by an area of erythaema. Swelling of the region is usual, and the injuries may leak serous fluid for days.

Generalised symptoms may follow severe stinging. In particular, retching and vomiting may

Brittle stars

These are beautiful little starfish found all around the Australian coast. They have a button-like central disc from which a number of flexible snake-like arms radiate a distance of up to 20 times the disc's diameter. These fragile arms easily break off (hence the creature's name). They are not thought to cause any harm to humans but, believe it or not, they have at times been mistaken for the blue-ringed octopus!

dominate the clinical picture. Such symptoms may begin an hour after the injury and can fluctuate. For example, when a young islander jumped onto a medium-sized *A. planci*, some 14 spines penetrated his foot and many broke off and remained embedded. Severe pain lasted several hours but the child's persistent vomiting caused the greatest concern. This recurred every 3–4 hours for 4 days.

First aid

Help the victim out of the water and remove any very loose spines. Immersing the region in hot but not scalding water may give pain relief. One expert

considers iced water may give relief. Medical attention should be sought for all but the most minor injuries. On some Pacific islands the natives believe the best first aid is to re-apply the crown of thorns' suction pads downwards on the injured region. This may give people something to do, but it does not relieve pain and may result in further injury. Likewise it has been thought that the application of a chemical meat tenderiser containing trypsin may break down chemical bonds in the toxin, but this is a waste of time.

Medical management

Local anaesthetics should be infiltrated around embedded spines prior to their extraction. Multiple and/or severe penetrations may require exploration under regional or general anaesthetic. Soft tissue X-ray should be considered. Management of the local injuries is as for deep, potentially contaminated wounds. (See management of stinging fish injuries, page 18).

In severe cases in which vomiting occurs, anti-emetics such as intramuscular prochlorperazine are usually rapidly effective. Sometimes dermatitis results from non-penetrating contact with this starfish. This apparently responds well to topical steroids.

MARINE CREATURES—OTHER MARINE CREATURES

Glaucus or sea lizard

The glaucus is a fascinating little animal that lazily floats around the major oceans of the world. It is known also as the sea lizard and the most common species is *Glaucus atlanticus*. The mantle, shell and gills of this carnivorous mollusc or gastropod have disappeared. This leaves it with a naked body, which increases the surface area for gas exchange but makes its lifestyle somewhat riskier.

They are beautiful and dainty creatures with lovely colours and movements. On the upper

side of their long, soft bodies are gently waving tentacles that are exquisitely patterned. They are seldom longer than 3 cm and drift along with their ventral surface facing upwards, buoyed by air in their stomachs.

This surface is usually a beautiful blue while their

DISTRIBUTION

undersides are generally a shiny white or light grey.

The glaucus attracts our attention because it recycles the undischarged stinging capsules or nematocysts from various jellyfish. Sometimes the weaponry is from minute marine creatures that cannot harm humans, but the glaucus becomes medically significant when it uses nematocysts from dangerous species, such as those from the Portuguese man-of-war (*Physalia*).

The creature floats on the surface, where it can gently attach to some innocent jellyfish as it potters along quietly. As the two drift along placidly, part of the jellyfish is eaten by the glaucus, which takes complete and undischarged nematocysts of the jellyfish into its gut. Over a period of time these nematocysts migrate through the body of the glaucus and are assembled at the tip of the gently waving tentacles. Whereas the jellyfish uses this weaponry to capture its prey, the glaucus uses it for defence.

Several other creatures are known to recycle undischarged nematocysts, including a species of sea cucumber, but the most interesting is a small octopus, *Tremoctopus violaceus*. The young octopuses pick up fragments of the tentacles from the Portuguese man-of-war and use them as both an offensive and defensive weapon. This is a smart octopus.

The glaucus is pretty smart also. Marine scientists have been arguing for years about the mechanisms that make nematocysts explode to release their poisonous coiled darts. The glaucus must know a thing or two to safely transport the nematocysts through its tissues and then reactivate them at the tip of its tentacles.

Human injury may be caused by

contact with the glaucus' tentacles when the nematocysts are triggered. The numbers and types of nematocysts will influence the severity of the injury. The affected area will not show the orderly lines usually associated with injuries due to stinging capsules, but will be scattered over the area of contact. There is generally a blotchy red patch over the injured part. Pain and swelling increases over the first 15 minutes after the sting and may persist for a number of hours.

Avoiding glaucus stings

The glaucus should never be touched and it is inadvisable to swim in its vicinity.

First aid

Until recently experts advised that vinegar should be poured over the affected region. However, now that it is known that *Physalia* nematocysts may be triggered off by this treatment it is recommended that ice-water packs be used instead. There have been no reports of nematocysts from the highly dangerous box jellyfish (*Chironex fleckeri*) being recycled by this creature. The application of vinegar is an essential part of the first aid for box jellyfish stings.

MARINE CREATURES—OTHER MARINE CREATURES

Octopus

If we believe one expert: 'A farmer in a cornfield is in more danger of being attacked by a pumpkin than a swimmer is of being attacked by an octopus.' Another believes that 'a large octopus is the most dangerous animal encountered by divers.'

What is the truth about octopuses? Apart from the deadly blue-ringed octopus, which is very common around the Australian coast, octopuses generally offer little threat to people. Divers have been killed by large octopuses on rare occasions, but it is extremely unusual for an octopus to attack a human.

One delicious case supposedly occurred in Victoria during World War I. A chaplain was leading a group of boys along a shelf of rock about 1 metre above the water when an octopus briskly left the water and wrapped its arms, which were more than 1 metre long, firmly around his body. He jabbed the creature frantically with the butt of his fishing line while a companion opened fire with a .22 calibre rifle, missing the octopus completely and fortunately also the clergyman. After further frantic jabbing, the octopus discharged black ink over everyone and retreated back into the sea. The chaplain was uninjured and no similar reports have appeared in the literature subsequently.

In the very rare situation in which a large octopus decides to grasp a diver firmly, they may have great difficulty escaping, particularly if the octopus has firmly anchored itself.

Octopuses are fascinating creatures for a variety of reasons. Their eyes and central nervous system are highly developed and experiments have shown that they have a remarkable ability to learn.

There are many types of octopuses which, like squids, cuttlefish and nautiluses, are cephalopods. (Squids and cuttlefish have six arms and two tentacles, whereas octopuses have eight identical arms.) The term 'cephalopod' implies 'head upon the feet', so their anatomy is quite odd. A sharp, parrot-like beak is found where the eight arms join up. The oesophagus passes from the beak through the brain and between the eyes. Its gut is situated in a mantle cavity in which seawater circulates. The creature can eject seawater from the cavity through a multi-

DISTRIBUTION

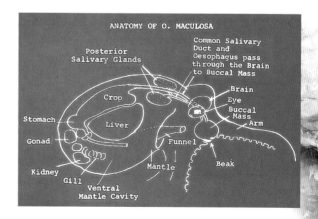

ANATOMY OF O. MACULOSA

Posterior Salivary Glands

Common Salivary Duct and Oesophagus pass through the Brain to Buccal Mass

Crop

Brain
Eye
Buccal Mass
Arm

Stomach

Liver

Gonad

Funnel

Kidney

Gill

Ventral Mantle Cavity

Mantle

Beak

directional funnel that gives it the additional advantage of jet propulsion to its normal swimming motion. A lot of octopuses can change their colour quite suddenly to camouflage themselves.

The mating habits of most octopuses are quite cute. The male keeps the female almost at arm's length while sperm is introduced into the female's mantle by the use of a single arm. If the male is shy, he can hide behind a rock and still become a father.

All octopuses can bite, and the injected saliva may cause itchiness and swelling. The ink they squirt out to allow their escape sometimes can produce surprising results. For example, in Chile a large octopus gave a naked diver a direct hit in the genitals. The result of this was pain, blistering and discolouration of the area.

The deadly blue-ringed octopus

There are at least five species of this little creature (genus *Hapalochlaena*), which is without doubt the most deadly octopus in the world. An adult

specimen may carry enough toxic saliva to completely paralyse 10 adult men. It was not realised that the blue-ringed octopus was potentially lethal until 1954 when a death occurred in Darwin following a bite. A young sailor walking back to the shore after spear fishing with a friend picked up a small blue octopus and put it on his shoulder for a few moments. He was unaware that he had been bitten. Shortly afterwards he complained of dryness in the mouth and difficulty in breathing. Soon he became nauseous, vomited and after a short trip to the Darwin Hospital was found to be cyanotic and not breathing, although his heart was still beating. Resuscitation attempts were unsuccessful. (It is now known that had this young man been given adequate and prolonged ventilation he probably would have recovered.) The minute bite site, which had been seen to bleed slightly after the octopus had been on his shoulder, could not be located at the post mortem.

The blue-ringed octopus lives all around the coast of Australia. The tropical species *H. lunulata* abounds in the north while the very common *H. maculosa* is found in southern parts. They are often found in relatively shallow water in shells, empty containers and sometimes mud flats may be literally alive with specimens at low tide. Sometimes they are found swimming in groups, but most lead a solitary existence.

No one would dispute that the blue-ringed octopus is a beautiful little creature. The total length of each arm is seldom longer than 10 cm and most specimens weigh less than 90 g.

The identification of the octopus is easy because at rest it has dark brown or ochre bands all over its arms and

Avoiding octopus bites

Blue-ringed octopus bites are easily avoided. The creature carries brilliant colours as a warning and it is important that the population at large is aware of this creature's existence and appearance. It should never be handled.

body with irregular little blue circles or figures of eight impressed on these bands. The colours darken dramatically if the creature is disturbed, with the bands becoming dark brown while the rings become a brilliant peacock blue. In daylight the creature's appearance is most striking. When the threat has passed, the colours of the octopus resume muted resting tones. Apart from producing highly toxic saliva, the octopus differs from other octopuses in that it does not have a functional ink sac, and the female carries her eggs with her all the time rather than leaving them to fend for themselves as other species do.

The salivary glands are particularly large and the toxin produced—tetrodotoxin—is an extremely poisonous substance. Tetrodotoxin is discussed in more detail on page 60. It is unique in that it is found in a wide variety of other poisonous creatures such as puffer and toad fish, a variety of shellfish, frogs and the Californian newt. (A fellow in California drank most of a bottle of whisky and then, apparently for a bet, swallowed a small newt and promptly expired.) The toxin causes paralysis by blocking the sodium channels in nervous tissue, an effect that wears off in time.

A young adult octopus weighing 25 g with venom glands weighing a total of 300 mg has enough venom to paralyse at least 750 kg of rabbits or, theoretically, 10 humans each weighing 75 kg.

Why does this octopus have so much of such a potent toxin? The reason is simple. The normal prey of the octopus is the crab. If it sails in to attack a crab it may well come off second best, so the octopus swims close to the crab and squirts saliva into the water surrounding it. (The octopus appears to be immune to its own toxin.) The crab observes this activity with some interest but in the

meantime inhales the toxin in the water and rapidly becomes paralysed. At this stage the octopus calmly descends upon the crab and proceeds to tear it apart.

The octopus has nothing to gain by biting a human and usually only does so when it has been restrained and kept out of water. It is thought that some envenomations have occurred when octopuses were trodden on in rock pools or perhaps prodded with a finger when resting in an underwater cavity.

Human fatalities and near fatalities follow a fairly similar pattern. The octopus, having been found stranded in a rock pool, is placed usually on the back of the hand or arm while it is shown to interested parties or carried up the beach. The victim is generally unaware of any actual bite, but symptoms of intoxication occur within 5–10 minutes of the live octopus being placed on the skin.

The symptoms commence with weakness and numbness about the face and neck combined with difficulty in breathing and nausea. Vomiting often occurs and severe cases may progress rapidly to a state of flaccid paralysis and apnoea. Cardiac function remains unaltered until anoxia becomes severe. In some cases there is little paralysis but evidence of cerebellar disturbances.

First aid and medical management

Bites by this octopus can produce a unique medical emergency. The pressure–immobilisation type of first aid should be applied immediately to the bitten area if this is possible, and should be left in place until the patient has reached medical care.

If breathing is failing it is essential that mouth-to-mouth resuscitation or some other form of ventilation be started. It has been established that in some cases respiration may have to be adequately assisted for many hours. If ventilation is adequate and prolonged, the chances of recovery are high.

If ventilation is adequate, the paralysed patient will remain fully conscious. One octopus victim who survived paralysis reported that while he was paralysed he heard one of the paramedics observe: 'It looks as if this chap has had it.' This did not cheer him up at all!

Port Jackson shark

The fisherman pulled a harmless 1 metre grey 'doggie' or 'dog shark' into his boat. It had been caught in water about 10 metres deep near Adelaide, South Australia. He picked it up by the tail with the intention of killing it when, to his annoyance, some part of the twisting creature spiked the back of his right hand. It was a clean wound, less than 1 cm across, and it bled only slightly. A few minutes later his hand was very painful, with pain spreading uniformly up the circumference of the forearm.

Within 10 minutes his arm was quite useless. He could not lift it, but this severe weakness was not due to pain, which soon became particularly intense in the right axilla. Subsequently he recovered and, like with other victims of this venomous shark, was unlikely to forget the experience. (One person stung on the foot by this creature in 1914 could vividly describe the episode more than 50 years later.)

Surprisingly, many professional fishermen are unaware that this shark is venomous and remain so by avoiding injury by deft handling of the creature rather than taking precautions.

DISTRIBUTION

The Port Jackson shark (*Heterodontus portus jacksoni*) was discovered and named by a member of the First Fleet under Captain Philip in Port Jackson, Sydney. As the late Gilbert Whitley wrote, its discovery aroused great interest because it was recognised 'as a relic of a bygone age, being the living representative of a family of sharks found widely distributed as fossils in Carboniferous rocks'.

This shark has a very wide distribution around the temperate parts of both Australia and New Zealand but it is not found in the cool waters around Tasmania. It has many common names, such as oyster crusher, dogshark, doggie, bullhead and sometimes by the Aboriginal name tabbigaw. It grows to a maximum of 1.4 metres and is a greyish light-brown with a darkish patch on the snout. The shark usually has a dark band as broad as the eye above and extending below the eye. Whitley described the blackish stripes on its body as resembling a harness.

Another species, which is rare, is the crested Port Jackson shark (*H. galeatus*). This is also venomous and is sometimes caught by deep water prawn trawlers in the ocean waters off southern Queensland. It may be distinguished from the other species by the presence of a high ridge over the eyes and the lack of the dark harness-like stripes.

The Port Jackson shark lives and feeds on the sea bed at depths to 200 metres. It eats oysters and shellfish, which it grinds up with its powerful jaws. It also enjoys crabs or sea urchins. The shark has a small mouth and its teeth are cusped in front for grasping the food, but are posterially enlarged to effectively crunch food. A finger presented to the shark may be promptly separated from its owner!

These creatures are gregarious and sometimes scuba divers find them stacked on top of one another on the sea bed. Divers sometimes call the shark 'pigs' because of this stacking habit and also because the mouth and snout have a pig-like appearance when viewed from the front. If you look for them you will usually spot at least one in the large tourist aquariums. They are docile and easily trained. (Trainer, watch your fingers!)

Immediately in front of each of the two dorsal fins is a fixed venomous spine. The venom apparatus is purely defensive and may have helped this slow moving and primitive creature to survive unaltered for millions of years. No research has been done on its venom or venom apparatus. Little is known about the few other existing venomous sharks, such as the northern hemisphere (Atlantic and Pacific) spiny dogfish (*Squalus acanthias*).

Penetration of the skin by the venomous spines may produce symptoms out of proportion to the apparent injury. Pain, swelling and local weakness occur at the same time. Like other envenomations by stinging fish, the most common immediate problem is the distress caused by local pain.

First aid

Pain relief can usually be rapidly obtained by bathing the injured area in warm water.

From all accounts, within 2 hours most symptoms of a Port Jackson shark's sting should have subsided.

For further information see first aid for butterfly cod, page 18.

MARINE CREATURES—OTHER MARINE CREATURES

Sea snake

A girl aged two was playing in the water on a beach near the Queensland resort of Yeppoon, near Rockhampton. She suddenly started screaming and her mother raced up to her and found a huge sea snake firmly wrapped around her daughter's left ankle.

The snake temporarily escaped and the mother rushed the child to the nearby ambulance station, firmly grasping the child's calf. After the wound had been washed she released her grip and within 30 seconds the child became drowsy and developed ptosis. On the way to the Yeppoon Hospital she started to vomit and showed respiratory distress.

DISTRIBUTION

It was touch-and-go for a while because she had received a massive envenomation. By the time she arrived at the hospital 20 minutes later, she was unconscious, cyanosed and had clonic movement of the limbs. She received seven ampoules of sea snake antivenom over the next 18 hours. This case was unusual because the multiple bites had led to a massive envenomation requiring more sea snake antivenom than had ever been used in a case before or since. Fortunately the little girl recovered.

Sea snakes are very common in the Pacific and Indian Oceans, but are not found in the Atlantic Ocean. Of the 50 known species, at least 32 have been found around the waters of northern Australia. They all have venomous fangs.

Sea snakes probably evolved from land snakes. They are graceful swimmers and have a vertically flattened tail to aid propulsion. These snakes are easily distinguished from eels because they have nostrils while eels have no nostrils or scales but have fins and gills. Sea snakes' nostrils point upwards to allow them to breathe on the surface of the water while the rest of their body is submerged. The nostrils have little valves that close when they dive. And dive they can! Some have been recorded at depths as great as 100 metres. The left lung is only small, but the right lung extends to the base of the tail and acts both as a reservoir for air and also as an aid to buoyancy. Sea snakes do not hiss like land snakes, but make a low-pitched gurgling sound.

Sea snakes frequently

shed their skins, probably to prevent a build-up of marine growth, which would slow them down. This sloughing of the skin may occur every 2 weeks for many of the snakes. Almost all sea snakes prefer relatively shallow water. However, some, like the yellow-bellied sea snake (*Pelamis paturus*), may be found hundreds of kilometres from land. At times they have been found in slicks consisting of millions of snakes drifting along peacefully.

The Bondi Beach case

In 1984, a 19-year-old man was swimming beyond the breakers at Bondi Beach in Sydney. He felt something bite his big toe and sensibly swam back to shore. When walking up to the beach he realised he was dragging his right leg and sought help from a life-saver. The latter saw two fang marks on his toe, made a provisional diagnosis of sea snake bite and immediately applied effective pressure–immobilisation first aid to the length of the leg. At this stage the patient had double vision. Later, in hospital, he received antivenom because of progressive muscle weakness, and made an uneventful recovery. A sample of sera taken before antivenom was later assayed at CSL disclosed the definite presence of snake venom, although the species involved was not certain. This case highlights the possibility of sea snake envenomation occurring in non-tropical waters. In the past, such envenomations may have gone undiagnosed and possibly ended fatally.

Most sea snakes are born alive at sea. However, one species, *Laticauda columbrina*, comes ashore to lay up to 20 eggs. Some tourists in the islands of Fiji have found it disconcerting when their holidays have coincided with the snakes' egg-laying season. These egg-laying sea snakes, or sea kraits, are rare in Australian waters, although one has been found near Sydney.

Sea snakes mainly eat fish and eels. A salt gland in the floor of the mouth excretes excess salt.

All sea snakes have fixed fangs with the venom duct opening near the tip. Although the venom of many species is extremely toxic, usually the output is very low. There are a number that are highly dangerous and they deserve individual mention (see below).

The output and potency of sea snake venom varies from species to species. Generally, they are of similar potency to the middle group of Australian land snake venoms. The venom of the beaked sea snake is the most toxic of all, deemed the sixth most toxic snake venom described. Most venoms contain neurotoxins, many of which have very strong myolytic actions. The latter activities are directed at skeletal muscle with little effect on heart or smooth muscle.

Although there are exceptions, the bite is not usually painful; at most a mild stinging may occur. Sometimes the relatively fragile fangs may break off and remain in the wound. As with the case of land snake bites, often no evidence of envenomation develops. If no first aid has been employed and a significant envenomation has occurred, rapid collapse may occur although this is unlikely.

General muscle aches, pains and stiffness of movement may develop within 30–60 minutes of the bite. There may be spasm of the jaw muscles. Moderate or severe pain may occur 1–2 hours later on passive movement of the limb muscles, and respiratory movement may be compromised. By 3 hours, myoglobinuria may be evident and plasma creatine kinase may become elevated. It is unusual to have any disturbances of coagulation or evidence of haemolysis. Death, when it occurs, may be early due to respiratory failure or later following renal complications.

First aid and medical management for all sea snakes

The pressure–immobilisation type of first aid (see page 186) has proved ideal for sea snake bites. They usually occur on the limb, particularly on the hands of prawn fishermen when clearing nets at night. The fact that this type of first aid can be left on for some hours when applied properly has proven advantageous when a port with medical help is some distance away.

Medical treatment is similar to the management of bites by land snakes. The antivenom of choice is sea snake antivenom, which has been shown to neutralise the 12 most important sea snake venoms. The sea snake antivenom is made by immunising horses with both tiger snake venom and beaked sea snake venom. If sea snake antivenom is not available, significant improvement may be obtained by the use of tiger snake antivenom.

Sometimes the diagnosis may be difficult to make. Fish and other marine stings are far more common than sea snake bites, and these usually cause immediate and intense pain, sometimes excruciatingly so. The fang marks of sea snakes are usually very small, with no local swelling and indeed may be at times very difficult to see. Thus, the lack of pain and small fang marks may be diagnostic, especially if associated with a positive venom detection finding and general muscle tenderness.

The olive-brown sea snake

This snake (*Aipysurus laevis*) is distributed from Brisbane to Exmouth Gulf in Western Australia. It is a heavily built snake that averages 1.2 metres length and is usually a dark purple-brown from above. The tail is nearly pure white. The young, which are born alive, are particularly large. Sometimes these snakes are stranded on beaches and they make very clumsy but usually successful attempts to get back to sea. It is best not to impede them. The olive-brown sea snake and Stoke's sea snake have fangs long enough to penetrate a wetsuit. Nevertheless, a wetsuit should give some protection by reducing the depth the fang may reach. The venom yields from this snake may be as high as 22 mg, and the venom is about as toxic as the venom of the Australian black snakes (genus *Pseudechis*).

Stoke's sea snake

This is a massively built snake with a very large head. It was one of these snakes that bit the little girl described above. This snake (*Astrotia stokesii*) is found from Sydney to the north-eastern parts of Western Australia. The head of this snake is usually dark brown or black, while the body is yellowish or dark grey. The belly is a faded ochre or cream colour. The snake may grow as long as 1.5 metres, and one such specimen was 26 cm in girth.

These snakes like reefs and also open water. They have been found in huge numbers drifting along in a slick. One such slick was recorded in 1932 in the Straits of Malacca; it consisted of a band 3 metres wide extending for about 96 km. The purpose of these slicks is not known, but they may enable safe sex (through safety in numbers) while the snakes travel to new feeding grounds.

The fangs of *A. stokesii* may be 6.7 mm long and easily penetrate wetsuits. Unlike the fangs of other sea snakes, the venom duct lies in a deep groove rather than being enclosed. This snake is a copious producer of venom with an output possibly as high as 152 mg. The toxicity of the venom in mice is similar to that of the Australian black snakes. The venom has a number of potent neurotoxins.

The beaked sea snake

This is clinically the most important sea snake in the world (*Enhydrina schistosa*) and it is widely distributed. It is found from the Gulf of Iran through the Far East to as far south as Rockhampton. It frequently causes fatal bites among Malaysian fishermen, usually after they have netted the snake at night.

The upper lip extends forward, giving it a beak-like appearance. The lower lip is deeply indented to receive the prominent nostril. The average length of this snake is 1.2 metres but it may grow to 1.5 metres. Usually they are a dull grey-green above with an off-white belly.

This sea snake rarely ventures into the open sea and generally lives around estuaries and tidal creeks, where it feeds almost totally on catfish. Like other sea snakes, it prefers to avoid people but becomes quite aggressive if interfered with. In captivity it is considered more likely to become angered than most other sea snakes.

The average output of this snake's venom is 8.5 mg with a maximum of 79 mg. The venom is more toxic than the other sea snake venoms, being only slightly less toxic than tiger snake venom. It contains at least five myotoxins and varies in properties from one geographical area to another.

Hardwick's sea snake

This is another heavily built sea snake (*Lapemis hardwickii*) that is often caught by trawlers in the northern waters. It is apparently common at low tide near Cairns. The snake is olive-grey or white above, with 30 or more bands that give it a zig-zag appearance. Its average venom output is some 5 mg and contains a number of myotoxins.

The sea kraits

Species of this sea snake (genus *Laticauda*) move onto land at times, hence the name sea krait. (The krait is an Asian land snake.) They are often beautifully banded and grow to a length of 1.3 metres. This snake is rare in Australian waters although one was found near Sydney and another in Tasmania.

MARINE CREATURES—OTHER MARINE CREATURES

Sea urchin

The well known politician was having his annual day off. Friends took him snorkelling near Cairns, and for the first 30 minutes or so he enjoyed himself enormously. However, as the sea roughened, the shallow water he was in slowly became murkier. He was not wearing a wet suit and unfortunately he knelt on something.

It felt as though a dozen red hot needles had been driven through his kneecap. He gave a terrible yelp and the others hurried to his assistance. The injured area had a series of puncture marks, some of which protruded fine dark spines. Over the next half-hour the pain and swelling increased and the victim was nauseated and vomited. He flew back to Melbourne the next day, leaving his concerned friends admiring his stoicism.

An attack of nausea and vomiting when approaching Brisbane nearly warranted his off-loading. But he made it back to Melbourne where he was coerced to obey doctor's orders for the next few days.

This representative of the people had knelt on a multi-spiked black sea urchin, which is considered the most common dangerous animal in tropical and sub-tropical waters. The black sea urchin (*Diadema setosum*) may be found as far south as Sydney. It has a spherical black body covered with needle-sharp hollow spines that may be 30 cm long.

DISTRIBUTION

These spines provide protection and are used for locomotion. Each spine is attached to the shell by a ball-and-socket joint and is moved by fine muscles.

The sea urchin is generally more active at night, when it feeds on plants and sedentary animals. In the water, it is impossible to touch the creature with bare hands without suffering a sting. The tips of the spines penetrate the skin with ease and often snap off. Only very strong protective clothing will prove adequate.

The flower urchin

The most dangerous sea urchin described is the flower urchin (*Toxopneustes pileolus*). This was not known to occur in Australia until it was discovered in Moreton Bay, Queensland, in 1960. Later specimens have been found as far south as Sydney Harbour. This urchin, which has apparently killed divers in Japanese waters, is covered with bright purple and white 'flowers' that are poisonous to eat. Its stout spines, only 8 mm in length, are extremely toxic. Contact with them may cause shock and respiratory failure. No cases of poisoning have been recorded in Australia.

Although venom glands have not been demonstrated in the spines, the effects of the stings suggest that a venom is released. A sting is associated with immediate burning pain followed by redness, swelling and continuous throbbing pain. The area is often discoloured blue from pigment released from the spine. Sometimes general effects such as nausea and weakness develop, especially when multiple stings have occurred. The wounds often become infected.

First aid

Carefully pull out any projecting spines. Bathing with warm but not scalding water may ease the pain.

Medical care should be sought for even minor injuries because, among other things, the likelihood of infection is high.

Even trivial stings can be uncomfortable for days or even weeks. Although some sea urchin spines are absorbed by the body in a day or so, the black sea urchin's spines may take many months to be absorbed and often cause chronic inflammation. The spines are detectable by X-ray and all extensive injuries must be appropriately X-rayed. If necessary, embedded spines must be surgically removed. If it has been decided to leave a spine or spines *in situ*, their absorption may be followed by X-ray studies every second month.

Without comprehensive management, however, a serious injury may lead to permanent disability.

Many Australian tourists suffer from sea urchin stings when overseas. In some islands the customary treatment carried out by the locals is to pound the stung area with rocks to pulverise the embedded stings. Although this may enhance the rate of absorption of the foreign bodies, it is far from the preferred management. The cure may prove worse than the disease.

MARINE CREATURES—OTHER MARINE CREATURES

Shark

Hank was the operator of a garbage barge at Heron Island on the Great Barrier Reef off the coast near Gladstone. In those days old Hank discreetly disposed of the Island refuse on the edge of a reef while the guests were having breakfast.

One morning he took Struan with him and the two set about emptying a number of 44-gallon drums of half-eaten turkeys and the like overboard. Within seconds fish were everywhere, but they shot through when half a dozen black-tailed reef sharks swung into action. They abruptly disappeared and all seemed calm as Hank and Struan continued tipping the remains of the previous night's smorgasbord over the side.

Suddenly, a huge shark appeared and swept

DISTRIBUTION

slowly past the barge, engulfing food as it went. As it passed Struan it rolled over slightly and observed him with a strange round eye about the size of a saucer. This tiger shark's companion then glided past, giving a good display of shark dentitia as it took half a turkey. The length of both was three-quarters that of the barge, which made them larger than 4 metres.

After a few more dramatic sweeps, one of the sharks then turned its attention to the barge. This turn of events was outside Hank's experience and with an air of feigned nonchalance he fired up the engines and propelled the barge over the reef proper in some 50 seconds flat.

Of the 350 species of sharks, 30 are known to have attacked humans. The most important are the white pointer, the grey nurse, the tiger shark and the mako shark (see also Shark Attack, page 2).

Sharks have been controlling marine populations effectively for more than 100 million years. They are designed beautifully and few predators are more successful. They have all the right equipment: their teeth may be as long as 5 cm. Unlike fish, the shark regularly replaces its teeth. Young sharks may do this every week and adults every 4–8 weeks. With such sharp teeth, very powerful jaws are not required. Even so, a large shark may bite at a pressure of 3 tonnes per square cm.

The shark has made a fine art of detecting prey. Lining its nasal sacs are extraordinarily sensitive cells that can detect enormously diluted fish blood or flesh. It is said that these sensors may pick up one part of food in 10 billion parts of sea water. When the hungry shark detects a stream of such food particles, it faces into the current and heads for the source.

Sharks also detect prey by picking up vibrations in the water made by injured creatures, or by people swimming. Having good vision as well as these other features means that a shark rarely misses its prey.

Shark attacks and fatalities hit the headlines but the actual statistics indicate the rarity of these dreadful occurrences. Between 1980 and 1990 there were 11 known fatal shark attacks in Australia. During this same period, 20 people died from bee stings, 19 were fatally struck by lightning, drownings accounted for more than 3367 people and 32,772 people were fatally injured in accidents involving motor vehicles. In the same period, crocodile attacks caused eight deaths. Thus the risk of shark attack is minuscule, particularly when the millions of hours Australians spend cavorting in coastal waters is considered. On the other hand, the infrequency of shark attack is little comfort to either the victim of a shark or a swimmer or surfer that sees one approaching. It is therefore wise to respect the advice of our coast guards and surf life-savers.

Injuries caused by an attacking shark vary enormously depending on the type and size of the shark. A determined attack will leave massive body wounds or amputations, and thus little chance of survival. Sometimes the teeth envelop the victim's neck or body yet the shark may not press on with the attack and spit the victim out. Most bites are single, with the flesh being torn away from the individual. Haemorrhage is usually massive.

Sometimes the only injury inflicted is due to contact with the shark's extremely coarse skin. This may cause parallel but shallow lacerations.

The white pointer

The white pointer or great white shark is the world's biggest and most feared shark. The largest ever caught and weighed was a 3312 kg specimen that measured 6.4 metres. They are found all around the world and unfortunately are particularly abundant in the Great Australian Bight. Like the mako, this shark is semi-warm-blooded. As a consequence, its muscles are more efficient, giving it a high attacking speed.

The grey nurse

The grey nurse shark has a most inappropriate name, being usually brown rather than grey and behaving nothing like a nurse. (The name 'nurse' is thought to have come from an ancient word 'nusse', meaning 'great fish'.) Growing to more than 4 metres long, its mouth has been described as 'a fang-lined chamber of horrors'.

The tiger shark

On many occasions, tiger sharks have been found to contain human remains and they also have cannibalistic habits. The tiger shark grows to a maximum of 7.4 metres (average 3.7 metres). It is second only to the great white shark for the number of attacks on people and boats. Its fearsome teeth and large mouth will take almost anything. Items found in these sharks, apart from human remains, include dogs, bags of potatoes (some of which had sprouted) and even a chicken coop with a few feathers and bones left inside. One shark had three overcoats, a rain coat and a driver's licence. Dr Ricky Chan of the University of New South Wales found three sharks that had each swallowed a sheep. He could not explain how the sheep had got there!

The mako shark

The mako, fast and strong, is often more than a match for big-game fishers. Growing to 4 metres, this shark can leap spectacularly into the air, and has sometimes landed in boats.

First aid

See also page 2.

The victim should be removed from the water: rescuers are rarely attacked. Attempt to stop the bleeding immediately by placing direct pressure above or over the bleeding artery. Move the patient as little as possible at this stage; stopping the bleeding has absolute priority over attempting to move the patient to waiting transport. Keep the patient's head lowermost, with the wounded parts raised if possible. Compress the bleeding area as firmly as possible: a rolled towel is ideal. If bleeding continues, leave the towel in position and firmly apply another one over it. The need to stem haemorrhage as soon as the patient is out of the water cannot be over-emphasised. If a wet suit is being worn, do not remove it. The ambulance and medical personnel should come down to the patient.

Medical management

Dr Carl Edmonds recommends that haemostasis should be established by any means available. He says this is one occasion where the use of tourniquets may be justified. Before moving the patient, top priority, if indicated, should be given to the infusion of intravenous replacement fluid and maintenance of vital functions. Dr Edmonds stresses that at all stages the first aid and resuscitation should take priority over the need for hospitalisation. He adds that many patients have died in transit, and he suggests that it could be more accurate to state that the victims died because they were transported.

Dealing with the injuries can only be tackled once the patient's condition is stabilised. The wounds are potentially contaminated with marine and other bacteria and may contain foreign bodies such as clothing and/or shark's teeth. Apart from these two factors, the management of a patient in hospital is similar to other equivalent trauma cases.

MARINE CREATURES—OTHER MARINE CREATURES

Sponge

A pretty sponge had been washed up on an Adelaide beach after a storm. It was a light brownish colour, some 25 cm wide, and the woman decided to collect it. She picked up the sponge, carried it home in her right hand, and placed it in a bucket of hot soapy water to clean it. About an hour after she had first picked it up her right hand developed severe stinging pain with erythaema and swelling, involving the right palm and the underside of the right forearm. Swelling and discomfort lasted several days.

A week after finding the sponge she took it out of the bucket with her left hand, which she described as her 'good' hand. As the reader might have anticipated, this hand became similarly affected. The penny dropped, and she went to see her doctor. They were both puzzled as to what might be done next. Antihistamines gave some relief, but it was 3 months before the irritation of her hands had subsided. The late Dr Ron Southcott of Adelaide, who researched stinging sponges, believed the sponge that effected her was *Neofibulania mordens*.

Although originally described as plants, sponges are animals. They were accepted as animals because they beat the flagella on certain cells to set up water currents. Sponges are the simplest of the multicellular organisms. They are made of a variety of cell types with differing functions.

Most sponges are marine, and all are sedentary although their sperm and ova float off to become free-swimming larvae. Sponges come in a wide variety of shapes and sizes and are of varying complexity. Their body plan is unique as no other multicellular animal uses its main opening for excretion rather than a mouth. The sponge is a living filter, with water constantly entering through the microscopic pores that riddle its entire surface area. Sponges belong to the phylum *Porifera* (pore-bearers).

In 1907 an embryologist by the name of Wilson conducted an intriguing experiment. He pushed a living sponge through fine silk, breaking it up into individual cells and debris. When the mixture was allowed to stand he discovered something quite surprising: the cells began moving and slowly aggregated into larger masses. After about 3 weeks a functioning sponge had re-formed.

The skeletons of sponges have been used for thousands of years. The Greeks used them as an aid for cleaning both their houses and themselves and found them great for padding helmets and leg armour. (No doubt they would also be handy for mopping up the blood.)

The Romans used them for multiple purposes, from paint brushes to substitutes for drinking cups. A significant example is told in the *New*

Testament (John 19:29): 'A jar full of sour wine was standing there. So they put a sponge full of the wine on a branch of hyssop and held it to [Jesus'] mouth.' (Hyssop apparently is an aromatic herb.)

The common bathroom sponge needs a lot of work done on it before it reaches the customer. When fished out of the sea, its dark tough leathery membrane is quite evil-looking. When cut in half it now looks like a slimy piece of raw liver. Sponges have to be cleaned, pounded and trimmed into appropriate shapes. Their tough elastic fibres make sponges remarkably hard-wearing, and they tend to outlast synthetic efforts.

The most dangerous Australian and New Zealand sponge is *N. mordens*, which is common in South Australian waters. It is mushroom-shaped, usually a beautiful royal blue colour, and may grow to 50 cm in height. The interior is a dull yellowish-brown. This sponge has a slimy exterior and people who touch it are not initially affected. After about an hour a 'pins-and-needles' sensation develops in the skin. Increased inflammation may occur, with the affected area becoming markedly swollen and painful. Resolution may take some weeks and there is often desquamation.

Dr Southcott discovered a classic description of the effects of this sponge in some correspondence written by a lighthouse keeper in 1890. A sponge had caused injury after it had been used to wash paintwork, and a sample of it had been forwarded to the South Australian Museum. There it remained for 80 years, where it was stored in a box with the accompanying correspondence.

The effects of the sponge are well described in the letters: 'at times his hands are swollen and purple with intolerable itching and terrible pain ... Some time after his hands began to burn and itch and for days he was like a madman.'

The writer warned that the sponge should not be touched if the hands were wet, and he asked if the museum authorities would kindly inform him of any discoveries they made about the sponges. It was 80 years before Dr Southcott could have informed him that the sponge involved was *N. mordens*. Dr Southcott established the effects of a fresh sponge applied to a small area of his skin, then carried out other studies. For instance, he found that the original specimen, when wetted, had lost its toxic effects but a sponge that had been dried for only 4 years and then wetted produced quite a moderate response when applied to his skin for 1 minute. He confirmed that dried sponge, whether fresh or old, is not toxic and wetting is required to activate the toxic agent, which is partially resistant to boiling or immersion in soap or formaldehyde solution.

In 1987, Dr Flachsenberger and his colleagues in South Australia looked at the structure of the spicules and tested various extracts made from *N. mordens*. The spicule arrangements appeared most intricate, extremely sharp, and offset in all directions. Some were sigma-shaped (like a short section of a corkscrew), giving them an additional

ability to drill into soft tissue. The spicules are made of silicon and thus cannot be metabolised. These scientists studied the effects of extracts on their own skins and found one that produced painful itching sensations lasting more than 4 weeks and becoming almost unbearable when the weather was warm and the skin perspired.

The extracts contained neuro-excitatory substances that were potent when applied to marine tissues, such as those from crabs and octopuses. If crabs were placed in beakers containing an extract they became very sluggish. This effect could be reversed by placing the crabs back in fresh seawater. The authors proposed that some sponge toxins play a defensive role against crabs. They observed that vast numbers of small crustaceans used other sponges as their hide-outs after removing the interior of the sponge. *N. mordens* is very rarely converted into a home by other creatures, perhaps because it is toxic.

The yellow sponge

The next most important toxic sponge is the yellow sponge (*Lissodendoryx* species). This is common in Port Phillip Bay, Victoria, but has a wide distribution and is sometimes brought to the surface by fishermen. It produces a severe contact dermatitis that Dr Southcott considered generally much milder than that of *N. mordens*, although the degree and persistence of the swelling can make a stung hand look like a grossly inflated rubber glove and require hospitalisation for more than a week.

The fireweed

Although not a sponge, the fireweed (*Lytocarpus philippinus*) should be mentioned, as the effects and management are similar to the stinging sponges. There are a number of species of stinging hydroids or seaweeds. The most feared is the fireweed, which is very common in Australia's northern waters and is found as far south as Moreton Bay. It lives both in coral reefs and sheltered coastal waters. Fireweed grows to 30 cm long and the slightest contact may produce severe stings. Pain develops within minutes and an erythaematous rash, which may blister,

often occurs. The toxins can produce general effects such as fever, malaise or gastrointestinal symptoms. In the Darwin area this creature is also known as the fire fern or poison weed.

Some of the other species of stinging hydroids prefer deeper waters. Most victims are inexperienced scuba divers.

Sponge divers' disease, common in the Mediterranean, has to date not been described in Australia. It is caused by stings of a sea anemone that grows on the sponges.

Except in the bathroom, it is best to avoid touching any sponge, especially those that have been washed up on a beach. Even a dried specimen may become dangerous when wetted.

On the bright side, plenty of good news has been published about sponges. Papers have been filling the journals describing a great variety of biologically active compounds isolated from tropical and sub-tropical sponges. They cover anti-inflammatory, anti-tumour and anti-microbial activities and they mimic just about every type of pharmacological activity described. Sponges produce chemical substances that astound the organic chemist. No doubt there will be some important benefits for therapeutics. Not bad for such 'simple' animals.

First aid

The exposed area should be gently washed in sea water or fresh soapy water.

No topical application is of proven value. Vinegar soaks have been claimed to give relief in the West Indies, but until the nature of the irritants is determined it is difficult to develop rational therapy. Local applications such as ice/water packs, local anaesthetic or antihistamine creams can be tried. Severe cases may require local and systemic steroids as well as antibiotics.

Dr Flachsenberger found that corticosteroids did not influence the reaction that sponge extract mixture produced on guinea pig skin, but when clinically facing gross inflammation due to toxic and mechanical factors it is hard not to reach for steroids. Provided infection is kept under control, steroids should not worsen the situation. There have been no reports of non-steroid anti-inflammatory drugs being used in these conditions, and they might be of some use.

MARINE CREATURES

Seafood Poisoning

Ciguatera

The fish was absolutely delicious. Caught earlier that day, grilled to perfection and served with a crisp, lightly perfumed white wine. The host looked around at his six companions with great satisfaction. Life was good. The coronation trout was good. His wife, who was near term, patted his arm with affection. He was a good cook, she thought, even though he did make a mess in the kitchen.

Six hours later, ciguatera struck. They all suffered abdominal pain, vomiting and diarrhoea. Soon some developed burning feelings in their hands and feet, itchy skin and muscle and joint pains. It was weeks before they had all recovered. The unborn child was affected, the mother describing it as shivering in her womb. A baby boy was delivered by Caesarean section 2 days later. He was quite ill with respiratory distress and a facial palsy, but made a full recovery over the next few days. It was noted he was slow to smile. No wonder.

Ciguatera is a very strange disease. There are several hundred types of fish that can accumulate the toxin. The toxic flesh of the fish tastes normal and the toxin is not destroyed by cooking.

Ciguatera occurs in both tropical and sub-tropical regions of the world. Its name is derived from a turban shell called 'cigua' that occurs in the Caribbean. When various fish were eaten in the region, they produced an illness similar to that which followed eating this little mollusc. As toxic fish were detected in other parts of the world, the illness produced was accordingly labelled ciguatera.

Ciguatera is in all the history books.

Everyone of note who cruised around the Pacific stirring up the locals or precipitating mutinies seems to have experienced ciguatera first hand. Captain Cook's crew aboard *HMS Resolution* suffered from it in 1774 in the New Hebrides. Captain Bligh, after the mutiny on *HMS Bounty* in 1789, noted in his log that he and his crew 'suffered a prodigious sickness' after eating a fish. The illness described most probably was ciguatera. It would not be much fun adrift in an open boat, without toilet paper, suffering from ciguatera and with Captain Bligh keeping a wary eye on you.

Avoiding ciguatera

In the Gilbert Islands, where ciguatera is common, suspect fish is often screened by first feeding it to the old or the infirm, who are the least productive members of that society and therefore not sorely missed if the fish prove toxic. This system works fairly well, but as far as is known is not practised elsewhere. Kits are being developed for toxin detection, but as yet are not available in Australia. In the meantime, to reduce the chances of suffering from ciguatera, the following suggestions will reduce the risk.

- Avoid eating large specimens of reef fish.
- Don't eat more than one meal of reef fish per day.
- Never eat moray eel, chinaman, red bass or paddletail fish. Commercial sale of these is illegal because of the risk involved.
- Be aware that problems may be encountered with coral trout, Spanish mackerel, reef cod, barracuda, emperor, groper and surgeon fish. Trevally and kingfish can also cause problems.
- If lucky enough to be staying at an Island resort, adopt the following cautious approach. For dinner have the same fish that other guests had for lunch that day, provided none of them have mysteriously disappeared. Keep this advice to yourself.

! SEAFOOD POISONING

Ciguatera is the most common form of fish poisoning in the Indo–Pacific region and the Caribbean. In 1987 it was estimated that in the South Pacific region, excluding Papua New Guinea, the annual incidence of ciguatera was one in 1000 people. In some islands in the Pacific, such as the Gambier Islands, ciguatera affects 20 per cent of the population each year. The occurrence of ciguatera significantly limits commercial fishing activities in many areas, which may keep the locals impoverished.

Tropical fish can become highly poisonous when they accumulate the toxin, called ciguatoxin, from the smaller fish they have eaten. The toxin itself originates in a microscopic plankton named *Gambierdiscus toxicus*, which was discovered near the Gambier Islands. This little organism is a dinoflagellate, a minute single cell planktonic organism that has similarities to both plants and animals (and is sometimes called a plant animal).

The dinoflagellate blooms among the algae on which herbivorous fish feed. In turn, the carnivorous fish eat the former fish, which in turn may be eaten by larger fish, which are finally caught and eaten by humans. None of the fish appear to be affected by the ciguatoxin. The moray eel accumulates particularly large amounts of the toxin, especially in its liver. These eels are an important source of the toxin for researchers and under no circumstances should these eels be eaten.

Outbreaks of ciguatera often follow disturbances to coral reefs by storms, earthquakes and human interference such as construction of jetties and dredging. Underground nuclear testing in the Pacific was believed to be implicated. Any such disturbances in the reef ecology may lead to a bloom of the dinoflagellate, and hence vast amounts of toxin progressing up the food chain. On other occasions there will be no apparent precipitating factor for an outbreak of ciguatera.

Scientists have been struggling to discover the secrets of ciguatoxin for years. It appears to be a mixture of toxins, one of which is water soluble. The main effects are due to the opening of sodium channels in the surface of nerves and muscles.

The syndrome of ciguatera may be described as follows. Usually after about 5 hours (range 2–12 hours) of eating the fish, nausea, vomiting and abdominal pain and sometimes severe diarrhoea occurs. Usually all people become ill, including those who may have only eaten a morsel of the fish. Prostration and general weakness then develop along with numbness and tingling around the mouth, which in 90 per cent of cases extends to the extremities.

In 90 per cent of cases a peculiar reversal of hot/cold sensation develops so that hot tea feels icy cold and ice cream may burn the mouth. One convalescing patient was seen blowing on his ice cream to cool it down! This temperature reversal may make showering both uncomfortable and possibly dangerous.

More than 80 per cent of patients suffer joint and muscle pain. Usually fever is absent and the patient avoids food and finds drinking water to be painful. Some 25 per cent of victims complain that their teeth feel painful or loose in their sockets. About 25 per cent of patients develop erythaematous rash.

Within 10 hours after the meal the acute symptoms have generally subsided. The patient will be left weak and exhausted and still suffering from numbness and tingling, which may last a week. Severe cases may take 2 weeks, or indeed months, to regain normal health. The numbness and tingling is exacerbated by alcohol, even in very small amounts. These symptoms sometimes return quite dramatically when non-toxic fish is eaten. Should toxic fish be eaten at a later date, the toxic effects are usually enhanced.

Ciguatera is usually easily distinguished from other seafood poisoning. Tetrodotoxin poisoning (e.g. from puffer fish, see page 59) produces signs and symptoms in a matter of minutes, as may bacterial contamination of seafood. The latter will not produce peripheral neurological effects.

First aid and medical management

If the patient is conscious and has not already vomited, s/he should be encouraged to do so. If the patient has collapsed, check that the airway is clear and give basic resuscitation if required.

Until recently there was no specific treatment for ciguatera and 1 per cent of severely affected people are thought to have died. In 1987, what appears to be specific treatment of ciguatera was discovered almost by accident. Dr Luis Jain, working in the Marshall Islands, had two patients comatosed with ciguatera poisoning. Both had suspected cerebral oedema so he treated them with mannitol infusions. The condition of both patients improved quite dramatically. Subsequent patients were treated in this way, with impressive results. In Queensland, where ciguatera is a recurring problem, Professor John Pearn and his colleagues found that an intra-venous infusion of 1.0 g/kg of mannitol over 45 minutes was of significant benefit, certainly in acutely intoxicated victims.

Crab

The woman thought it was a beautiful crab. Its body was a speckled reddish-brown and its eyes were bright red. Her husband had also caught three small lobsters and the whole catch went into the soup pot and provided breakfast for five people. The results were disastrous.

Soon after the meal, the family members went off to their different tasks. As the last one departed, the husband began to feel ill. With a shock he realised he had been poisoned when a pig, which had been fed the remains of the breakfast soup, vomited and died. The poor man was shortly told that his wife, who had left home to peddle the

remaining crabs, had collapsed on the road. He went out to help her but also fell down and was carried home. His wife, who now could neither speak nor move, soon died and by midday the husband had also expired. Meanwhile the other three people had collapsed and been taken to hospital. They were less severely affected and recovered over a few days. Six chooks that had wandered up and pecked at the husband's vomit were later found dead.

The toxic crab that killed these Japanese people is found in northern Australian waters, as are several other highly toxic species. Knowledge of how poisonous these crabs may be varies from one area to another. Most Australians are unaware of the danger, whereas the Palauans of the Caroline Islands have made use of their toxins from time to time. Apparently their rulers have ceremoniously committed suicide by nibbling upon poisonous crabs. During the Spanish invasion in the 17th century, a female chief took the option of eating poisonous crabs rather than surrendering to the enemy. A better idea would have been to ask them to come and discuss the matter of surrender over a bowl of crab soup!

Research in recent years has added to the number of species of crabs known to be poisonous. Almost all toxic crabs belong to the family Xanthidae. Members of this family are the most common crabs found in and around tropical reefs. They vary enormously in appearance, habits and size. The claw tips characteristically are dark or black, hence the common name for the family:

Lophozozymes pictor

Carpilius convex

SEAFOOD POISONING

'black-fingered crabs'. These crabs tend to walk around rather than swim and, being slow-moving, are easily caught. Many species are out and about during daylight hours. This activity and their often bright colour increase the chance of capture.

Of the 16 poisonous members of the family *Xanthidae,* five are large enough to be well worth cooking. Such potential meals include *Zosimus aeneus, Lophozozymus pictor* and *Carpilius convexus. Z. aeneus,* which is the largest of the toxic crabs, has been found as far south as northern New South Wales. Professor Robert Endean, who triggered off research into toxic crabs in Australia, found two very toxic species in Moreton Bay, Brisbane, in 1983. The more dangerous was *Atergatis floridus* or shawl crab, which has an intricate lacework pattern on its back. Since that find, more toxic crabs have been identified in Australia, including those belonging to the families *Portunidae* and *Grapsidae.*

On the bright side, no endogenous toxin is produced by the Australian mud and sand crabs. Speaking of large crabs, it should be noted that the coconut crab (*Birgus latro*), a terrestrial crab weighing up to 2 kg, has been reported as toxic.

A variety of toxins have been isolated from poisonous crabs. All are water-soluble, tasteless and heat stable. These facts account for the severe poisoning that can follow the drinking of soup made from these crabs. Indeed, one writer compared the drinking of such a soup to swallowing a bowl of poison.

In the crab, the distribution and concentration of the toxins varies with the species. In some cases, the gastrointestinal tract, in particular the hepatopancreas, is the major site of the toxin. For the others, the danger is in the musculature of the limbs. Either way, the toxin tends to diffuse into the cooking water, lowering the level in the crab tissues. This could make the flesh safer to eat ... perhaps as safe as Russian roulette.

To date, three crab toxins have been isolated. All have been previously associated with other poisonous marine creatures. The first one isolated was saxitoxin. Saxitoxin, with a molecular weight of 299 Daltons, is responsible for paralytic shell fish poisoning (see page xxx). Some crabs have been shown not only to have saxitoxin but also

some variations on this toxin that block sodium ion channels, thus causing paralysis.

The second toxin found in crab flesh is tetrodotoxin (see page 60). This very potent low molecular weight substance is widespread in the animal kingdom and also causes paralysis by blocking sodium channels.

The third toxin isolated is palytoxin. This is a rather mysterious toxin that was first found in the flesh of certain fish that had fed on an anemone-like organism, *Palythoa*. Palytoxin, which has a higher molecular weight than the other two toxins (2681 Daltons), has proven a difficult substance with which to work. In particular, its pharmacological actions have defied precise identification. It appears to cause excessive movement of positively charged ions across membranes and may even create new channels. The immediate effect is widespread tissue malfunction which, in experimental animals, is a euphemism for rapid death.

In humans, the speed of onset of illness is in proportion to the dose of toxin ingested and absorbed. After mild poisoning, the only evidence of the toxin might be a numbness or tingling of the mouth and tongue, perhaps followed by nausea and vomiting. In severe cases, nausea, vomiting and collapse may occur within 30 minutes of the meal, with death following within an hour, presumably from respiratory paralysis.

Medical management

If the patient is conscious and has not already vomited, he or she should be encouraged to do so. Vomiting should not be induced in the unconscious patient. Urgent hospitalisation is essential, as is respiratory and circulatory support in many cases. There is no specific antidote to any of the three main toxins involved in crab poisoning.

The diagnosis is usually straightforward, particularly when a group who have shared the same meal are involved. Ciguatera (see page 53) may present in a similar fashion but its onset is usually some 2 or more hours after the meal was eaten. Crab meat, like any other prepared food, may become contaminated with bacterial and viral infections.

The diagnosis of poisoning can best be confirmed by professional identification of the crab involved. The toxins in the food, vomitus or post mortem samples may be detected by using highly specialised chromatographic techniques or mouse toxicity tests. Some people have screened crab meat of dubious safety by feeding it mixed up with rice to adult cats. In one such test, all three cats involved were dead within an hour.

Allergy to the crab meat can occasionally be severe and life-threatening. Such reactions, which can explosively develop within seconds of starting the meal, may range from gross swelling of the face, mouth and respiratory passages to anaphylactic shock and death. Prompt administration of adrenalin and maintenance of the airway may be life-saving.

Paralytic shellfish poisoning

Paralytic shellfish poisoning (PSP) has occurred in New Zealand but, to date, proven major outbreaks of this poisoning have not occurred in Australia. However, since 1993 the stage has been set for outbreaks, not only after consumption of marine molluscs but also from freshwater shellfish that have accumulated toxin from blue-green algae.

Some 100 million tonnes of shellfish are eaten throughout the world each year. Apart from their importance as a food source, molluscs are regularly pinpointed as a cause of human illness and death. The bivalve molluscs are especially dangerous because of their ability to accumulate and concentrate toxins, bacteria, viruses and heavy metals. Most feed by continuously filtering large volumes of seawater daily. The shellfish are usually unaffected by the accumulated nasties.

PSP is a biological poisoning resulting from the consumption of shellfish that have accumulated a very potent neurotoxin. The neurotoxin originates in minute single-cell planktonic organisms called dinoflagellates. The toxins are generally referred to as phytotoxins or algal toxins.

Certain conditions may lead to a dramatic increase in the number of dinoflagellates present, producing red tides or algal blooms. These mainly occur in summer. The sea may become discoloured, with the water turning red, yellow-brown or milky-white. It may even have the consistency of thick soup. The factors responsible for these massive population explosions are not fully understood, but pollution and the presence of inorganic nutrients like phosphates when combined with sunlight and warm water are all favourable. These red tides, which sometimes produce luminescence, may precede the onset of an epidemic of PSP. The tides on occasions appear innocuous to marine creatures in general, but at other times there is widespread death of shellfish, fish and birds. Sometimes the most dramatic of red tides is not associated with any apparent toxicity, and the reverse may also occur.

It is estimated that more than 300 people die worldwide each year from PSP. Perhaps 10 per cent of victims succumb where medical facilities are inadequate. Sporadic outbreaks occur in Europe, Japan and especially North America. Less common but severe outbreaks have occurred in South Africa, Papua New Guinea and South America. The number of people involved may be small, but even the remote possibility of an outbreak has significant commercial implications. The export of Australian scallops to the United States, for example, involves mandatory and regular monitoring for the presence of toxins. Furthermore, an outbreak of PSP in one area often leads to a dramatic decline in consumer demand for shellfish from other areas. Such is the power of the modern news media. In America, the secondary effects of an outbreak may cost the industry millions of dollars. An episode of PSP has at times had severe repercussions on tourism in the area where it occurred.

Once the shellfish has absorbed the toxin there is no rapid way of rendering them safe. The shellfish that don't die from the direct effects of the toxin will take weeks or months to lose toxicity.

Several species of dinoflagellates are associated with PSP. The most important are of the genus *Gymnodinium* and *Alexandrium*. The identification of these, their subspecies and other less incriminated dinoflagellates is a specialty all its own.

! SEAFOOD POISONING

Research has shown that the toxins tend to accumulate in the hepatopancreas of mussels and clams, and they can become toxic when the seawater contains as few as 400 dinoflagellates per mL. At this level the water is not even discoloured. On one occasion in Japan, shellfish became toxic when there were as few as 20 cells per litre. If the affected mussels are transferred to dinoflagellate-free salt water, by 12 days they have lost half of their toxicity. However, it may take up to 1 year for poisonous shellfish to become safe for human consumption.

Experimentally it has been found that mussels can filter 20 litres of water per day. They can ingest 3 grams dry weight of dinoflagelate in 24 hours when in contact with red tide water. Such a quantity could contain as much as 180 mg of toxin. Cooking the shellfish may reduce their toxicity by 70 per cent, but if the liquid is consumed about 50 per cent of the original toxicity may be ingested.

In 1957 the first of 18 types of PSP was isolated from the butter clam, *Xaxidomus gigantea*. Saxitoxin, considered to be 50 times stronger than curare, remains the most important of the PSP toxins. It is known to be produced by at least four species of dinoflagellates. In its pure form it is a white hygroscopic material that is soluble in water but only partially soluble in alcohol. Its molecular weight is 299 Daltons and its chemical formula is $C_{10}H_{17}N_7O_4$. The PSP toxins are relatively heat stable and all contain positively charged guanidino groups.

These toxins cause paralysis by blocking the extracellular aspect of sodium channels in both muscle and nerve cell plasma membranes. The negatively charged carboxyl group at the entrance to the sodium channel interacts with the positively charged guanidino group on the saxitoxin or saxitoxin-like molecule. The paralysis caused by PSP toxins is produced by a mechanism somewhat similar to that of tetrodotoxin (see page 60).

Saxotoxin, which is the most potent of the PSP toxins, has been the most extensively investigated. In 1935 Dr Charles Kellaway, who was Director of the Walter and Eliza Hall Institute in Melbourne, investigated the crude toxin. The preparation he used had come from poisonous mussels selected in Oregon, USA. Dr Kellaway's pioneering work demonstrated the extremely rapid and potent curare-like action of this extract in a range of animals. Saxitoxin is one of the most potent naturally occurring poisons known. It has been estimated that an oral dose of less than 0.5 mg would be sufficient to kill an adult human. There is no known antidote to this toxin.

An outbreak of poisoning can have very serious consequences. In July and August 1987 there was an outbreak of PSP in Champerico, on the Pacific coast of Guatamala. Some 187 people developed characteristic neurological symptoms and 26 died. A species of clam harvested from local beaches was considered the culprit. Children under the age of 6 years had a 50 per cent fatality rate, whereas in adults the rate was 7 per cent. In an outbreak in Taiwan in 1986, 116 people were affected, two of whom died within 4 hours. In Mexico in 1989 an outbreak caused 99 cases and three died. Ten deaths occurred in 1991 during an outbreak in Chile. From these statistics it is clear that PSP is dangerous.

Since dinoflagellates incubate better under warm conditions, shellfish are more likely to be toxic during the months that contain the letter 'r' in their names. Apart from this tip, trial and error is the only way to determine whether shellfish are safe to eat: a silver spoon that tarnishes in the cooking pot is not indicative of toxic shellfish, nor can an 'expert' tell whether a shellfish is poisonous by merely looking at it.

Symptoms of PSP generally develop within 30 minutes of eating affected shellfish. Burning or tingling sensations may occur around the face, lips and tongue, with steady progression to the extremities. Soon these sensations change to numbness, and voluntary movements become more difficult. Gastrointestinal disturbances are not common. Paralysis of the upper and lower limbs develops progressively. In severe cases, paralysis of respiratory muscles may result in respiratory arrest and death. Most patients remain conscious and surprisingly calm about the condition. Often they describe their condition as feeling as if they are floating in the air. Others complain of headache and dizziness. Sometimes salivation and intense thirst and even temporary blindness occurs.

In time, major outbreaks of PSP will occur in Australia. A combination of pollution and the emptying of ballast tank waters by overseas shipping has contributed to recent disturbing findings. Marine dinoflagellates known to be associated with PSP have been found in a number of places, especially Port Philip Bay in Melbourne, the Derwent River in Hobart, and in the Port Adelaide River in Adelaide. Major blooms have occurred in southern Tasmania in 1993, and cases of human poisoning have apparently occurred. Analysis of shellfish from various areas has found high to extremely high levels of potential PSP toxins. At times, shellfish farms have been closed down because of this finding.

Another startling report involved the discovery of PSP toxins in freshwater blue-green algae. A survey of the Murray–Darling Basin confirmed that these algae produce the full range of PSP toxins previously isolated from the dinoflagellates. Considerable stock deaths occurred during the bloom of algae in the Darling River in 1991. Therefore the advice is to leave freshwater shellfish well alone when these freshwater blooms occur.

First aid and medical management

If the patient is conscious and has not vomited, as is usually the case, then vomiting should be encouraged by the use of an emetic such as liquid ipecacuanha. This should not be given to children younger than 6 months. If respiration is compromised, assisted ventilation should be given. Hospital treatment should be sought as a matter of urgency in all cases.

There is no specific antidote, but in most cases the effects of the toxin wear off in about 12 hours. Theoretically, an anticholinesterase might accelerate recovery in milder cases. There is one report in which haemodialysis was carried out for 2 successive days and, with supportive therapy, resulted in full recovery. This report involved two brothers who, when reaching the intensive care unit, were found to have a total absence of muscular activity.

The differential diagnosis of PSP is usually straightforward because of the food that has been eaten and the clinical syndrome. Poisonings to be excluded include ciguatera (see page 53), puffer fish poisoning (see below) and scombroid poisoning (see page 62) as well as other acute paralytic illnesses such as botulism, myasthenia gravis and periodic paralysis.

A standard mouse assay technique for the detection of saxitoxin and other toxins in shellfish is carried out by health authorities in most countries. An extract is made from the edible portions of the shellfish and its toxicity, or lack of toxicity, is compared with a standardised toxic solution available from the United States Food and Drug Administration. This assay is used to monitor commercial shipments, particularly to the USA, as well as to investigate outbreaks.

Toad and puffer fish

The businessman was pleased to be back in Japan. He had enjoyed his years in Australia, but he had missed certain things his homeland had to offer. He popped the thin slice of fugu in his mouth and he noted with satisfaction that it produced a pleasant tingling sensation over his tongue.

DISTRIBUTION

The raw fish had been exquisitely arranged in the shape of a flower: an extremely expensive flower, and a potentially lethal one. The chef had a difficult-to-get licence to prepare fugu from specially selected toad fish. He took into account seasonal and other factors to select only flesh of low toxicity. One mistake and he could have a dead customer or two and lose more than his licence.

Our businessman swallowed another cup of sake, some more fugu and generally became more euphoric, and noisier. He was lucky to have such a good expense account as others aren't so fortunate. At least 75 Japanese die each year from toad fish poisoning, in most cases due to inexperience.

From time to time, deaths occur in Australia when people eat puffer fish. The fish are very easily

SEAFOOD POISONING

caught and on one occasion a destitute young couple both died after eating fish caught near Eden in New South Wales. Sometimes the fish has been eaten despite obvious evidence of its toxicity. On one occasion, a piece of fish being prepared for a meal was thrown to a pet magpie. Shortly after, the bird was seen staggering about in the grass and then fell over, twitched and died a few minutes later. You would think such an event would make the cook pause to think, but it didn't. We will come back later to the remarkable experience of the 14-year-old boy who on the same day nearly shared the fate of his young magpie.

It is interesting that although both the ancient Egyptians and Chinese knew of the dangers of puffer and toad fish, Europeans seemed unaware of it. Poor Captain Cook nearly died in 1774 after eating a little bit of the liver of a large toad fish in New Caledonia. To make matters worse, he had bought the fish from the locals who knew not to eat it. They must have thought him a real Charlie.

There are hundreds of types of toad and puffer fish, and they are found throughout the world. They have several common features, the most important being that their teeth are fused together with a single gap in the middle. They thus appear to have four wide front teeth and are therefore called tetrodotoxic fish. Another feature in common is that they lack scales and have a rather leathery skin. One can thus appreciate the wisdom of the *Old Testament* advice that any fish without scales should not be eaten as it was 'unclean' (e.g. see Leviticus 11:9).

Many of the tetrodotoxic fish have highly descriptive common names such as puffer fish, toad fish, toado, globe fish, swell fish and balloon fish. Others are surrounded by long spines such as the porcupine fish. Many of these fish can inflate themselves into near-perfect spheres using either air or water. When so inflated, and with their usually large bulbous eyes, they are not an attractive sight.

Incidentally, their teeth and jaws are particularly strong and effective in despatching crabs, which are their favourite meal. Occasionally they may take a finger or a toe. A 5-year-old girl had two toes nipped off by a toad fish in Shute Harbour, Queensland, in 1979.

Puffer fish, which are common around wharfs and jetties, are probably one of the easiest of fish to hook. They usually have a maximum length of about 15 cm, but the giant toad fish found all around Australia and elsewhere grows to 76 cm. It is believed this is the species that Captain Cook mistakenly munched.

Many of these fish contain tetrodotoxin (TTX), which is one of the most toxic naturally occurring poisons known. It is found in most tissues of the fish, especially the gonads and liver. The concentration of the toxin varies seasonally and from species to species (hence the knowledge and skill required to prepare fugu). TTX is not destroyed by washing the flesh of the fish, or by cooking. It is tasteless. Some people washing toxic fish have noticed a tingling sensation in their hands as small amounts of TTX has penetrated their skin.

TTX was first isolated by Japanese workers in 1910, but it took more than 50 years to elucidate its unique structure. It has a molecular weight of 319 Daltons and is one of the few natural toxins produced by widely differing species. For example, TTX is found in the blue-ringed octopus (see page 38), the Californian newt, some types of frogs and a variety of shellfish.

TTX has a specific effect on nerve fibres, where it halts the passage of action potentials by blocking the sodium channels. This effect is greatest on the peripheral nerves but also involves sensory and

autonomic nerve fibres. The excitability of muscle fibres, especially skeletal muscle, is markedly reduced.

The effects of eating part of a puffer fish occur within 10–45 minutes. The speed of onset usually reflects the severity of poisoning. Victims may get nausea but vomiting (unfortunately) is uncommon. The degrees of poisoning are as follows:

Grade 1: numbness around the mouth without gastrointestinal symptoms.

Grade 2: numbness of the tongue, face and elsewhere, with early motor paralysis and loss of coordination. Speech is slurred and the patient may be thought to be drunk or drugged.

Grade 3: Still conscious, but widespread paralysis, hypotension and loss of voice.

Grade 4: Severe hypoxia, near-complete paralysis and hypotension. Death may occur due to respiratory failure.

Death has occurred as rapidly as 17 minutes after eating the toxic fish. The first recorded death in Australia occurred in 1821, and the victim died 20 minutes after eating a toad fish. The account of his death concluded that he must have been a stranger to the colony because the locals knew the fish to be poisonous.

Like victims of the blue-ringed octopus, those suffering puffer fish poisoning remain fully conscious when paralysed, provided they are adequately ventilated. It is said that in the 19th century in Japan some severely paralysed victims recovered some days after eating the fish to find they were facing imminent burial or cremation.

This brings us back to the 14-year-old boy who nearly suffered the same fate as his pet magpie. He later described being conscious, but fully paralysed on a ventilator in hospital, as follows:

I can't remember much at all except for hearing voices in the distance, but it was only faint ... but I heard nurses later on and they were trying to talk to me, especially one who said 'good morning' and 'good night'. I could also hear surgeons talking mumble jumble ... I tried to move and talk but that was impossible. They usually told me what they were going to do ... it was terrible because they opened my eyelids every now and then and I found out I could see, but just couldn't open my lids. They always used a torch, which was very disturbing.

He improved suddenly 24 hours later and made a complete recovery.

One weird aspect of puffer fish poisoning worth mentioning is the supposed use of this toxin by the Haitians to produce zombies (or the so-called living dead). The idea was to give selected individuals a dramatic change in their lifestyle for fun and profit. The victims would be given a healthy dose of puffer fish extract mixed with other substances, and in a day or so would be dead and buried. When no one was about, they would be dug up and hopefully revived with certain stimulants. If all had gone to plan, the toxin would have slowed both breathing and circulation so low that they were considered dead. However, when revived they would be fit and strong, although their minds weren't quite what they used to be. They would therefore be useful to sell as a labourer some distance away where they were not known. In their zombie-like state they would carry out orders but would be unlikely to go on strike or ask for a pay increase.

In 1986, scientific examination was made of some zombie potions but they did not appear to be particularly dangerous at all. Then again, if you were in the zombie business you would be unlikely to hand over your best brew to the first scientist that wandered in and asked for a bucketful of it.

Dead toad fish are often washed up on beaches and dogs being exercised may eat them. Some die, some don't. A Jack Russell terrier once ate a piece of porcupine fish on Beaumaris beach in Melbourne. Next morning the little dog had a staggering gait and the vet thought that all would be well since he had survived so far. Next day the dog was completely paralysed, except for his head. Because the owner was so fond of the dog, it was left for 6 days in the veterinary hospital on intravenous fluids.

At the end of this time its legs were still completely paralysed. It was mentally alert, could masticate and swallow food and breathe. At this stage, the vet rang CSL to see whether the dog should be put down or not. With fingers crossed,

SEAFOOD POISONING

the vet was advised that the effect of TTX should wear off in time. The dog went home, paralysed, and travelled everywhere strapped onto a skateboard. Progress was slow but 6 weeks later there was full recovery with no evidence of brain damage. A letter from the happy owner concluded that the dog 'still moves like greased lightning and refuses to come when called'.

First aid

If the patient is conscious, he or she should be made to vomit by the use of an emetic such as Syrup of Ipecac. This is not to be given to an infant under 6 months of age.

Medical treatment should be promptly sought in all cases as prolonged and effective artificial ventilation may be required. Maintenance of airways, breathing and circulation in transit may be life-saving.

Tracheal intubation and prolonged mechanical ventilation may be required. Gastric lavage may be useful. Severe cases may have fixed dilated pupils, which in this type of poisoning does not necessarily indicate brain stem death. There is no specific antidote. Provided severe hypoxia has been avoided, and vital functions are maintained, there is ample evidence that the effects of the toxin will wear off within 24 hours or so. Anti-cholinesterases may or may not play a role in reversing the neuromuscular block.

The diagnosis of TTX poisoning is usually clear cut, especially when a number of individuals are involved, as is usually the case. Furthermore, puffer fish are easy to identify. With ciguatera, the symptoms develop later and are different (e.g. reversals of hot and cold sensations may occur). Other types of marine poisoning, such as those due to contaminated fish, usually will lack the neurological signs observed with TTX poisoning. Paralytic shellfish poisoning (see page 57) is easily excluded.

Scombroid poisoning

The South Pacific Underwater Medical Society (SPUMS) is a wonderful society. The annual meeting is a gem, usually held on some unspoilt remote island with abundant sea life and wonderful diving opportunities. The members come from all medical specialties as well as the Navy and top diving schools.

The 1985 meeting was held in the Maldives, which consists of nearly 2000 low lying coral islands a little south-west of India. The islands are unspoilt and the crystal clear water abounds with life and tourists.

The Maldivian meeting was a great hit with delegates, but because of the remoteness, fish dominated the diet. On the final night, barbecued fish again was the main course, but fortunately it was left largely untouched.

The Editor of *SPUMS Magazine*, however, decided to have the fish and was given a larger than usual helping. As he recalled later, the fish tasted excellent. After a couple of post-dinner drinks, he made his way to his bed. His skin felt a bit itchy and he thought he had been bitten by

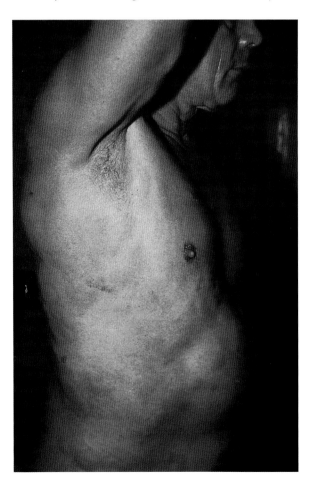

mosquitoes. Before going to sleep he noticed there were some itchy blotchy spots on his skin.

He woke with a jolt at 1 am. He was itching all over, his face felt swollen and he had a strange numbness in his mouth. As he later recounted, 'I could still smile, but in repose I looked as if the end of the world was nigh.' To his alarm, the rash was now widely spread and was obviously not due to mosquito bites. The penny then dropped: he had eaten tuna, which is a member of the scombroid family, and now had an obvious histamine rash. He diagnosed scombroid poisoning and took a promethazine tablet and two betamethasone tablets and managed to get back to sleep.

Unfortunately there was a 6 am departure by boat from the island to get to the nearby airport. At this stage he was itching madly all over and would have been a splendid case presentation at the meeting had it not just concluded. With everyone running around packing diving gear and settling their bar accounts, our victim did not attract the attention he deserved. At least one colleague took photographs of his rash when he temporarily stopped scratching. After more promethazine and betamethasone, he was loaded into the boat.

At the airport the poor fellow could hardly stand, and by the time he arrived at Singapore he was ready to collapse. His blotches came and went for some days, worsening every time he tried to reduce the dose of betamethasone. It was 2 weeks before he was blotch-free. As we see below, there is a possibility that steroids may prolong the effects of the poisoning.

Scombroid fish poisoning is the most common cause of ichthyotoxicosis in the world. The disease follows the ingestion of improperly handled fish, usually of the scombroid family, such as tuna or mackerel.

The fish are perfectly edible when first caught, but a tasteless, heat-stable toxin (or toxins), called scombrotoxin, accumulates if they are poorly stored. It is certain that high levels of histamine accumulate in the spoilt fish. All these scombroid fish normally contain large amounts of free histidine in their muscles, and this may be decarboxylated by bacteria to form histamine. Histamine is absorbed poorly from the gastrointestinal tract and

is also easily inactivated by the intestinal mucosa and liver. Since high doses of oral histamine may be given to volunteer subjects with little or no effect, scombrotoxin is probably not histamine alone, but may be a number of substances including potentiators of histamine absorption.

Knowledge of scombroid poisoning was advanced in 1990 when a doctor at Vanderbilt University in Nashville, Tennessee, started to tuck into one of 25 servings of marlin on offer in the staff cafeteria. He noticed a peppery taste and smartly, in more sense than one, stopped eating it. Three others went down with severe scombroid poisoning before the cafeteria stopped serving the fish. Tests showed that the level of histamine and histamine-like products excreted was some 20 times the normal quantity in these victims. These studies clearly indicated that scombroid fish poisoning was associated with a sufficiently high level of circulating histamine to cause toxicity. It was further concluded that the source of the histamine was from the fish rather than endogenously released histamine.

The fish is sometimes described as having a peppery or metallic taste. The illness starts suddenly, usually about 90 minutes after eating. The main symptoms may include hot flushes, sweating and a bright red rash that may be itchy and distressing. Diarrhoea may occur, but vomiting is uncommon. Most cases will begin to recover within 3–6 hours. Although severe poisoning may occur with bronchospasm and hypotension, no deaths are reported in the modern literature.

Medical management

Mild cases who only suffer brief flushing or minor rash may need no treatment, but should be given parenteral antihistamines if the condition either fails to improve or worsens. Severe poisonings should receive parenteral antihistamines. A combination of H_1 and H_2 antagonists should be used. The literature suggests there is no role for corticosteroids in this condition; in fact, these may prolong the clinical course. If the poisoning is severe—with bronchospasm, hypotension and airways difficulties due to angio-oedema—treat aggressively with airways control, intravenous fluids, antihistamines and adrenaline.

SEAFOOD POISONING

Poisoning from canned fish

Scombroid poisoning has followed the consumption of canned fish that contained the heat-stable toxin. Common offenders have been sardines from Morocco, which have caused at least seven outbreaks in the UK. Outbreaks have occurred after eating tuna that has been canned in Taiwan, Fiji, Peru, Malaysia, Japan, Thailand and the Philippines.

In Australia, Dr David Smart has reported seven cases of scombroid poisoning involving the Western Australian salmon, *Arripis truttacus*. Both outbreaks occurred in March, with the fish being caught in South Australian waters. Tests performed on some of the fish demonstrated levels of histamine as high as 243 mg per 100 grams. No bacteria were cultured from the samples.

In severe scombroid poisoning, if vomiting has not occurred consider gastric emptying by careful gastric lavage.

Analysis of the histamine content of the fish by fluorometric assay will confirm the diagnosis. The normal level of histamine in fish is less than 0.02 mg per 100 grams. Any sample in excess of 2 mg per 100 grams of fish muscle is most likely to be toxic. Occasionally there have been outbreaks of fairly definite scombroid poisoning in which histamine was not detected in the fish.

Because of its characteristic features, scombroid poisoning can be distinguished from other types of fish poisoning due to the presence of true toxins such as ciguatera (see page 53) or puffer fish (see page 59) poisoning. Scombroid poisoning must be distinguished from allergy to fish. Usually, allergy to fish will manifest itself within 30 minutes of ingesting the fish. Otherwise, the signs and symptoms are somewhat similar and the treatment is the same. In the case of allergy to fish, only the allergic person will be affected by the particular dish and, on analysis, the histamine level of the sample will be within safe limits. A person who has suffered from scombroid poisoning will be able to eat similar fish without untoward effects on later occasions, provided it has been stored correctly.

Turtle

Last century a lucrative soupmaking industry wiped out thousands of giant turtles in the waters off northern Australia. Heron Island, for example, was a veritable slaughterhouse, and this almost led to the extinction of turtles in the immediate area.

Nothing was wasted. The flesh was boiled to make soup, which was canned on the spot, and the shells (tortoiseshell) were used to make ornaments, spectacle rims, hair combs and so on.

By the turn of the century, when investors were starting to get a reasonable return from the turtle industry, things went terribly wrong. Green turtle soup had become a standard item on European menus, even challenging brown Windsor soup in the UK. Brown Windsor soup did not kill diners, but green turtle soup did. There was no way of predicting which batches were toxic, and the market folded overnight. This was good news for the turtles.

Turtles are now protected creatures in Australian waters, except in some areas where they are traditional food for the local inhabitants, such as those around the Torres Strait Islands.

In Australia, the green turtle is usually safe to eat, although overseas deaths have been attributed to this animal. It is the flesh of some of the other five large sea turtles that causes problems.

For example, in 1935 it was reported that five breastfed infants died in northern Queensland after their mothers ate hawksbill turtle flesh. This must have been a slip-up in traditional behaviour because the naturalist MacGillivray, who was on *HMS Fly* in 1849, recorded that native women who were suckling were forbidden to eat hawksbill turtle or its eggs, although the latter are not known to be poisonous.

Some of these animals are so large they represent a magnificent feast for a village population. Reports of unfortunate results include 300 people in a southern Indian village affected by such a feast. The death rate in this case was low, but in other cases 25 per cent of diners have died. The death rate among children is usually twice that of adults and one in four was usually being breastfed.

Zoologically, turtles and tortoises both belong

to the order Testudines. In Australia, the word 'turtle' is usually applied to the sea-going species while the freshwater species are referred to as 'tortoises'. Unlike some other countries, Australia has no non-aquatic tortoises. Terrapins are freshwater tortoises (or turtles).

Marine turtles have no teeth. They have paddle-like feet with one or two short claws. A big turtle can cause serious injuries to people with its powerful jaw and claws.

Turtles have no movable ribs to assist breathing but have two pairs of ventral muscles that aid air intake. Their vertebrae, like their ribs, are fused to the exoskeleton.

Turtles have no sense of taste but their sense of smell is acute, both on land and in the sea. Sea water is regularly monitored for important smells by flushing it through the nasal passages. Their eyesight is well developed and they have colour vision.

Although turtles are cold-blooded and their temperature is related to the ambient water temperature, some heat is generated via muscular activity.

In 1987, the journal *Nature* reported two amazing findings about leatherback turtles. One was that a large leatherback captured near Nova Scotia had a body temperature of 25.5°C, which was 18°C above the water temperature. The second finding was that they routinely dived at least 1200 metres while hunting for jellyfish, exceeding the record for air-breathing animals previously set by sperm whales. The same article disclosed that half the dead leatherback turtles found washed up on the world's beaches had the remains of plastic bags in their gut. They had apparently mistaken floating plastic bags for jellyfish.

Turtles can stay underwater for hours without suffering brain damage. They appear to have a protective mechanism that slows brain activity to save oxygen while they are holding their breath for these long periods. This discovery has triggered research by pharmaceutical companies to find drugs with similar effects that could benefit stroke victims.

On land, marine turtles are easily captured because they are helpless when tipped on their backs. Their progress on land is slow and laborious, but thanks to their buoyancy they can swim steadily for great distances. As they swim, they use their front flippers much like birds use their wings, while the hind limbs act as both rudders and elevators. Even the largest turtle can reach speeds of 7 km/h for short distances, and during migrations they can cover 40 km/day for days at a time. Dr Col Limpus and colleagues at Queensland's National Parks and Wildlife Service have tagged Queensland turtles and found some migrate further than 2600 km and have turned up as far away as the Solomon Islands and Fiji.

The late naturalist Eric Worrell described sea turtles resting on the surface with their flippers raised. The locals told him this behaviour indicated a shark was cruising underneath and the turtles were trying to protect their flippers.

Turtles live a long time, some more than 100 years. It is difficult to determine their lifespan in the wild.

Marine turtles are the most fertile of all reptiles. The green turtle may nest 11 times in one season, laying 50 or more eggs every 2 weeks. She does not usually breed in successive years. Turtles return instinctively to the same beach to nest, often having travelled enormous distances from their normal feeding grounds.

Sexual maturity does not develop until the age of 30–50 years. The adult female has enormous paired ovaries that produce follicles greater than 2.5 cm in diameter. The oviducts are up to 6 metres long and sperm may be stored in them for use later in the breeding season.

The eggs of the sea-going turtles look like ping-pong balls. The female comes ashore at night,

SEAFOOD POISONING

usually to a spot she has picked with pinpoint accuracy and at a site above the high tide mark, where she excavates a depression up to 2 metres wide. She uses her hind flippers to deepen one end for the eggs, which are laid one or two at a time and sometimes emerge 1 second apart. During all this activity she seems fairly oblivious to the closest of human observation.

Between 50 and 132 eggs may be laid, after which the flippers and body movement are used to fill in the next site. She will then make her way slowly back to sea, the whole exercise having taken 2–3 hours.

About 2 months later, the hatchlings emerge and the battle for survival begins. Many baby turtles hatch but few make it to the sea. Gulls, hawks and lizards queue up for their meals at hatching time.

The sex ratio of the hatchlings was discovered by Dr Limpus to be related to incubation temperatures. He found eggs laid on the warm brown eastern Australian beaches produced mainly females, but the cooler white beaches of the nearby coral reefs produced mainly males.

The hatchlings neither feed nor sleep until they have reached deep offshore water. They can be disastrously disoriented by artificial lights, and this is evident when bright lights around a resort centre attract the creatures inland rather than seawards.

Turtles have been often seen weeping, particularly when egg laying. In the past it was speculated that this was to keep sand out of the creature's eyes. It is now known that their tear glands are the primary osmoregulatory organs from which excess salt is secreted.

Turtle poisoning is uncommon now in Australia, especially because the creatures are largely protected. Outbreaks of poisoning, with occasional deaths, occur in the Indo–Pacific region and tourists should be cautious should they have the chance to sample turtle meat or soup.

Scientists have named the toxin responsible, chelonitoxin, but to date have not found out much about it. The evidence suggests it has accumulated in the creature as the result of its diet. Possibly the toxin has been passed along the food chain, having arisen in poisonous algae or invertebrate animals, as occurs when fish cause ciguatera (see page 53).

The main reason researchers believe the toxin

comes from the turtle's diet is that the toxicity is sporadic and may occur at different times of the year. In some areas, such as the western Philippines, hawksbill turtles can be eaten routinely, whereas in other places they are often highly poisonous.

The toxin may accumulate more in the viscera of the animal rather than in other parts, such as the skeletal muscle. It all sounds a bit risky.

The toxin presumably is a neurotoxin and is tasteless and not destroyed by cooking. This factor was clearly evident when tinned turtle soup was drunk on the other side of the world.

Nausea, vomiting and diarrhoea may begin within a few hours or even a week after ingestion of a toxic turtle meal. Hyposalivation, lethargy and diminution of deep reflexes may be followed by coma and death.

The victims do not exhibit some of the classical features of ciguatera, such as reversal of hot/cold sensation.

The toxin is unusual in that breastfed babies may die, with the mother showing no ill-effect whatsoever. Another uncommon feature is the development of large mouth ulcers that may take months to heal in those who survive.

At autopsy, liver, kidney and bowel damage may be found.

The diagnosis is often self-evident and the exact species involved can usually be determined because the shell is generally kept for other purposes.

Most cases occur in remote areas. It is not possible to determine which turtles are toxic and most people shouldn't be eating them anyway. There is now an embargo on international trade in marine turtle products under the Convention for International Trade in Endangered Species.

First aid

If the patient is conscious, but has not already vomited, he or she should be encouraged to do so. If the patient has collapsed, check that the airway is clear and give basic resuscitation if required.

There is no specific treatment for turtle poisoning and cases must be managed by first principles. Ensure that ventilation is adequate. Intravenous rehydration and close monitoring of vital functions should improve the chances of survival.

Australia's turtles

The hawksbill turtle

The hawksbill turtle (*Eretmochelys imbricata*) is found throughout the tropical parts of the Indo–Pacific region. It has three known breeding areas in Australia: the Torres Strait islands, the Wessel Islands off the Northern Territory, and near Port Hedland in Western Australia. It may be found as far south as southern NSW waters.

The length of its shell, or carapace, is less than 1 metre. The average adult is some 60 cm in length and its colour is olive with darkish-brown mottlings. The creature's maxillary sheath somewhat resembles the bill of a hawk, hence its common name. Its dermal plates were the main source of tortoiseshell, which was highly valued for making combs and the like.

Its diet is mainly fish. The flavour of its reddish flesh and its eggs is not considered to be as good as some other turtles. If necessary, Aborigines in northern Australia will eat this turtle after removing its scent glands, or poison glands, as they call them.

The loggerhead turtle

The loggerhead turtle (*Caretta caretta*), like the other marine turtles, has a wide distribution in tropical and temperate waters. Occasionally it may travel far outside its normal habitat; some have been found in southern Australia.

The loggerhead turtle is brown, feeds on fish and crustaceans, and may weigh as much as half a tonne. Although the flesh is only fair eating, its eggs are considered a great delicacy when fresh.

The green turtle

The green turtle (*Chelonia mydas*) has several breeding grounds, from North-West Cape in Western Australia to Lady Elliot Island near Bundaberg, Queensland. It is called the green turtle because of the colour of its fatty tissue. The shell is usually a greenish brown with dark mottling. A mature female's shell may measure 1 metre in length and she may weigh as much as 300kg.

The green turtle is the only sea-going turtle that ventures onto the beach merely to sun itself; other species only come ashore during the laying period, and then only at night. This sunbaking habit may prove a fatal mistake if a hungry local comes around the corner.

The green turtle feeds mainly on the marine vegetation but is known to eat jellyfish, including the deadly box jellyfish. This is a further good reason for its preservation.

The leatherback turtle

The leatherback turtle (*Dermochelys coriacea*) is a rare turtle with a tough skin that is embedded with bones rather than a continuous true shell. It is the most widely distributed of all sea turtles, being found as far away as the Mediterranean.

It also is the world's biggest turtle, growing at times to 3 metres in length and 750 kg in weight. This makes it the world's second largest reptile, the largest being the estuarine crocodile.

Fish make up most of this turtle's diet and its throat is lined with long spines that prevent the prey escaping.

The flatback turtle

The flatback turtle (*Chelonia depressa*) is a close relative of the green turtle but is smaller and its colour is olive-yellow. This turtle has a large nesting site near Bundaberg in Queensland, and is unusual in that it lays its eggs throughout the year.

SNAKES

Snake facts

Australia is home to more than 100 species of snake, 25 of which are dangerous to humans. In fact, some of these are among the deadliest in the world, both in terms of venom output and toxicity.

Snake venom is produced in two large glands in the sides of the head behind the eyes, and passes through a duct into a canal in the fangs. The fangs of Australia's venomous snakes are hollow so that the venom may be injected into the victim efficiently. As it bites, the snake controls the amount of venom it injects by contracting muscles around the venom glands.

Some Australian snakes may produce copious amounts of venom. For example, the taipan produces enough venom to kill 12,000 guinea pigs. It is not known why they produce so much venom, but it could be to compensate for their small fang size, which makes it difficult for some of them to hold large struggling animals.

When they do try to hold on after they bite, the chewing action they make usually causes more venom to be injected. Some snakes can even rotate their fangs forward to a degree. The death adder has the most effective envenomation apparatus and it can move its fangs significantly.

Snakes replace their fangs from time to time and occasionally have only one functioning fang. Thus it is possible to be effectively poisoned when only one fang mark is visible. In fact, snake fangs are so sharp and thin that sometimes it is difficult to see fang marks with the naked eye.

Snakes produce venom in order to paralyse their prey. The venom contains strong neurotoxins that prevent the victim's nerves from stimulating its muscles. The victim's struggles weaken, it cannot escape and its breathing fails, leading to its death. Snake venom can also contain other toxins that may damage the muscles directly, prevent blood clotting at wound sites or even damage red blood cells. Venom may even contain factors that assist its spread through the victim's body.

Snakes usually swallow their victim's head first because limbs, feathers and the like tend to 'flatten' against the victim's body, streamlining it as it is swallowed. Apart from the fangs, snakes have a number of teeth that point towards its stomach, ensuring that its meals only move in the one direction. The snake's lower jaw can also dislocate to enable larger prey to be swallowed. The snake later opens and closes its jaw to move it back into position.

The digestive juices of snakes only work when their body temperature is sufficiently high. Thus many snakes kept in captivity will die if the temperature of their environment is inadequate. In this situation they stop digesting. They usually regurgitate as otherwise the meals in their stomachs would rot and they would die from 'food poisoning'.

Snakes are cold-blooded. While Australian snakes do not hibernate during the cooler months,

Identifying snakes

Body colour is often a poor means of identifying a snake, unless it is a 'classically' coloured tiger snake or a red-bellied black snake. Instead, examining head shields and counting scales is the most reliable way to identify a snake. The important scales to count are the body scales (which are counted diagonally), the ventral scales and the subcaudal scales. Noting whether the anal plate is divided or not can also be crucial. Note, however, that subtle variations can make identification difficult, even for experienced snake experts.

they remain dangerous if their daily nap is disturbed. Let sleeping snakes lie!

In general, though, snakes will go to considerable lengths to avoid humans and will bite only when accidentally trodden on or when people reach into hollow logs or long grass without looking first. Always wear stout shoes and adequate clothing if you are in 'snake country'. Never wear sandals or thongs in thick grass or along river banks. Keep grass cut around playgrounds and vacant allotments, and do your best to keep rodent populations down as these prove irresistible to hungry snakes.

All snakes are deaf, but they can still 'hear' you approaching by detecting vibrations in the ground. The eyesight of some snakes is poor and such snakes may not notice an animal until it moves. Snakes have a keen sense of smell even though their nostrils don't smell very efficiently. Instead, they flick their forked tongues along the ground and in and out of their mouths, depositing tiny particles into two sensitive smelling organs called Jacobson's organs located in the roofs of their mouths.

Snakes regularly shed their skin, especially fast-growing snakes during the summer months. At first the transparent scale covering their eye becomes opaque, and thus 'clouds' their vision for a day or so. When their eye clears the snake looks for an object to rub against so that it can break out of its old skin. First the skin over the snout and lips is pushed back and turned over the head, and then the old skin is turned inside out, much like the removal of a stocking.

Snakes move slowly, most species reaching a maximum speed of 7 km/h on level ground—little more than a brisk walk for humans. They are even slower on smooth surfaces because they need to grip the surface to move forward. Although they are slow travellers they can nevertheless strike like lightning if they are held incorrectly, flexing their bodies rapidly to turn on their foolish captor.

Their flexibility comes from a spine containing 180–400 vertebrae, to each of which is attached a pair of ribs by a ball and socket joint. As snakes move, each part of the body follows the same winding course. All snakes can swim, and some ardent swimmers enjoy a diet rich in frogs.

While snakes are usually born alive or in a thin sac from which they soon escape, the taipan, the small-scaled snake, the mulga and the brown snakes lay eggs.

Most snakes are cannibals, but there remains a myth that mother snakes will swallow their young if alarmed to protect them. This myth has arisen from observations of unborn snakes emerging from their mother soon after she has been killed.

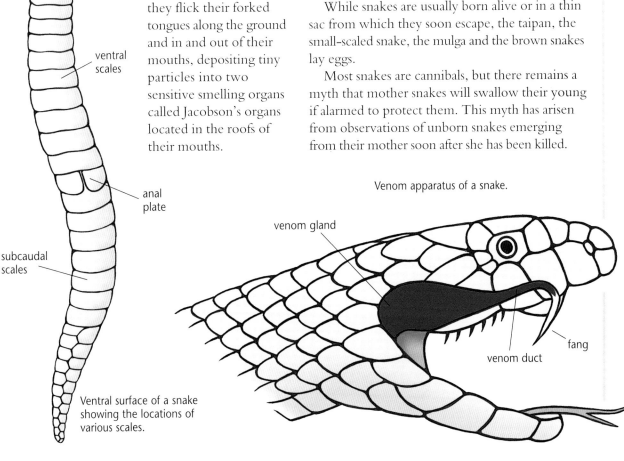

ventral scales

anal plate

subcaudal scales

Ventral surface of a snake showing the locations of various scales.

Venom apparatus of a snake.

venom gland

venom duct

fang

SNAKES

Collett's snake

If there is one snake any self-respecting snake fancier wants in their Australian collection, it is Collett's snake. As a result, most bites by this beautiful snake are inflicted upon herpetologists and snake fanciers who have fulfilled this ambition. It may be attractive, but it is a very dangerous snake. Many collectors have suffered serious illness either because of the direct effects of the venom components or because they have developed a life-threatening allergy to certain venom proteins. A mere scratch from a fang may set off an anaphylactic reaction.

Collett's snake (*Pseudechis colletti*) is one of the less known members of the black snake family and inhabits a huge area in central and western Queensland. This snake, which was first described in 1902, is of solid build and its head is barely distinct from its neck. Its colour is variable, with individual body scales almost randomly coloured and producing a regular band or spots ranging from cream, pink, red or brown.

This snake's scales are impressive. They can look like artistically arranged and polished tiles. The dorsal surface varies in colour and the belly is usually light yellow or orange. The overall colour of the snake changes as it ages. Like other members of the black snake family, its anal plate is divided.

DISTRIBUTION

The average length of a mature snake is 1.2 metres and the maximum length recorded is 2 metres. The snake is mainly active at night and hunts other reptiles, frogs, birds and small warm-blooded animals. It lays eggs, usually numbering 13 per clutch. The newborn reach 37 cm in length and are ready to bite from day one! Collett's snake must be considered a generally placid reptile but if transgressed upon will adopt a threat display, flattening its entire body.

Little research has been done on its venom and the average yield when the snake is milked has not

been determined. Tests in mice have shown the venom to be slightly more toxic than that of its close relative, the king brown or mulga snake (*P. australis*), which is a common cause of serious snakebite in northern parts of Australia.

Two myolytic proteins have been isolated from the venom of Collett's snake, and both have a molecular weight of near 14,000 Daltons. The myolytic activity of these toxins in rats easily puts their plasma creatine kinase levels through the roof. This interesting venom warrants further research.

Human victims tend to develop coagulation disturbances, moderate haemolysis and, without prompt treatment, rhabdomolysis may be severe. There has not been much evidence of straight neurotoxicity, although a number of victims have lost their sense of smell for some months after being bitten (see also red-bellied black snake, page 81).

First aid

The pressure–immobilisation type of first aid (see page 186) should be applied as soon as possible. Venoms from the black snake group are more likely to cause local tissue damage than those from most other Australian snakes. It is important to bear this in mind and remove first aid measures as soon as possible after the patient has reached medical aid.

Although black snake antivenom is quite suitable for treating bites by this snake, usually it is better to use the smaller volume tiger snake antivenom, which is known to neutralise this venom. Unfortunately, tiger snake antivenom is not often held in the normal distribution range of this snake because other antivenoms are in greater demand and their purchase is given preference.

For more details of antivenom usage, see page 190.

SNAKES

Common brown snake

A few days before Christmas 1991, a group of friends were having afternoon drinks on the bank of the Murray River at Berri, South Australia. One of the drinkers, a 35-year-old, spotted a snake swimming across the river straight towards him. While the others threw rocks at the snake, the victim-to-be got up and, as an observer said, 'dived in the river like Tarzan'. He seized the snake from behind but it turned and bit him vigorously. When he came out of the river he took vengeance on the snake by ripping its head off. He refused medical treatment. However, an ambulance was called and reached the site some 15 minutes later. On the way to hospital the patient collapsed and could not be resuscitated. Death occurred some 35 minutes after he had been bitten.

The foolish behaviour of this fellow and the dangerous combination of alcohol and the extremely potent brown snake venom produced a disastrous outcome.

The snake was later identified as a common or eastern brown snake (*Pseudonaja textilis*), which in recent years has been responsible for most Australian deaths from snakebite. The venom sometimes appears to cause sudden and unexpected deaths when only small amounts of venom have been injected by the snake. There is clearly something very odd about this snake's venom.

The common or eastern brown snake is found in a broad area of eastern Australia, sweeping from the Gulf of St Vincent right up to Cape York Peninsula. No snakes of this genus are found in Tasmania. It rarely exceeds 1.5 metres and the

DISTRIBUTION

longest
described was
2.4 metres. The colour of
specimens varies enormously. They may be light
brown, orange or even black. Young ones may
show a number of dark bands.

The common brown snake is particularly fond
of rodents and is often attracted to sheds and other
buildings on properties.

Unlike most other dangerous Australian snakes,
it is rarely active at night, even when the weather
is hot. One fellow found this out when he crawled
into his sleeping bag to find that a brown snake
had already retired for the night. Both got a great
surprise and the snake managed to inflict an
effective bite before it slithered away.

When a brown snake is angry its body takes up
a characteristic pose of an 'S' shape, with the head
raised high off the ground. This is why some bites
occur high on the victim's leg. Another unusual
feature is that when it strikes it does so with its
mouth wide open, possibly because its fangs are
quite short.

When venom is 'milked' from this snake the
average yield is less than 10 mg, which is quite

Sudden collapse after snakebite

A 48-year-old man staying at a caravan park at
Kirra, Queensland, saw a snake near his
caravan. As a passer-by had informed him that it
was a non-poisonous tree snake he picked it up
and threw it away. However, the snake managed
to bite him on the finger in the process. He
returned to his caravan, appearing to suffer from
no ill-effects. Thirty minutes later when he was
talking to his wife, he collapsed suddenly in mid-
sentence and became unconscious. He was
transferred promptly to hospital but failed to
respond to any therapy and was declared dead
75 minutes after he had been bitten. At post
mortem, trace quantities of brown snake venom
were detected at the bite site.

This disturbing case and others like it stress
the danger of brown snakes in particular. Snakes
should only be touched by expert reptile
handlers—and even they seem to get bitten all
too often. Of some 30 top snake experts in
Australia, at the time of writing, only two have
never been bitten by a snake!

low compared with our other dangerous snakes.
However, the venom is the second most toxic
snake venom in the world and the main neurotoxin
present in it is the most toxic snake neurotoxin
ever isolated. Apart from a number of other neurotoxins, the venom can cause a severe consumptive

coagulopathy. Although the venom of this snake does not cause muscle damage—as do some other snake venoms such as tiger snake venom—it appears to have several other unpleasant properties including a direct renal toxin and a component that causes direct thrombocytopaenia.

It is not understood how the venom causes sudden collapse in some patients. The matter is being investigated by Dr James Tibballs at the Royal Children's Hospital in Melbourne, who has found that the venom causes severe cardiovascular depression in closely monitored anaesthetised dogs. The venom-induced hypotension seen in these animals mimics closely the sudden collapse in some patients.

First aid

The pressure–immobilisation type of first aid (see page 186) should be applied promptly and left in place until medical care is reached. If systemic envenomation has occurred, brown snake antivenom is the antivenom of choice. If this is not available, polyvalent antivenom should be used.

For more details of antivenom usage, see page 190.

SNAKES

Copperhead snake

The copperhead was lazily sunning itself in a paddock in far eastern Victoria. Like all snakes it was completely deaf, but its body detected the ground's vibrations as the tractor approached. By the time the huge tractor wheel stopped beside it, it was fully alert but uncertain where to go. When the heavily built young man jumped off the tractor and landed on the copperhead, both were taken by surprise, and both engaged in some frantic activity. The half-squashed snake bit the aggressor firmly on the ankle. In response, the tractor driver jumped up and down on the snake, rendering it almost two-dimensional. This no doubt increased the rate of venom absorption.

When he had got his breath back, the young man set off on the tractor to the small bush nursing hospital 5 km away. Upon arrival he had a headache and was vomiting. A nursing sister had a headache too: she had no antivenom.

After a very rough 5-hour trip from the high country to a base hospital, he arrived semiconscious and cyanotic. He was intubated and, after some five ampoules of antivenom, was transferred to Melbourne where further antivenom was given. His high plasma creatine kinase level was a laboratory record, and skilful management avoided renal failure. He made a slow but complete recovery and for some time was a local celebrity, especially down at the local pub. In fact, he was lucky not to be in the local cemetery.

DISTRIBUTION

This case occurred in 1978, a year before the pressure–immobilisation type of first aid became standard first aid for snakebite in Australia. Had he not jumped up and down on the snake, and had he had the benefit of the new type of first aid, he may not have had such a brush with death. In retrospect it was agreed that he should have been flown to the base hospital rather than bounced up and down on all those mountain tracks.

Copperheads (genus *Austrelaps*) stand out from all the other highly venomous Australian snakes because of their tolerance of cold. Only in freezing conditions will they seek refuge in animal burrows for a brief period of semi-hibernation.

Copperheads are limited to the south-eastern parts of mainland Australia and all but the south-west of Tasmania. In New South Wales, the copperhead is only found in the high country, whereas in the other states it extends to many lowland areas.

It is now generally accepted that there are three species of copperheads. The main species of copperheads is *A. superbus*. These are the largest, and are lowland snakes found in Victoria, Tasmania and south-eastern South Australia. In New South Wales and the eastern high country of Victoria, the darker and usually shorter copperheads have now been named *A. ramsayi* or alpine copperheads. Near Adelaide, especially in the Adelaide hills, pockets of small snakes called pygmy copperheads are a third species, *A. labialis*. *A. superbus* may be found on the Bass Strait islands and the pygmy copperhead inhabits Kangaroo Island.

Copperheads are fine looking snakes. They have a small head that is barely distinct from the neck, and tend to be stockier than tiger snakes. The body colour of *A. suberbus* is extremely variable, ranging from a very dark brown to a rich light copper colour. To see one of the light coloured specimens in bright sunlight is a memorable experience, viewed of course from a safe distance.

Sometimes a dark dorsal stripe is present and in some specimens, two outer rows of scales may be pink or red, creating a red stripe down the side of the snake. A snake so coloured might be mistaken for a red-bellied black snake, but fortunately the treatment of bites by either is identical. The belly of the snake is usually yellow, cream or grey. Like the tiger snake its anal plate is undivided, which allows them to be distinguished from brown snakes (whose anal plate is always divided).

The average length of a mature *A. superbus* is 1.2 metres, with the longest ever recorded measuring 1.83 metres. *A. ramsayi* is usually only about 60 cm and tends to be a lot darker in colour, but has very conspicuous white-tipped scales on its upper lip. The pygmy form, which also has distinctive white bars to its upper lip, is even smaller.

Copperheads prefer a mild to cool climate and may be active on cold days when other snakes are dormant. They have been found above the winter snowline on Mount Kosciusko. Skiers beware! It feeds on frogs, small mammals and reptiles, and hunts at night if the weather is particularly hot. When food is plentiful, large numbers of these snakes may be found congregated in and around swamps. Swimmers should be wary of the odd floating stick as this snake loves to take a dip.

The copperhead is a habitual cannibal and will often eat its own progeny. For this reason, it is not common to see copperheads sharing the same cage in reptile collections.

The snake reaches maturity at 2 years. Mating

occurs in spring and up to 20 little copperheads are born alive and wriggling, not hatched from eggs, and are usually much lighter in colour than their parents.

This snake is shy, retiring and basically good natured as far as our venomous snakes go. Usually they will only strike in anger after considerable provocation, so copperhead bites to people or animals are rarely reported. When it is annoyed, it flattens its neck in a cobra-like fashion, as does a tiger snake, but it is a slower and less accurate striker. The average length of its sharp hollow fangs is 3.3 mm and the maximum length is 4.5 mm. The average quantity of venom milked from this snake weighs 26 mg when freeze dried. The maximum recorded is 85 mg. These yields are from *A. superbus*; the other species have lesser outputs.

Tests in mice have disclosed that the venom of *A. superbus* is the twelfth most toxic snake venom in the world. It is known to be strongly neurotoxic and can cause significant coagulation disturbances. Experimentally, the venom has been shown to cause rhabdomyolysis in mice and monkeys.

Strangely enough, fewer biochemical studies have been done on this venom in modern times than on the other important Australian snake venoms. The only significant work on this venom in a number of years was published in 1993 by Professor Salen and his co-workers at the Box Hill Hospital in Melbourne. They discovered that the venom of the copperhead has a very potent inhibiter of platelet aggregation. This component will prove a useful research tool and one wonders what else awaits discovery.

First aid and medical management

Apply the pressure–immobilisation type of first aid (see page 186) if possible.

Antivenom should only be given if there is clear evidence of significant systemic poisoning. Tiger snake antivenom (initial dose 3000 units) is the appropriate antivenom. If this is not available, polyvalent antivenom is the next choice. Swabs from the bite site, serum or urine samples may come up positive in the CSL Venom Detection Kit. The positive result will be seen in the tiger snake venom well, confirming the appropriate type of antivenom that may have to be used, but not of course giving specific identification that a copperhead was involved.

Copperhead venom sometimes produces marked local swelling and erythaema. This alone is not an indication for antivenom.

If antivenom is given early, the neurotoxic effects of the venom will be rapidly reversed. Coagulation defects should be sought and treated with adequate antivenom to neutralise venom procoagulants. In significant cases, replacement therapy with fresh frozen plasma should be undertaken. If rhabdomyolysis occurs, a high urine output should be maintained. Infusions of mannitol and the alkalinisation of urine with sodium bicarbonate will assist renal protection.

SNAKES

Death adder

Ten people were walking along a forest track in Indian file. The tenth person suddenly screamed with alarm as a death adder he had trodden on buried its long fangs into his foot. The footsteps of the other walkers had all been within inches of the camouflaged death adder, but only when touched did it strike.

Therein lies the special danger of this snake.

Unlike most other snakes, it does not slip away quietly at the approach of a human. It is a night hunter and tends to be sluggish during the day. All snakes are deaf but are sensitive to ground

DISTRIBUTION

vibrations made by footsteps. Because death adders tend to remain put, even when discovered, the alternative name of 'deaf adder' is appropriate.

Death adders are found in all states of mainland Australia except Victoria. They are also a frequent cause of serious snakebite in Papua New Guinea. There are at least three species, the most important one being *Acanthophis antarcticus*.

The death adder has an almost triangular head and a short, fat body, giving it a viper-like appearance. Its colour varies considerably from one area to another, ranging from light reddish brown to dark grey. Its body, which has irregular transverse stripes, may reach a maximum length of 1.1 metres. *Acanthophis* is Greek for 'spiny snake', and this refers to either the rugose scales or spiky tail.

This snake is not a particularly active hunter. It half buries itself in leaf litter or sand and curls up so that its head is close to the worm-like tip of the tail. It attracts curious rodents, lizards and even small birds by flicking the little tail back and forth. It has excellent eyesight for a snake, and the strike rarely misses when the prey is within range.

The snake also rarely misses when it strikes out at a human, and certainly doesn't waste its venom on inanimate objects such as sticks. Its fangs are quite long with an average length of 6.2 mm, and they can rotate forward so that at the time of strike they are at right angles to the skin. The venom is pumped down the hollow sharp fangs quite deeply into the tissues. Death adders are copious venom producers, with an average output of some 85 mg. A yield of 236 mg from a single snake is a record that has stood since 1929.

The venom is the ninth most toxic snake venom in the world and is highly neurotoxic. The neuro-toxins appear to be mainly postsynaptic curare-like in action, and their effects are very rapidly reversed with antivenom. The venom does not produce significant coagulation disturbances nor does it damage skeletal muscle.

First aid

Apply the pressure–immobilisation type of first aid (see page 186) if possible. Practically all death adder bites occur on the lower extremities and are therefore amenable to this type of first aid.

Death adder antivenom is the antivenom of choice. If this is not available, polyvalent antivenom may be used. Antivenom can reverse the paralysis dramatically, even many hours after the bite has occurred, because the neurotoxin has not deeply penetrated the tissues and also has not caused structural changes. In other cases of Australian snakebite this quite dramatic reversal of paralysis is not seen when treatment has been seriously delayed

The absence of both coagulation disturbances and the possibility of renal damage as a consequence of myolysis also make the management of death adder bites easier. Some clinicians have used anti-cholinesterase (Edrophonium) drugs with some success in death adder envenomations. Such therapy should be seen only as an adjunct to antivenom usage, especially in significant envenomations.

For more details of antivenom usage, see page 190.

For more details of antivenom usage, see page 190.

SNAKES

Dugite

The 61-year-old tourist was a very fit woman who had a passionate interest in Australian flora. She was so engrossed photographing wildflowers at Cervantes in Western Australia that she stepped back onto a brown coloured snake that bit her quickly and disappeared. She was taken to the local Community Health Centre and lapsed suddenly into unconsciousness.

No antivenom was available, and the Royal Flying Doctor Service made a mercy dash with antivenom from Jandakot 245 km away. She was declared dead an hour and a half after the bite. An autopsy was carried out 2 days after her death and there were few positive findings other than a small retroperitoneal haemorrhage. Swabs from the bite site were taken and venom of the genus *Pseudonaja* was detected.

It was considered highly probable that the snake involved in this woman's sudden death was the dugite. It is most unusual for a previously healthy adult to die from snakebite after such a short period of time. Even in the absence of antivenom, death following severe envenomation by most of the highly dangerous Australian snakes rarely occurs in less than 7 hours. However, in recent years it has become apparent that snakes of the *Pseudonaja* genus may cause sudden and unexpected deaths, often with minimal findings of significance at autopsy.

The dugite (*Pseudonaja affinis*) is found in the southern parts of Western Australia, and is the cause of most serious cases of snakebite near Perth. Some specimens have been found in South Australia but the majority inhabit the area west of the Darling Ranges. It is the most dangerous snake found on Rottnest Island, and other sub-species await visitors to other islands in the region such as Boxer Island. One quite dangerous sub-species (*P. tanneri*) is named after Charles Tanner, the only man in Australia who has been immunised with snake venom.

DISTRIBUTION

The threat to humans by the snake is enhanced by its excitability and its tendency, if surprised, to bite first and then slither away. In most cases, however, this particularly alert snake would have retreated unseen after detecting the approach of the human.

The head and neck of juvenile dugites may be black but there is considerable variation in body colour. Likewise adult dugites vary in colour. Near Perth the adult dugite usually has a greenish-brown or olive body, while the head may be lighter in colour. Often there is a scattering of dark scales over the body, and thus in some areas it is known as the spotted brown snake. These dark scales are entirely dark brown or black and randomly arranged. The belly is yellow or olive, with quite attractive light pink or grey spots. However, the colour differs to the south-east from Eucla to west of Esperance, where spotting is much darker and heavier and some adult snakes are entirely black.

The maximum length reached is some 2 metres. The snake has more body scales than the common brown snake, which does not occur in the same area. The anal plate of the dugite is divided; in contrast, the other most important dangerous snake in its region, the western tiger snake or norne, has an undivided anal plate.

The dugite mainly feeds on mammals, frogs, lizards and small birds. It often enters sheds or even houses in search of mice. Its temperament is far more nervous than that of the other brown snakes, making it all the more dangerous. The snake prefers sandy country to swamps and does its travelling and hunting during the day. Unlike tiger snakes it tends to go to sleep when the sun sets. It lays 13–20 eggs.

The prey is killed by both the effect of its venom and constriction. Like other members of the genus *Pseudonaja*, when angered it raises its body in an 'S' shaped configuration with its head flattened like a cobra, and strikes repeatedly while hissing surprisingly loudly. Because it tends to raise itself, dugite bites may be delivered higher on the body than bites by a tiger snake, which tends to strike in a more level fashion.

When the dugite is milked it produces on average some 5.7 mg of venom, with a maximum yield recorded of 17 mg. There has been very little work done on the output of this snake and these figures must be considered tentative.

The bite delivered by the fine fangs of this snake may not be especially painful, but usually some local bleeding and

bruising develops. Vomiting, headache, diplopia and difficulty in swallowing may develop over the next 30 minutes or so if sufficient venom has been introduced to cause systemic poisoning and if first aid measures are not applied. Sometimes sudden and unexpected collapse and death may occur and this may be due to intravascular coagulation associated with myocardial ischaemia.

The venom is strongly neurotoxic but does not appear to produce muscle damage, as does tiger snake or taipan venom. Clinically, the haematological effects of this venom are quite dramatic. Marked thrombocytopaenia, depletion of serum fibrinogen, prolonged prothrombin and activated partial thromboplastin time have all been described. In most cases the coagulation disturbances dominate the clinical scene.

Dr James Tibballs at the Royal Children's Hospital in Melbourne studied the effectiveness of brown snake antivenom in dogs. His surprising finding was that, compared with brown snake envenomation, the dose of antivenom required to prevent the effects of dugite venom was five times greater than might be expected by the number of units of neutralising activity in the ampoule. Obviously the number of units

allotted to an antivenom is only a rough guide to its effectiveness. In fact, when venom/antivenom mixtures were injected, some 10–25 times the recommended dosage of antivenom was required to prevent coagulopathy.

First aid

The pressure–immobilisation type of first aid should be used (see page 186). In Australia, more than 99 per cent of snakebites involve the extremities, and thus this type of first aid is suitable. If applied correctly it can be left on safely for hours and should not be removed until the patient has reached medical care.

Practitioners should be aware that sudden collapse may occur after bites by snakes of the brown snake species. Make sure before the first aid measures are removed that an intravenous line is in place and that antivenom and injectable adrenaline are at the bedside in case they need to be used. The antivenom of choice is brown snake antivenom, and a number of vials may be required. If this is not available, polyvalent antivenom may be used. For more details of antivenom usage, see page 190.

Coagulation problems may need special attention and platelet counts should be performed regularly. When antivenom therapy is adequate, replacement therapy with fresh frozen plasma may be considered. To date, platelet infusions have not been used.

SNAKES

Mulga or king brown snake

In 1982 at Windorah in outback Queensland, a large snake bit a 3-year-old boy on his right arm near his elbow. The frantic mother rang the Royal Flying Doctor Service headquarters in Charleville. A medical team was promptly dispatched, scheduled to arrive 2 hours later. The mother was advised to get a bandage, but came back to the telephone saying she could not find one but had found some old pantyhose. She was then instructed how to bandage the child's arm firmly from the fingers upwards and to keep it in place until help arrived.

Mother and child then stayed close together, with the former looking back and forth from the clock to the child. We'll return to this case later.

The snake that bit the little boy was a mulga snake or king brown snake, which when milked can produce more venom than any other snake in the world.

Pseudechis australis is better called the mulga snake than the king brown snake as the latter name confuses all but the experts. The snake is actually a member of the black snake genus (*Pseudechis*), and its venom is not neutralised by brown snake anti-venom. Patients could possibly die if they were given brown snake antivenom instead of the recommended black snake or polyvalent anti-venom. Hopefully other names it is called, such as the 'Darwin brown snake', will fall into disuse.

DISTRIBUTION

The mulga snake is widely distributed in Australia and found in all states except Victoria and Tasmania. It does not like extremes of climate. The mulga is one of the largest of Australia's dangerous snakes and is considered good eating by the original settlers of Australia. The average length is 1.5 metres and it may grow as long as 3 metres. It has a broad, blunt head that is slightly distinct from the neck, and its body is thick set. The colour of the snake is usually a uniform light brown but may be dark or olive. Its belly is a pinkish cream colour but it never has the pink or orange blotches that may be seen with taipans and common brown snakes. Its anal plate is invariably paired.

The mulga snake avoids the heat of the day by hunting at dusk or in the evening. It has a habit of appearing on verandahs or in the rafters of buildings.

Mulga venom differs in two ways from the other important Australian snake venoms. First, it may produce a considerable degree of local tissue damage (with other Australian snakes, changes at the bitten area are usually minor and in many cases insignificant). There can be a lot of swelling and the fang marks are inclined to ooze serosanguinous fluid for hours after the bite. If the blood supply is severely reduced, say with an arterial tourniquet (this is a 'no-no' for snake-bite!), severe tissue damage and gangrene may occur. One fellow had to have his thumb amputated following this combination of mulga bite and bad first aid.

Mulga venom lacks toxins that cause paralysis. However, it has a potent myotoxin (named mulga-toxin) that can cause widespread muscle damage and presumably rapid immobilisation of its prey. Like most of the local snake venoms, this venom also contains powerful prothrombin activators and haemolysins.

Now back to our mother and son. The Flying Doctor kept in radio telephone contact with the mother while in the air. At 5.30 pm, she reported that her child was vomiting and so a nurse who had just arrived was asked to give an intramuscular injection of stemetil. The vomiting soon ceased. The doctor arrived at 6.30 pm and the little fellow was conscious and in no distress.

The pantyhose bandage was found to be firmly in place and the circulation to the bitten limb, as estimated by the colour of the extruding fingers, was considered to be normal. An intravenous line was put in and it was decided to leave the bandage in place and fly the child back to Charleville.

He remained well, and was bright and alert on

It feeds on rodents, lizards and fish and quite likes eating other (presumably smaller) mulga snakes. The female may lay 11–16 eggs in a clutch.

If provoked, the mulga snake can be extremely aggressive. It flattens its entire body and may strike with great speed, often inflicting multiple bites and 'chewing' at the bite site, injecting considerable venom as it does.

When milked, this big snake produces a lot of venom. Its average output of 180 mg is greater than that of any other Australian snake. It became the world champion venom producer in 1986 when the herpetologist, John Cann, milked a 2.5 metre mulga and obtained 2.5 mL of liquid venom, which when freeze dried weighed 1350 mg. This yield was more than double the previous obtained from this snake and surpassed the 900 mg yield obtained from the Asian snake, the king cobra. John Cann and his brother George had considerable trouble holding this snake because of its strength and girth. The game duo milked the snake again 5 weeks later and obtained 920 mg of freeze dried venom. This snake literally flooded the snake venom market!

However, the toxicity of mulga venom is much lower than that of most of the other dangerous Australian snakes. The venom of at least 11 snakes is more potent, but what the mulga lacks in toxicity it makes up for in volume.

admission. With antivenom on hand, the panty-hose compression bandage was removed, having been in position for about 4 hours. The child subsequently developed signs of systemic poisoning with haematuria, coagulation disturbances and a positive finding of snake venom in his urine. He responded satisfactorily to antivenom and was discharged home 7 days later. The myolytic effects of the venom were clearly indicated; the day after he had been bitten his serum creatine kinase had risen to 27,500 units/L (normally 20–200 u/L).

This case deserves as much publicity as possible. It is really a text book case of how the death of a child in the outbreak was prevented by the use of good first aid and the skills of the Royal Flying Doctor Service.

First aid and medical management

The management of mulga snakebites is similar to Australian snakebite in general. Promptly apply the pressure–immobilisation type of first aid if possible (see page 186). More than 95 per cent of snakebites in Australia occur on the limbs and therefore are amenable to this type of first aid.

Black snake antivenom is the antivenom of choice. If this is not available, polyvalent antivenom should be used.

Because of the size of this snake and its venom output, significant systemic poisoning usually follows bites by this snake. The prompt administration of adequate antivenom early after the appearance of general poisoning should result in a rapid cure. All cases of bites by this snake should be regarded as serious. If possible, coagulation profiles, serum enzymes (in particular, creatine kinase) and renal function should be monitored closely. Severe cases may require multiple doses of antivenom and fresh frozen plasma.

The bitten limb may warrant special attention because of swelling and discomfort. Rest and elevation are essential and may have to be continued for some days. The patient's tetanus prophylaxis should be updated.

Sometimes an abscess may develop at the bitten area, probably due to tissue damage rather than bacteria.

SNAKES

Red-bellied black snake

'Nice lizard Mummy, nice lizard.' The farmer's wife was stirring a pot when her 4-year-old son entered the kitchen and made these comments. She kept stirring for a moment, but when she looked around she got one heck of a shock. The 'nice lizard' her young son was firmly grasping by the neck was a red-bellied black snake more than 1 metre in length. The back half of the snake twitched like a cat's tail as it was dragged across the kitchen floor.

Soon afterwards the Commonwealth Serum Laboratories received a telephone call from a small hospital in Gippsland, Victoria. Apparently the woman's husband had driven over the snake, which was then found by the child. There were clear fang marks on one hand, but otherwise he appeared unaffected (which is more than could be said for the snake). It had been finished off by a ritual beating.

The family members now had their breath back and were anxiously awaiting the next development. Fortunately, the snake had not injected enough venom to make the child ill, and after observation overnight he was allowed to return home. He was fortunate, as this shy and beautiful snake, if provoked, can easily produce sufficient venom to kill a child. Indeed, one of the first cases of death from snakebite recorded in Australia is

DISTRIBUTION

believed to have been due to a red-bellied black snake. It is worth quoting the poignant report that appeared in the *Sydney Gazette* on 4 October 1804:

> *The following lamentable circumstances occurred last week in the district of Hawkesbury:- A fine boy, the eldest son of Mr John Howorth of that place, was employed in tending his father's stock; and in the course of the unfortunate day alluded to, was bit in the left arm by a large black snake. Growing sick and faint soon after, the poor little fellow went home, to chill with horror the hearts of his afflicted parents, who had to witness his almost immediate dissolution.*

You don't get prose like that in the popular press nowadays. Indeed, after such an occurrence in these times the grieving parents are more likely to have a microphone shoved under their noses and be asked how they feel about the death of their child.

The red-bellied or common black snake (*Pseudechis porphyriacus*) is found along the length of the heavily populated eastern coast of Australia, from northern Queensland through New South Wales and Victoria and extending slightly into South Australia. It is not found in Western Australia, the Northern Territory or in Tasmania. The poisonous imported cane toad (*Bufo marinus*) is causing the demise of this snake in many northern areas as death may follow either grasping or swallowing the toad.

The back of the snake is a shiny purplish black, and its snout is usually light grey. It gets its name from the bright red or orange coloured scales on its sides. The belly of the snake is usually dull red

or pink and the tail region is black. While this snake's colours are reasonably constant from one area to another, there is a tendency for specimens found in the northern parts to have light cream, pale pink or sometimes black bellies. The average length of this snake is 1.25 metres and the maximum recorded is 2.55 metres. Unlike that of tiger snakes, the anal plate is divided, a property it shares with the common brown snake.

This snake is active only during the day and is fond of well-watered areas where its large appetite can be satisfied. It is partial to small rodents, lizards, frogs, birds, fish and eels and has a strong tendency towards cannibalism. The great naturalist, the late David Fleay, had a specimen he named 'Cannibal Bill'. Over a period of 6 years this snake would often eat snakes of almost its own size.

'Cannibal Bill' was extremely placid and a very good performer. In 1954 David described how it did a royal command performance for Queen Elizabeth on a Government House lawn. While Her Majesty activated her movie camera, 'Cannibal Bill' obligingly swallowed a dead mouse. Members of the royal entourage, especially the security people, sighed with relief when he was safely back in his box. Had it been an angry and hot taipan, a few significant lines may have been added to the history of the British Empire.

The red-bellied black snake is a very good swimmer and can remain submerged for lengthy periods. Sometimes it will lie motionless on the surface of the water and may be mistaken for a stick. People fishing, especially those who have had a few beers, have had memorable experiences when idly moving such flotsam from

near their lines. It is surprising how often the snake is dropped in the boat rather than back in the water. Furthermore, there is no way the startled snake is going to curl up and go to sleep. Dispatching the snake with a shotgun might fix the snake but it also has a tendency to rupture the petrol tank or sink the boat!

The young of this snake are born alive and number from 12 to 20, although broods as large as 40 have been recorded. Sometimes the young are born in a membranous sac from which they escape within an hour of their birth. The young, which are usually born in February or March, have the appearance of miniature adults and may be up to 30 cm long.

When disturbed, this snake will almost invariably attempt to escape into the undergrowth or a crevice under ground. If cornered it will hiss loudly and make bluffing strikes with a flattened neck. Although this snake scared the pants off the early settlers in New South Wales because of its size and abundance, a number of other venomous Australian snakes are much more dangerous.

When the snake is milked the average venom yield is 37 mg with a maximum of 94 mg recorded. Although the venom is less toxic than many other Australian snake venoms, on a global basis it is slightly less toxic than the king cobra, and more toxic than the most important American rattlesnake venom.

Experimentally, the venom has been found to produce mild coagulation defects in animals, with the predominant effect described to date being rhabdomyolysis. The main toxin has phospholipase A activity and a molecular weight of some 13,000 Daltons. It has been demonstrated to produce myoglobinuria in mice. This toxin is fairly similar to the main toxin in tiger snake venom.

Like with bites by other members of the genus *Pseudechis*, there tends to be more local reaction than is typical of snakebite in Australia. Pain and quite marked swelling occur and the regional lymph nodes may become especially tender and swollen. Local infection may subsequently be a problem. In herpetologists and others more prone to receive snakebites from time to time, the local swelling is often far more severe, most probably because of the development of an allergy. Indeed a current study on the serum of some herpetologists has disclosed the presence of IgE antibodies directed at components present in the venom of the red-bellied black snake. The presence of these antibodies suggests that there is a distinct possibility that a significant general reaction will develop in these people should they receive even a very minor envenomation by this snake.

Children are more likely to suffer a significant poisoning than adults because of their smaller size and inability to escape. If sufficient venom has been injected, and effective first aid is not in place, systemic symptoms may occur within 15 minutes or so in either adults or children. Headache, vomiting and abdominal pain may develop, and traces of fresh blood may be seen in the vomitus. Laboratory investigations may demonstrate the presence of a coagulation disturbance, and elevation of the plasma creatine phosphokinase and myoglobinuria may occur.

Although no deaths have been recorded in recent times from red-bellied black snakebites, there have been some uncommon effects of the snake venom reported.

Epilepsy in people with no previous history has occurred after envenomation by this snake. It has been seen after envenomations by other snakes from time to time, but the impression is that a preponderance have followed bites by *P. porphyriacus*.

Loss of smell and taste has persisted for months and even years following a bite by this snake. These complications should be avoided by prompt and adequate antivenom therapy if the indications for such treatment are present.

First aid and medical management

In more than 95 per cent of cases in Australia, snakebite has occurred on the extremities and the pressure–immobilisation type of first aid may be used (see page 186). In the rare instances when the bite has occurred on the trunk, it may be possible to apply direct pressure to retard venom absorption to some extent. For further information on antivenom usage, see page 190.

Incorrect selection of antivenom is a common problem in the management of red-bellied black snakebites. Three antivenoms effectively neutralise this snake's venom. The one that should be used in most cases is the small volume tiger snake antivenom, which contains 3000 units per ampoule and usually has a volume of 8 mL.

Alternatively, black snake antivenom is designed primarily for the treatment of the king brown snake or mulga (*Pseudechis australis*), which is the same genus as the red-bellied black snake. However, the mulga is a prolific venom producer (see page 79), and holds the world record for venom production. The average venom output of the mulga snake is 180 mg, and so an ampoule of black snake antivenom contains 18,000 units in a whopping 20 mL of a 17 per cent purified equine protein solution. The antivenom of last choice, polyvalent antivenom, is even larger at 50 mL. Because the possibility of both immediate reactions and delayed serum sickness is increased in proportion to the quantity of foreign protein that can be given, it is clearly in the patient's interest in most cases to use the small volume tiger snake antivenom when treating systemic poisoning by a red-bellied black snake.

Often red-bellied black snakebites with merely moderate local effects have not only been given antivenom when it was not warranted but have been given 18,000 units of black snake antivenom. Apart from not being particularly good medicine, it is fairly expensive therapy.

At times polyvalent antivenom has been used for the treatment of red-bellied black snakebites even when tiger snake antivenom was beside it in the pharmacy refrigerator. Not a good idea.

Venom from the red-bellied black snake may give a positive result in two wells in the CSL Venom Detection Kit, and should indicate that the choice of antivenom is either tiger snake antivenom or king brown antivenom. As explained above, tiger snake antivenom is clearly the antivenom of choice.

The instructions to the Venom Detection Kit must be read very carefully. If the venom concentration is very high the Kit may go into overload. In this situation the test must be repeated using a sample that has been further diluted.

It would be useful if hospital pharmacists clearly tagged the black snake antivenom as the antivenom of second choice in the management of bites by the red-bellied black snake.

Rough-scaled snake

In May 1992, a sudden and unusual snakebite death occurred near Tomewin in northern NSW. A previously healthy 40-year-old woman returned home at dusk with her husband after a shopping expedition. As she walked from the car she said something had bitten her but did not seem unduly perturbed. After entering the house she complained of headache, lay on the floor, and soon became unconscious. She died some 30 minutes after being bitten.

At post mortem, two tiny bleeding sites were noted on the lateral border of her right foot, associated with some subcutaneous haemorrhage. These two marks were 4 mm apart. Nothing else of significance was found.

Snake venom was detected in extracts from the bitten area and also the victim's urine. While further investigation of the post mortem

DISTRIBUTION

samples was limited by the resources available, it would appear probable that the snake involved was the Clarence River or rough-scaled snake (*Tropidechis carinatus*). This snake is common in the area and the fang marks would be compatible with its bite.

It is peculiar for a healthy adult to die so rapidly under the circumstances described. The amount of venom involved was not great

and there was no suggestion that an extraordinarily unlikely intravenous injection of venom had occurred. Although small quantities of venoms from the brown snake family (genus *Pseudonaja*) are known to sometimes cause sudden and unexpected deaths, venoms from other Australian snakes have not been implicated in such deaths. The exception is when a snake handler has developed an allergy to snake venom, but this woman had no past history of snakebite.

However, a number of cases of bite by this snake have produced rapid onset of systemic poisoning. A botanist bitten by an adult specimen later described that within a minute everything appeared grey, his gait became staggering and then he collapsed. A zoologist who had mistaken the snake for a harmless one was unconscious less than 10 minutes after being bitten. Both these men recovered after antivenom therapy.

This snake poses special problems for children and can cause very rapid death in domestic animals. A cattle dog attacked a rough-scaled snake that had bailed up her owner's 6-year-old daughter, and was dead within 10 minutes. The snake was not seen to bite the dog, which was experienced in dealing with snakes.

A few years back, a practical joker reached into a bag as he stood at the bar in a Sydney social club and pulled out a small snake that he believed was a harmless carpet snake. The snake immediately showed its displeasure and quickly sank its fangs into his hand three times. Five minutes later, after a spasm of coughing, the man collapsed and died. The coroner attributed his death to the combined effects of snake poison and alcohol. The snake was identified as a rough-scaled snake. The deceased may well have been allergic to the venom.

Naturalists have found that captivity does not mellow this snake, which is always ready to strike. The late Charles Tanner, a distinguished Australian herpetologist, recorded that one specimen he had in captivity for quite some time would become airborne with alarm if he merely peered into its cage. It is obviously not the sort of venomous snake to pass around to your mates in a pub.

The rough-scaled snake is very common around the Clarence River region of New South Wales, extending in a broad band up the coast to northern Queensland. It is, however, absent from a central area between Rockhampton and Tully.

The common keelback (*Amphiesma mairii*) is often confused with this dangerous snake. The keelback is a harmless aquatic snake that occurs in the same area. It rarely bites, even under extreme provocation, and may be distinguished from the rough-scaled snake because it has 15 rows of keel body scales whereas the latter has 23 rows. Its anal plate is divided whereas the anal plate of the rough-scaled snake is single.

The maximum length of the rough-scaled snake is 1 metre, with the average specimen reaching 70 cm. Its colour is olive green to greenish brown, and it has dark banding. Its body scales are strongly keeled, and hence the description (rough-scaled). The snake is active day and night, and in hot weather may prefer night activities. It is pugnacious. If trodden on or disturbed, it may lunge fast and furiously while frantically hissing. Apart from being a fast mover when it comes to biting, its fangs are quite long (5 mm) for such a relatively small snake.

For many years the average yield when milking this snake was given as 5 mg. However, in 1997 Peter Mirtschin obtained an average of 15 mg over 115 milkings of seven specimens. Although this output is not particularly high, the venom is complex and highly potent. In mice it is more toxic than the venom of the Asian king cobra (*Ophiophagus hannah*). It contains a number of neurotoxins, one of which also has strong myolytic activity. It also may cause severe coagulation disturbances.

First aid

If a person is bitten, the pressure–immobilisation type of first aid should be used (see page 186) and these measures left in place until the patient is safely hospitalised.

The venom is effectively neutralised by tiger snake antivenom. If this is not available, polyvalent antivenom can be used.

Small-eyed snake

She was a super fit 56-year-old physiotherapist who loved hiking and was wearing her usual hiking gear: blouse, shorts and canvas shoes. Having briskly picked her way through thick blackberries to the top of a hill near Powelltown in Victoria, she paused while her companions caught up with her. While she waited she spotted a small snake, barely 60 cm long and dark brown in colour, retreating deeper into the blackberries. She took no special notice of it because it was small and she had seen many snakes when she went hiking almost every weekend.

Back in the city later that evening, she had difficulty swallowing and felt particularly tired. The next morning bilateral ptosis was present and her pupils were dilated when she awoke. On examination there was total external opthal-moplegia and complete bilateral ptosis. She was admitted to hospital and intensively investigated because of the possibility of a stroke or an impending cerebral thrombosis. A CT scan of her brain and angiograms disclosed no abnormalities. Two days after she became ill her eye signs had only slightly improved but she was profoundly weak and had commenced to pass pink-staining urine.

DISTRIBUTION

On the third day she was as weak as a kitten and the possibility of snakebite was considered. Examination of her legs revealed a number of deep scratches and bruises; in fact, she could have had half a dozen snakebites on either leg. She was still seriously ill with photophobia, bilateral ptosis and difficulty in speaking.

On specific questioning it was revealed that she may have had contact with a snake and that the snake involved had a small head. Considering the evidence, it appeared possible she might be a victim of the shy and secretive small-eyed snake.

It was then found that her plasma creatine kinase was greater than 70,000 IU/L and myoglobin was present in her urine. This woman was clearly suffering a severe generalised rhabdomyolosis of delayed onset.

It was a long and tough haul before she fully recovered. The rhabdomyolysis continued but renal damage was avoided and by the fourth week her creatine kinase level had dropped to 1800 IU/L. She suffered a great deal of muscle and joint pain but slowly things improved. By the fourth week her ptosis had resolved completely and her swallowing improved.

It was very hard for someone who would run 6 km daily and swim 1.5 km twice weekly to find herself doing a feeble dog paddle in the rehabilitation pool. But 3 months after the illness commenced she could swim 1.5 km and had completed a 9 km bushwalk.

The small-eyed snake (*Cryptophis nigrescens*) is a potentially dangerous snake that is particularly shy. It has a close relative, *C. pallidiceps*, which is known as the secretive snake found in the Northern Territory. The small-eyed snake is found in a broad band down the eastern part of Australia from Cape York to southern Victoria. It may be found both in coastal plains and in the mountain ranges. It does not inhabit Tasmania.

It is a delicately built snake whose back is a glistening gunmetal black. When it is preparing to slough its skin, its back may be grey or dark brown. The colour of the belly varies from cream, pink or white and it usually has dark blotches. The head is small and uniformly black, and is flattened and distinct from the neck. The sheer 'blackness' of this snake may lead the inexperienced to consider it a member of the black snake family (genus *Pseudechis*), but the anal plate is always single whereas it is divided in the genus *Pseudechis*. The average length of this snake is less than 40 cm, and the maximum recorded is 1.2 metres.

Humans hardly ever make contact with this snake because it is a very shy creature and is rarely active during the day. It lives under boulders and sheets of bark and sometimes as many as 28 adults have been found in a tightly knotted semi-

hibernating group under appropriate cover. Its diet consists of small reptiles and frogs, but it is highly cannibalistic in captivity. The litters are never more than seven, and the young are born free. Although very timid, when cornered or angered this snake will bite with the same speed and determination as the more dangerous snakes.

The average venom output of this snake is about 5 mg when milked. The milking is usually carried out by getting the snake to bite through a tightly stretched latex membrane over an appropriate container. If fine plastic tubes are pushed over the fangs, then a yield as high as 30 mg may be obtained from a single specimen.

The venom is far less toxic than that of most of the other important venomous Australian snakes, yet by international standards it must be considered highly potent. The venom was studied in a single monkey and the small dose used produced a slight ptosis and moderate rhabdomyolysis. A toxin named Cryptotoxin has been isolated from this venom, and it has strong myolytic activity in experimental animals but no detectable neurotoxic effects. Further research on this rather unusual venom is overdue.

Bites by this snake are most uncommon and usually only involve amateur herpetologists. However, there appears to be something pretty sneaky about this venom. Usually the only effects of bites have been local stinging, with or without swelling, and sometimes a moderate headache. On occasions, the swelling may not occur for some days after the bite. For example, a snake collector travelling in a train noticed that his hand became itchy some 4 days after a bite. Soon the hand began swelling slightly and he put it in his pocket. When he arrived at his destination it was too swollen to remove from the pocket.

In 1965 a 20-year-old man whose hobby was collecting reptiles was bitten on his finger by a small-eyed snake. He ignored the bite because he believed the snake to be harmless, having previously been bitten by this type of snake with no apparent effects. However, 3 days after this bite he was admitted to hospital complaining of a stiff neck and an inability to open his mouth. His complaints could not be demonstrated objectively and he was sent home after an injection of tetanus toxoid. Five days later he was very sick indeed, and was admitted to hospital with severe muscle pain and weakness of his lower limbs.

The young man was transferred to the Cairns Base Hospital where a diagnosis of leptospirosis was made on the basis of pyrexia, muscle pain and dark urine. He was commenced on antibiotics but over the next few days muscle pain and weakness increased, and his output of dark brown urine fell. He died of renal failure, secondary to myoglobulinaemia, 10 days after the bite had occurred.

This was the first case of myoglobulinaemia reported after snakebite in Australia. Subsequently it was found that if treatment with antivenom was delayed, the majority of the most important Australian snake venoms had the ability to cause significant muscle damage. The most unusual features of this case were the late delay of significant symptoms and the occurrence of severe muscle pain, which has not been described following bites by other Australian snakes.

Some researchers have suggested that the deaths of cats and dogs following nocturnal encounters with this snake may be quite common. In Queensland, veterinarians studying the effect of the venom in dogs noted that vomiting and diarrhoea occurred initially, and in severe cases death from renal failure occurred 6–10 days later. They noted that the illness of some of these experimentally envenomed dogs could be mistaken at first sight for cases of distemper. These workers stressed that envenomation by this snake should be considered in the differential diagnosis of domestic animals presenting with vomiting, diarrhoea and progressive weakness. They found that a post mortem diagnosis could be made by a histological examination of the muscles of the tongue, pharynx or larynx. Of course, snakebite in animals is far more likely to be due to the other more widely distributed dangerous snakes.

Larger animals are more likely to survive an envenomation. For example, a 50 kg male labrador dog was bitten by a 45 cm *C. nigrescens*. He and the pet cat promptly killed the snake. The cat was unaffected but the dog was described as being nervous and spooky all night. Next day it was lethargic and for the next 6 weeks remained extremely weak and moved about 'like an old man'. He lost condition and his coat became filthy. After 6 weeks he steadily improved and later was reported to be in excellent health. At no stage was this animal's urine examined but it appears most likely to have suffered from severe rhabdomyolysis.

First aid and medical management

The pressure–immobilisation type of first aid should be applied as soon as possible (see page 186). Tiger snake antivenom is the antivenom of choice. Swabs of bites, serum samples and urine samples will be detected in the CSL Venom Detection Kit as belonging to the tiger snake group.

For more details of antivenom usage, see page 190.

In bites by this snake, special care must be taken to preserve renal function by maintaining high urinary output, alkalinisation of urine, etc.

SNAKES

Small-scaled or fierce snake

The world's most toxic snake venom was only a relatively recent discovery, probably because the snake lives in remote areas and contact with humans is rare. Until 1974, no specimens had been found in the 20th century and the two museum specimens collected in the 19th century had had their names changed a number of times. There was a lot of confusion until it was finally agreed that these two pickled specimens were related to the taipan. They were labelled 'western taipans' and practically forgotten.

Unbeknown to all and sundry, another specimen

DISTRIBUTION

had been sitting in a large jar since 1967 at the Australian Reptile Park at Gosford. A herpetologist had spotted it in the channel country of south-west Queensland but incorrectly identified it as a common brown snake (*Pseudonaja textilis*). The snake did not want to be captured and gave the expert two powerful bites as he and his companions tried to catch it.

One thing led to another and the snake was killed, but the victim became very ill by the time the party reached the nearest homestead. It was 5 hours from the time of the bite before the Flying Doctor reached him from its base at Broken Hill 724 km to the south. By this time the patient had gone through a period of unconsciousness and incontinence.

Unfortunately, it was decided not to give him antivenom until he got back to Broken Hill because of his prior history of allergy to antivenom. These days appropriate premedication would be given and antivenom would not be withheld if indicated. His systemic poisoning increased and he had a cardiac arrest when he was being taken off the plane some 9 hours after the bite.

The herpetologist was resuscitated and, acting on this expert's mistaken belief that the culprit was a brown snake, his doctors gave him brown snake antivenom. In the meantime, the snake involved was heading east in preservative to the Australian Reptile Park at Gosford, NSW.

At Broken Hill, the wrong antivenom did little to improve the patient's condition and he remained partially paralysed. Seventeen hours after the bite, haematuria and bloody diarrhoea developed and he was then transferred to Adelaide and remained in hospital for weeks. This man never fully regained his former good health.

When the offending snake finally arrived at the Australian Reptile Park it was more closely examined and identified as a taipan. Some years later, with new guidelines, it was proven to be the rare western taipan, and so our herpetologist became the first recorded case of an envenomation by this rather special snake.

The survival of this man is quite remarkable considering the potency of the snake venom involved and the lack of specific antivenom. It also highlights the danger of interfering with

snakes when you are in an area remote from civilisation, even if you are an expert.

In 1974 there was a plague of the long-haired rat in western Queensland. A CSIRO scientist, Mr John Wombey, was investigating this plague when he found a large brown-coloured snake. Studies with Jeanette Covacevich, the Curator of Reptiles at the Queensland Museum, confirmed it to be a specimen of *Oxyuranus microlepidotus*, which has three common names: the western taipan, the small-scaled snake or the fierce snake.

This discovery aroused great excitement, and in no time at all further specimens were found in this remote area. They were maintained and milked of their venom by the late Charles Tanner at his Reptile Park at Cooktown. For the first time, this snake and its venom could be closely studied. Tests on its venom made it world famous and placed it firmly in the record books.

It is quite an event when an important new venom arrives at a laboratory for investigation. First, it had to be determined whether existing antivenoms could neutralise the venom. Tanner had provided plenty, as the first seven specimens produced an average yield of 44 mg. A maximum yield of 110 mg came from a 1.8 metre long male.

Allen Broad at CSL tested whether taipan antivenom would neutralise this venom. The first step in this work was to determine the precise toxicity of the venom, and he soon discovered that minute doses of venom, which he predicted would not kill mice, wiped out every one of them. It was some weeks before a dose of venom could be found that was low enough not to kill mice. He found the venom was four times more toxic than taipan venom and eventually proved that it was the most toxic snake venom ever described in the world. Broad later followed this work on to establish that the ten most venomous snake venoms in the world are all Australian. Fortunately he found taipan antivenom effectively neutralised this new venom.

All Australians can be very proud of the potency of our snake venoms. The figures are quite remarkable. For example, the LD_{50} of fierce snake venom for 1 kg of mice is 0.01 mg, whereas the equivalent LD_{50} for the Indian cobra is 0.50 mg and the LD_{50} for the relatively weak American rattlesnake is 11.40 mg.

It is not certain why our snakes have developed such extraordinarily potent venoms. One theory is that instead of developing huge fangs and jaws for hanging onto their victims, they have developed potent venoms and thin fine fangs with the venom duct opening near the tip. Thus, rather than having grooved fangs like many overseas snakes, Australian snakes most effectively deliver their very toxic venom, quickly paralysing the prey which may only get a few metres away. Nonetheless, when you consider the number of rats that could be killed by the average output of the fierce snake, it does seem somewhat excessive.

Further examination of the venom showed that while it differs biochemically from taipan venom, it has the same range of life-threatening activities. It is strongly neurotoxic, with both fast and slow acting toxins. The main toxin is a presynaptic neurotoxin that produces structural damage to nervous tissue. The resultant paralysis is barely reversed by antivenom, so early treatment with antivenom is important when indicated. The venom can also provide severe disturbance of coagulation and widespread lysis of skeletal muscle. This may cause myoglobinaemia and lead to acute tubular necrosis.

The distribution of the fierce snake is not specifically defined yet. Most specimens have been found in a large area in the channel country of south-western Queensland and also the adjoining areas of South Australia. Last century, one was found near Bourke in New South Wales and there is a possibility that they occur as far south as near Mildura. Specimens have been found near Coober Pedy in South Australia. The distribution of this snake is far greater than first thought.

The average length of the fierce snake is 1.7 metres and the maximum size recorded is nearly 2 metres. Its build is similar to the taipan but its head is a glossy black, although this may fade somewhat in captivity. The body is dark brown above, often with dark flecking which may merge to form bands towards the tail. The belly is cream-coloured and the eye is black. The diameter of the eye is less than its distance from the mouth; in the case of the taipan, the diameter of its large eye is greater. There are also subtle scale, skull and

Dangerous Liaisons

All the victims of fierce snakes have so far been herpetologists or snake handlers. In March 1984, a male fierce snake, which was only 3 weeks old, bit the hand of the distinguished South Australian herpetologist Peter Mirtschin. Appropriate first aid was applied and he reached the local hospital within 12 minutes. Twenty minutes after the bite he was suffering from a severe headache, had difficulty speaking and it was decided to give him taipan antivenom despite his past history of reactions to antivenoms. He received the recommended premedication, including subcutaneous adrenaline, had no adverse reactions, and his recovery was uneventful. He was given prednisolone for 2 weeks in the hope of preventing serum sickness. No serum sickness developed. Apart from demonstrating the danger of an almost newly hatched snake, this case appears to demonstrate the value of appropriate premedication and post-antivenom steroid therapy.

The next case occurred in 1988, and was almost a disastrous repeat of the 1967 episode. A 65-year-old herpetologist who had been bitten on 15 previous occasions (receiving antivenom on three occasions) was collecting fierce snakes in the remote north-east of South Australia, 1000 km from Adelaide. A fierce snake bit him effectively on the chest and in no time at all he was suffering from nausea, vomiting and episodes of unconsciousness. When seen by the Flying Doctor some 3 hours after the bite, he had ptosis and it was decided to withhold antivenom therapy because of his past history of antivenom allergy. On the flight to Adelaide, he became hypertensive and recommenced vomiting. Upon arrival in Adelaide 7 hours after the bite, he was seriously ill with marked paralysis and a severe coagulation defect. He was not premedicated with subcutaneous adrenaline and when the case was published, the reporting doctor casually stated that 'he suffered the expected allergic reaction to initial antivenom therapy with rash, bronchospasm and hypertension'. After six ampoules of taipan antivenom and intensive management of problems such as impending renal failure, the patient recovered. Fortunately he was put on steroids and delayed serum sickness, which is almost inevitable after such a massive amount of antivenom, did not occur. Hopefully the lessons to be learned from this episode are clear.

A number of other cases have occurred. One was particularly well managed. In this case Dr Ken Smith and Dr Arunasalan Ambikapathy reported two odd things in the *Medical Journal of Australia* (20 July 1992). One was a surprising delay in the onset of envenomation (8 hours after the bite), and the other was thrombocytopaenia associated with the appearance of giant platelets, which have not been reported in cases of snakebite before. One wonders what will be found next.

other morphological differences between the two. Its fangs are shorter than those of the taipan, but it is highly effective when injecting venom.

Much has yet to be learned of the habits of this snake. It feeds extensively on the long-haired rat, which lives in extensive burrow systems in the 'ashy downs' areas of south-west Queensland. When conditions lead to a decline in the rat population, the snake may shelter and fast in the empty burrows. In times of drought, it may retreat from the heat deep into the cracks that characteristically appear in this area. The climate in this region is extremely harsh, with summer temperatures of 45°C or so, while freezing conditions may occur in winter.

Charles Tanner successfully bred fierce snakes in captivity and determined that the snake lays 9–12 eggs that hatch after some 66 days. The average length of the newly hatched was 40 cm and they were highly dangerous.

Tanner found little in their behaviour to warrant the name 'fierce'. He said they were generally quite placid in captivity and thrived peacefully on laboratory rats. On the other hand, the taipan is described in captivity as alert and nervous. Although the snake is placid when managed by an expert herpetologist, it is highly ferocious when provoked.

First aid and medical treatment

If bites have occurred to the limbs, apply the pressure–immobilisation type of first aid (see page 186). If systemic envenomation has occurred, taipan antivenom is the antivenom of choice. If not available, polyvalent antivenom should be used. The CSL Venom Detection Kit will give a positive result for taipan venom if fierce snake venom is present in the sample.

Bites by the fierce snake can be extremely serious, so prompt effective first aid, vigilant clinical and laboratory monitoring, adequate antivenom (if indicated) and supportive therapy is essential even for what might be considered trivial bites. For more details of antivenom usage, see page 190.

Taipan

Until 1955 there was no antivenom for taipan bites, so a good dose of its venom was curtains for many a cane cutter in northern Queensland. The taipan was no fool; it was rarely captured and thus no venom was available for antivenom research. This situation was suddenly changed by an encounter at a garbage tip.

On 28 July 1950, 20-year-old Kevin Budden died of snakebite at Cairns. This young Sydney snake collector spotted a 1.9 metre taipan emerging from rubbish at the municipal tip. The strong snake struggled furiously as he carried it some distance as he sought help to bag it. At the last moment the snake managed to bite him viciously on the thumb. Once the snake was bagged, Kevin had to restrain some newly brave bystanders from killing it. He was adamant that the snake should be sent down south to the CSL for research. The injected venom soon went to work and the progressive paralysis was unaffected by tiger snake antivenom. He died the next day.

Considerable press interest followed the transfer by air of the 'killer snake' from tropical Cairns to chilly Melbourne. The great naturalist, David Fleay, who was then living in Melbourne, was coerced into milking the angry prisoner. When he carefully opened the outer of the two bags containing the snake he discovered that the snake had already escaped from the inner bag. It rocketed out in an exceedingly savage temper. The snake was skilfully restrained with a snake stick and David carefully grasped it at the base of its head before milking it. As it struggled

DISTRIBUTION

he noted that it had extraordinary muscular power. A few minutes later, after venom had been collected from the snake, David could sense muscle cramps coming on as a result of the intensity of his grip. With some difficulty, the snake was rebagged and all present sighed with relief.

When the liquid venom had been dried, it weighed an amazing 128 mg. Despite the fact the snake had delivered a fatal bite several days earlier, it could still produce sufficient venom to kill more than 12,000 guinea pigs! Some snake. This initial milking was sufficient to get research underway that resulted in the issue of taipan antivenom to hospitals in 1955.

The taipan (*Oxyuranus scuttelatus*) is Australia's longest venomous snake. The largest recorded measured 3.35 metres. Unless he was extremely tall, an experienced snake collector would have a problem catching such a specimen.

The taipan is a most elegant snake, with a head that is long and narrow and a surprisingly delicate neck. The snake fixes the viewer with a particularly intelligent look. The eye is large and the pupil is circular. The mature snake is uniformly either light or dark brown above, with a creamy yellow belly. One admiring naturalist described this undersurface as having an iridescent mother-of-pearl 'bloom'.

Taipans are found along the eastern parts of Queensland, including the whole of the Cape York Peninsula. They are also found in the northern parts of the Northern Territory and as far west as the Kimberleys.

It is a particularly shy snake; if it senses humans in the vicinity it will attempt to slip away quickly. If cornered or attacked, however, it will strike with unequalled ferocity. Prior to attacking, several coils of its body may be raised off the ground and the tail waved back and forth like an angry cat ready to pounce.

Its appearance is sinister. When hunting for food, it will freeze motionless when the quarry is spotted, and then hurl itself at the victim to register a bite almost too fast to follow. David Fleay, who observed many such attacks, noted that the prey died so quickly from the venom that the snake did not have to restrain it in any way.

Taipans are particularly fond of rats and mice, and this increases their chances of human contact. They are too smart to eat poisonous cane toads (other snakes like the king brown do, and as a result their numbers are falling).

The female taipan lays up to 20 eggs that hatch 12 weeks later. The newly hatched snakes can measure up to 0.56 metres, and can probably give a lethal bite.

The fangs and venom of the taipan are impressive. Their fangs are the longest of any Australian snake and may be up to 13 mm. They can inject venom effectively because the venom duct opens near the tip of these very sharp fangs. The average output of the venom when the snake is milked is 120 mg, and the maximum recorded is some 400 mg. Tests at the Commonwealth Serum Laboratories have demonstrated that this venom is the third most toxic snake venom in the world. When output and toxicity are considered together, it is no wonder that sometimes children have died within a few minutes of receiving multiple bites from an alarmed taipan.

Taipan venom is a powerful mixture of neurotoxins that act both in a curare-like fashion and may also cause presynaptic paralysis. One neurotoxin can also cause severe skeletal muscle damage with release of myoglobin, which in turn may produce renal failure. The venom has a direct prothrombin activator and victims will almost invariably have a coagulation disturbance.

First aid and medical management

If possible, the pressure–immobilisation type of first aid should be applied as quickly as possible (see page 186). It is very uncommon for a taipan not to envenom effectively. If applied correctly, the first aid measures will be comfortable and should not be disturbed prior to reaching hospital.

Taipans still kill

A recent review of snakebite deaths in Australia included two due to taipans. There were lessons to learn from both of them.

One man died 60 minutes after being bitten by a taipan. Although reaching hospital promptly, there was some reticence to the use of antivenom because of possible side-effects. By the time this reluctance had been overcome it was too late. Oddly enough, both parents of this victim had been bitten in the past by taipans. They had been successfully treated with antivenom. No further comment is necessary.

The other death involved a camper in far north Queensland who spotted a large snake and unsuccessfully attempted to kill it with a shovel. He was bitten and ran about for a while before killing the snake with a shotgun. He was then taken off to medical care but it took 3 hours to reach the Edward River Hospital. A loose bandage had been put over the bite site, but this had come off by the time he reached hospital. He died shortly after, and tests on his tissues at the Commonwealth Serum Laboratories detected large quantities of taipan venom.

Two lessons arise from this last case. Don't try to kill a highly venomous snake when you are in a remote area and, if you do get bitten, apply effective first aid.

The taipan is a snake among snakes. Next time you see a display of venomous Australian snakes, seek it out and admire its grace and form from a safe distance. No doubt it will look at you appraisingly.

Taipan antivenom is the antivenom of choice and should be used in preference to the polyvalent antivenom whenever possible. An ampoule of taipan antivenom is large, containing 12,000 units of activity in some 40 mL. This volume is designed to neutralise the average output of the taipan, but sometimes a number of ampoules are required.

Generally, the sooner the antivenom is given, the more effective it will be. Instructions are enclosed with the ampoule regarding premedication, and these should be closely adhered to. For more details on antivenom usage, see page 190.

Venom Detection Kits have been useful in diagnosing taipan bites. Once the diagnosis of systemic poisoning by a taipan is confirmed, or even strongly suspected, antivenom must be given.

SNAKES

Tiger snake

A grandmother was convalescing comfortably after her coronary. The doctor had put her on anticoagulants and she was set to go home the following morning. She had slept soundly but woke suddenly at 6 am to find a 1 metre tiger snake on her bed savaging her right forearm.

A loud yell brought the duty staff into the ward and, as they later agreed, the woman gave them very clear instructions. She ordered the doors to be closed and a long handled shovel passed through the window. The snake was not only dispatched but given a ritual beating.

The local doctor then had the difficult problem

DISTRIBUTION

of controlling the bleeding tendencies she had developed, but overcame the problem with extensive antivenom therapy. She went home a few days later than expected and was pleased to be back at home in the kitchen with her cat.

Nothing about tiger snakes surprised this doctor. A year earlier he had treated a small child who had claimed that a snake had come out of her bed-room cupboard, bitten her and retreated. Her parents thought she had a bad dream and put her back to bed. Only a swift antivenom therapy by the astute doctor saved her life when she was found critically ill the next morning. A snake had, in fact, come through a hole in the back of the cupboard, and tests showed tiger snake venom present in the little girl's serum.

It is unusual for tiger snakes to enter houses, but they may be seeking mice and thus be drawn into buildings. Tiger snakes don't go out of their way to bite people, but they will respond with fury if they are trodden upon, attacked or restrained. A small child who accidentally stands on a tiger snake may receive multiple bites and become critically ill within minutes. Several toddlers have died in recent years after such encounters.

The mainland or eastern tiger snake (*Notechis scutatus*) is a common cause of serious snakebite in Australia. It is found from the high country west of Brisbane down through the eastern parts of New South Wales, most areas of Victoria and towards Adelaide.

This is a solidly built snake. Its broad head is barely distinct from its neck. Its colours vary considerably; it may be pale brown or almost black and crossed with some 45 yellowish bands, hence its common name of tiger snake. Some-times the snake has no bands at all, and this can lead to incorrect identification. Occasionally albino tiger snakes are found.

The maximum length of a tiger snake is 1.2 metres. There is a single undivided anal plate, which distinguishes it from the eastern brown snake for which the plate is divided. This can be useful information. Tiger snakes prefer river flats and swampy regions, and are often active on summer nights around rivers, dams and camp sites. Like the French, they are very fond of frogs. The snake does not lay eggs and the young are born free, usually up to 30 per litter.

People are often bitten at night when they come out to turn off hoses on back lawns. Avoiding tiger snakes can be as simple as using a torch around camps and farmhouses at night, and keeping properties free of mice. It is essential to wear stout shoes and adequate clothing in snake country and make sure that grass is kept cut, especially around playgrounds. If you see a tiger snake, leave it alone unless it is endangering life and you have a suitable weapon.

If alarmed, the snake can become extremely aggressive and will flatten its neck, hiss malevolently and take on a sinister 'cobra-like' appearance. When striking, it usually raises itself no higher than 30 cm (the eastern brown snake may rise much higher). Its fangs average 3.5 mm in length and are very sharp, hollow, and they very effectively introduce venom.

When tiger snakes are 'milked', the average output is 35 mg. The maximum output recorded to date is 189 mg, which was obtained from a snake 1.5 metres long.

No Australian venom has been studied as thoroughly as the tiger snake's venom. It has a wide variety of components, but the clinically most important are those that disturb coagulation and the neurotoxins. The coagulation disturbance follows the activation of prothrombin, which defibrinates the blood plasma.

The neurotoxins have three main effects. There are several postsynaptic or curare-like neurotoxins that produce their effects quite rapidly, but fortunately are very easily reversed by antivenom. The third neurotoxin works more slowly and produces paralysis by its presynaptic effects. This toxin causes damage to the nerve membranes, which is very difficult to reverse with antivenom when established. Unfortunately this same neurotoxin also has strong myolytic activity that may lead to the breakdown of skeletal muscles, gross

elevation of creatine kinase and myoglobinaemia. Renal failure may develop. The venom also has some haemolytic effects that are usually not clinically important.

A study on the toxic effects of tiger snake venom in animals some years ago determined that this venom is the fourth most toxic snake venom in the world. A bite from a tiger snake is usually moderately painful. The fang marks will usually ooze if venom has been introduced. Sometimes only one fang mark will be seen (snakes regularly lose and replace their venomous fangs), and sometimes the fang mark is barely discernible. On some occasions the fang mark has not been found until post mortem. Usually there is little local damage produced by tiger snake venom, although the force of the head of the striking creature may cause some bruising in the area.

If sufficient venom has been introduced to produce systemic effects, and effective first aid has not been applied, then signs and symptoms may develop within 5–10 minutes. Early and possible transient syndromes consist of a severe headache and vomiting. As a general rule, if a child vomits, he or she will require antivenom. Next come signs and symptoms caused by the fast acting postsynaptic neurotoxins. These usually consist of ptosis and blurred or double vision, followed later by voluntary muscle weakness. Usually coagulation disturbances will be evident within 30 minutes. For more details of antivenom usage, see page 190.

Allergy to tiger snake venom sometimes develops among both snake collectors and laboratory workers. Sometimes snake collectors have suffered from both severe allergic reactions and the neurotoxic effects of the venom at the same time. This may prove a challenging clinical situation.

The immunisation of people with toxoided snake venoms has been carried out in a number of countries. In Australia, one snake handler was immunised regularly with modified tiger snake venom and developed a moderate degree of immunity. However, this fell quite rapidly when the injections ceased. Unlike with tetanus, the immunised person does not have a chance to develop an anamnestic reaction to the venom and can be rapidly overwhelmed.

However, there is sound basis for the development of a modified venom or venoid for use in valuable domestic animals. Many cats and dogs die from snakebite in Australia each year, and this number could well be reduced if they were given some degree of protection.

If hospital pharmacists have out-of-date anti-venoms that show no signs of cloudiness, local veterinarians will gratefully take stock of them. Provided they have been stored correctly, they should still be of some clinical value in treating domestic animals. Animal owners have to pay the full cost of the antivenoms, which in many cases restricts their use.

First aid

Prompt and effective treatment of tiger snake envenomations is important, especially because of the possibility of the development of rhabdomyolysis. The vast majority of bites occur to the limbs, so the pressure–immobilisation type of first aid can be applied (see page 186). Tiger snake antivenom should be used, with most patients requiring one or perhaps two ampoules of this antivenom. Each ampoule of antivenom contains 3000 units, which is sufficient to neutralise the average output of this snake. Polyvalent antivenom should be used if tiger snake antivenom is not available.

SNAKES

Tiger snake—black

Many years ago an elderly female doctor was on a hiking trip in Tasmania. When Nature called she received a rude shock. A black tiger snake had bitten her on the bottom while she was having a wee.

She was so embarrassed that she did not tell her companions until she became quite ill some hours later. She subsequently became a statistic.

Another statistic was a 47-year-old chap who handled tiger snakes for fun and profit. He was last photographed holding one in each hand, which most herpetologists would consider a passport to hospital. In 1977 he was bitten by one of his snakes and his audience was rather disappointed when the show stopped a minute later. He had dropped dead. Although it was suggested at the time that the snake had injected its venom intravenously, it is more likely that he had developed allergies to the venom of his charges.

There are a number of subspecies of the black or island tiger snake (*Notechis ater*). Apart from the islands of Bass Strait and Tasmania, they inhabit parts of the Flinders Ranges, both the Yorke and Eyre Peninsulas and a number of South Australian

islands, in particular Kangaroo Island. A dangerous subspecies is found in the south-western part of Western Australia, where it is known as the Norne. There it is restricted to the area west of the Stirling Ranges but south of the Moore River. Although some of the Western Australian tiger snakes have yellow bands one scale wide, the others tend to be black and some are very black indeed.

DISTRIBUTION

Black tiger snakes are the largest of all tiger snakes. The maximum length of the snake varies considerably, with those found in the Flinders Ranges seldom over 90 cm long and those on Chappell Island in Bass Strait reaching 2.4 metres!

The black tiger snake shows some fascinating evolutionary variation, particularly in Bass Strait and Tasmania. In this region both small and larger land masses were separated from the mainland around 10,000 years ago. The venom and habits of many of the different species and subspecies of these snakes have evolved to suit the most available prey. They are sometimes active at night, but only in particularly hot weather.

The Chappell Island tiger snake (*Notechis ater serventyi*) was named by the late Eric Worrell after the scientist Domenic Serventy. Dr Serventy had spent many years on the Bass Strait islands studying the habits of the short-tailed shearwaters or mutton birds. Chappell Island is the home of thousands of these mutton birds, providing ample fodder for a thriving population of black tiger snakes.

The average tiger snake eats two chicks and several eggs early in summer. They accumulate large reserves of fat from these meals, and eat little or nothing for the rest of the year. When the chicks grow too large to be eaten they and the snakes co-exist comfortably in the same burrows. For these reasons, Chappell Island can support a dense population of black tiger snakes, and is considered by many to be the most snake-infested place in the Southern Hemisphere.

This particular snake is surprisingly sluggish,

but when angered will give more than it will take. If its body temperature has been raised by basking in the sun or being snuggled up beside a large mutton bird chick, its biting reaction may be lethally brisk.

The eating habits of the Chappell Island tiger snake vary quite surprisingly to those of its very close relative on the neighbouring King Island. The King Island snake, which is smaller and also feeds on mutton bird chicks, is a voracious cannibal of its own kind, but the Chappell Island snake would rather die of starvation than eat one of its own or another type of snake. In captivity, however, the Chappell Island snake—deprived of mutton bird chicks—will eat all sorts of things ranging from mice to strips of liver and even sausages. Most snakes are far more fussy eaters.

The young of all black tiger snakes are born free, with an average litter of 25. Newborn Chappell

Island snakes may be 30 cm long and survive on skinks before they are large enough to tackle a mutton bird chick.

Venom production by black tiger snakes is impressive. As might be expected, the Chappell Island snake is king with an average milking yield of 74 mg and a maximum recorded output of 388 mg. The toxicity of the various black tiger snake venoms varies from place to place. When the toxic proteins present in these venoms are separated electrophoretically it is fascinating to see the subtle differences from east to west or north to south. Some are more toxic than the mainland or eastern tiger snake, whereas the venom from those on Chappell Island is half as toxic (although its average output makes up for this deficiency).

The venoms are similar in action to mainland tiger snake venom. They contain potent neurotoxins, one of which may also cause skeletal muscle damage. The venom can rapidly defibrinate plasma by activation of prothrombin and also has haemolytic activity.

The clinical effects of a significant systemic envenomation by black tiger snakes may include headache and vomiting, ptosis and progressive paralysis of the larger muscle groups, including those involved in respiration. Marked haematological changes may occur and renal failure subsequent to rhabdomyolysis may develop within 24 hours.

First aid

Apply the pressure–immobilisation type of first aid if possible (see page 186).

Tiger snake antivenom is the appropriate antivenom and the initial dose recommended is 6000 units (i.e. double the normal recommended initial dose). This double dose reflects the known high output of venom by most of these snakes. For more details of antivenom usage, see pages 190.

SNAKES

Western brown snake or gwardar

He had enjoyed his time at the pub, and the only job to be done on returning home was to fill some cans with water. While doing this, a large brown snake reared up and bit him on the right thumb. He responded by killing the snake, but neither applied first aid nor sought medical attention. In fact, he decided that since it had been a long day it was time he went to bed. He noticed no symptoms of snakebite poisoning and was soon 'in the land of nod'.

Next morning he had more than a hangover. He certainly had a headache but he was also suffering from diarrhoea, abdominal pain, vomiting and marked general weakness. He was quite alarmed when he went to the toilet: all he could do was pass a small quantity of extraordinarily dark urine. He wondered where the beer had gone.

He turned up for medical attention at the hospital at Woomera in South Australia about 15 hours after he had been bitten. He was in big trouble, having tangled with what was later positively identified as a gwardar.

DISTRIBUTION

After appropriate premedication, including adrenalin, he was given one ampoule of polyvalent antivenom intravenously and flown to Adelaide. On arrival there 24 hours after the bite he had no signs of neurotoxic paralysis but had a coagulation abnormality, thrombocytopaenia and his renal output was near zero.

Intensive therapy was required, including two more ampoules of polyvalent antivenom and seven ampoules of brown snake antivenom over 24 hours. Haemodialysis was carried out for 12 days until diuresis occurred, after which he rapidly improved. The clinicians involved considered the patient suffered from acute tubular necrosis, although this was not confirmed by renal biopsy because of the presence of a coagulopathy.

The young man was more than lucky to survive as snake venom and alcohol is a dangerous mixture.

The western brown snake or gwardar (*Pseudonaja nuchalis*) is a common and important

with the maximum clutch recorded numbering 35 eggs. On hatching, the young snakelets measure 20 cm.

Although this snake is said to be more placid than the common or eastern brown snake (*P. textilis*), it will prove just as bad tempered if provoked and may inflict a number of bites in rapid succession. When it is alarmed it raises its head and upper body into an 'S' shape.

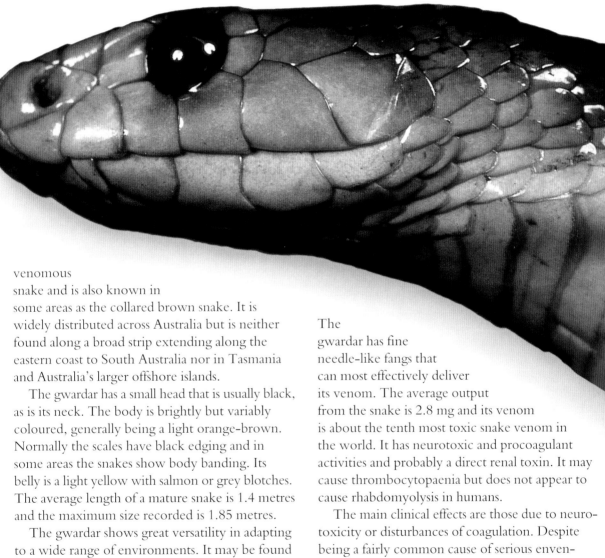

venomous

snake and is also known in
some areas as the collared brown snake. It is widely distributed across Australia but is neither found along a broad strip extending along the eastern coast to South Australia nor in Tasmania and Australia's larger offshore islands.

The gwardar has a small head that is usually black, as is its neck. The body is brightly but variably coloured, generally being a light orange-brown. Normally the scales have black edging and in some areas the snakes show body banding. Its belly is a light yellow with salmon or grey blotches. The average length of a mature snake is 1.4 metres and the maximum size recorded is 1.85 metres.

The gwardar shows great versatility in adapting to a wide range of environments. It may be found from the sparsely vegetated low rainfall desert areas of interior Australia to the dry sclerophyll forests (woodlands) of higher rainfall. Like other brown snakes (Genus *Pseudonaja*), it is only active during the day except when the weather is especially hot. Its diet consists of frogs, rodents and small reptiles. The females lay an average of 20 eggs each year

The
gwardar has fine
needle-like fangs that
can most effectively deliver
its venom. The average output
from the snake is 2.8 mg and its venom
is about the tenth most toxic snake venom in the world. It has neurotoxic and procoagulant activities and probably a direct renal toxin. It may cause thrombocytopaenia but does not appear to cause rhabdomyolysis in humans.

The main clinical effects are those due to neuro-toxicity or disturbances of coagulation. Despite being a fairly common cause of serious enven-omation in Australia, there are very few published case reports of envenomations proven to be due to this snake. Several of them describe dramatic collapse occurring shortly after what was considered a minor envenomation, such as following a bite by a juvenile snake. One of these instances involved a snake handler who had suffered previous bites and may have had an allergic reaction. The other responses, however, are similar to the sudden collapses that may end fatally following bites by the common brown snake (see page 71).

First aid and medical management

The pressure–immobilisation type of first aid should be applied as soon as possible (see page 186). If applied correctly it may be safely left in position until the patient reaches hospital and can be carefully assessed.

The antivenom of choice is brown snake antivenom. If this is not available, polyvalent antivenom should be used.

Bite site swabs, serum and urine samples may come up as positive in the CSL Venom Detection Kit, and the findings will indicate brown snake antivenom as the agent that may have to be used. Severe envenomations may require a number of ampoules of antivenom.

Other Snakes

Bandy-bandy or ringed snake

This is a particularly pretty snake (*Vermicella annulata*) and is found in most parts of Australia except Tasmania and the south-east and south-west parts of the mainland. It is very easy to identify, having evenly sized pure black

DISTRIBUTION

and white bands the length of its body. This shy nocturnal snake rarely grows longer than 60 cm.

Nothing is known of the actions of this snake's venom apart from a demonstration in 1934 by Dr Charles Kellaway that its bite could cause the neurotoxic death of a 1.5 kg rabbit within 15 minutes. A woman bitten by this small-fanged snake is said to have suffered symptoms similar to a protein allergy.

It is not known if any existing antivenom will neutralise this venom, but the need is extremely unlikely to arise. Should a critical illness develop, either tiger snake antivenom or polyvalent snake antivenom could be beneficial.

A transitory hypotensive episode after a bite from this snake would not be an indication for antivenom. Only minor local effects might be expected after bites by immature specimens. The bitten limb should be rested and antihistamines and analgesics used if necessary.

Bardick

This snake (*Echiopsis curta*) is only found in the southern parts of Australia but only in the western areas of Victoria. It can grow to a length of 60 cm and superficially resembles a small greenish death adder. The herpetologist, John Coventry, considers it a most aggressive snake as it opens its mouth ready to bite immediately it is disturbed. Children

More snake facts

Some 80 of the 130 species of snakes in Australia are venomous. Ten of these produce some of the most toxic snake venom in the world and rightly receive much attention.

Many of the less venomous snakes may also cause problems. Much has yet to be learned about these snakes and the effects of their venom. The venom of some snakes has never been investigated and selection of the appropriate antivenom, which may have to be used, cannot be done with confidence.

Although several snakes considered below are unlikely to produce a severe illness in an adult, the effects of their venom on a child or an invalid may be another matter. Before dealing with these snakes there are three important aspects of snakebite that are particularly relevant.

First, whenever help is sought in the management of a snakebite it is important to know the length of the snake involved. It is surprising how often a bite by a baby snake will cause panic and even set off a full-scale medical alert. Gerard Krefft, the father of Australian herpetology, made the following generalisation in 1869: 'An Australian snake that is not thicker than a man's little finger, whatever may be its length, cannot by its bite endanger the life of an adult human being.' Since some of our snakes are extraordinarily venomous, Krefft's rule should be modified with a reference to the length of a snake. It would be reasonable to say a snake neither thicker than a man's little finger nor longer than 25 cm is unlikely to produce a significant illness in adults or children.

Unfortunately there are even exceptions to this guide. Many herpetologists and snake handlers develop an allergy to snake venoms and severe life-threatening reactions may arise following bites from even the smallest snakes. Although IgE antibodies have been demonstrated in the sera of some well-known Australian snake experts, they are determined to continue in what was already a hazardous occupation. Even a tiny newborn snake could cause their demise by anaphylaxis (always remember the drug of choice for anaphylaxis is adrenaline).

Second, the mere presence of fang marks does not mean the snake has injected a significant amount of venom and is not an indication for the administration of antivenom. In the majority of snakebite cases, no significant systemic poisoning develops. Fang marks are, of course, the cue to apply the pressure–immobilisation type of first aid (see page 186) to retard any venom that may have been injected.

One can, however, generalise about the likelihood of systemic poisoning in certain cases. For example, a small child receiving multiple bites from a highly venomous snake is far more likely to become seriously ill compared with a healthy adult receiving a single bite from a snake that is considered only marginally dangerous. The fangs of our venomous snakes are like fine hypodermic needles and occasionally the fang mark may be difficult or impossible to find even in a case that has ended fatally. Sometimes there are no classical fang marks present but merely scratches or just a single fang mark. They may miss with one fang or only have a single fang as snakes regularly shed and replace their venomous fangs.

Third, a high proportion of snake venom components move centrally via the lymphatic system. Reducing the lymph drainage from the bitten limb accounts, in part, for the effectiveness of the pressure–immobilisation type of first aid. To various degrees snake venoms cause tenderness and/or enlargement as they pass through the regional lymph nodes. This is a feature of many other types of venoms.

For many years enlargement or tenderness of regional lymph nodes was considered an indication for the administration of antivenom. This is no longer an accepted reason for specific therapy. In minor bites, particularly by small, immature or less venomous snakes, the only detectable effect of venom is on the regional lymph nodes. Sometimes this effect is worsened by over-zealous palpation.

sometimes bring this snake to school, but to date it has not caused any serious illness. Swelling may occur at the bitten area but coagulation defects have not developed.

The main importance of this snake is that its venom may be detected as death adder venom in the CSL Venom Detection Kits. Although people bitten by this snake are unlikely to require anti-venom, further work should be done on its venom, particularly from an immunological point of view.

Black whip snake

This fast moving snake (*Demansia atra*) is found from the Kimberley in Western Australia to eastern Queensland. From above it is black, olive or light brown. The head, which has dark spotting, is narrow

DISTRIBUTION

and its neck is delicate. White gaps of skin may appear between the anterior body scales when the snake is angered. The body is elegant, whip-like and almost 2 metres long.

This has been described as the fastest moving Australian snake. Its diet consists of small mammals and lizards and is usually only active during the day. It is nervous and will only bite if it is restrained. The maximum recorded venom yield is 16.4 mg and its toxicity is very low by Australian standards.

A 4-year-old girl was bitten on the hand by a 1 metre long black whip snake near Bundaberg, Queensland. Quite gross local swelling and bluish-red discoloration developed over a few hours. The appearance was described as 'rather frightening'. There was little pain and no blistering. The only systemic sign was an irregular pulse. The hand was kept elevated for several days and returned to normal. No information is available on suitable anti-venom but tiger snake antivenom might be helpful.

Black-bellied swamp snake or marsh snake

This snake (*Hemiaspis signata*), which grows to about 80 cm, inhabits coastal regions of both Queensland and New South Wales. It may deliver a painful bite and the bitten area may be swollen for days. In 1993 a young man, whose health was already frail, was hospitalised for 2 weeks after being bitten near Gosford. It is the most common snake in that area.

Broad-headed snake

This attractive snake (*Hoplocephalus bungaroides*), also known as the yellow-spotted snake, is becoming rarer because it is particularly popular among amateur snake collectors. The snake has a surprisingly limited distribution, being found in mountains and rocky parts of the coast within a radius of no more than 250 km from Sydney. The very broad head and characteristic colour allow its easy identification. Inexperienced people can mistake it for the harmless diamond python or even a tiger snake. From above, the body is a glossy black and is crossed by narrow yellow bands. Yellow scales are also found on the head and are particularly striking on the upper lip, where yellow-black barring occurs. The snake grows to around 75 cm, the maximum recorded being 1.25 metres.

DISTRIBUTION

The broad-headed snake is usually active only at night and inhabits rocky areas, particularly in the Hawkesbury sandstone region. It often climbs trees and feeds on small birds, mice, frogs and small reptiles. The young are born free and may number 20.

If disturbed it may become very pugnacious, curve its neck into an S-shape and strike repeatedly and accurately. The average yield of venom obtained when this snake is milked is 12 mg and the venom is considered to be about as toxic as that of the red-bellied black snake (see page 81). The venom has powerful procoagulant and neuro-toxic activity that is only feebly haemolytic.

Effective bites by this snake may cause some pain and swelling. Severe headache, vomiting and collapse have been reported.

The antivenom of choice is tiger snake anti-venom.

Brown tree snake

This is a rear-fanged snake (*Boiga irregularis*) that is venomous but not considered dangerous to people. It is nocturnal, tree-dwelling, and found along the coastal regions of eastern and northern Australia, extending from near Sydney to Derby in Western Australia. Its average length is 1.4 metres.

On 24 August 1983, a herpetologist at the Healesville Sanctuary in Victoria was feeding a brown tree snake some dead mice when it 'swallowed' two of his fingers and would not let go. He felt the fangs penetrate his forefinger. For 10 minutes he tried to remove the snake and finally succeeded by immersing it and his hand in a bucket of water. Some 15 minutes later he had stomach cramps and nausea and by 60 minutes he was continuously vomiting. Next day he felt as though he had a severe hangover. The index finger remained very swollen for several days.

Nothing is known about the venom of this snake. An essential part of the first aid for its bites would appear to be a bucket of water!

Brown-headed snake

This little known nocturnal snake (*Glyphodon tristis*) is found on eastern Cape York Peninsula

and neighbouring islands. It is dark brown to black with a maximum length of 90 cm. This snake was thought to be fairly innocuous until it bit a man on Lizard Island in 1989. He had had a few drinks and was playing with the snake when he was bitten at 10.15 pm. Shortly after, the bitten area became red and inflamed and the arm numb to the elbow. At midnight he was found on his bed in severe pain rolling about with abdominal cramps. He became shocked and suffered apnoeic spells. During the night he had episodes of vomiting and watery diarrhoea. Next day he was airlifted to Cairns and given an ampoule of polyvalent snake antivenom because of persistent symptoms, partic-ularly abdominal pain and headache. No sudden improvement occurred and so effective use was made of pethidine. He recovered over the next few days. His clotting profile on admission to hospital was normal and a swab from the bitten area was negative in the Venom Detection Kit. (The bite site had been well washed a number of times.)

This snake had been thought to be almost harmless, but the venom does not appear to be neutralised by any existing Australian antivenoms. Fortunately the toxicity of the venom, at least in mice, is considerably lower than that of all other Australian snake venoms assayed to date.

Dr James Tibballs of the Royal Children's Hospital in Melbourne has shown that the venom causes hypotension in dogs, associated with a thrombocytopaenia and a small reduction in serum fibrinogen. Mr Peter Hobbins, while still an Honours student at the University of Melbourne, found the venom to be biochemically and pharma-cologically complex. It had the potential to cause moderate paralysis and directly affected cardiac tissue. This research cannot explain why the Lizard Island man became so ill nor select an antivenom that may neutralise the venom of the brown-headed snake.

Curl or myall snake

This snake (*Suta suta*) is found in a patchy fashion in all states except Tasmania. It is light brown to reddish above, and the head's dark colour ceases abruptly over the neck. The

DISTRIBUTION

undersurface is creamish. Most mature specimens are less than 35 cm long and the maximum described is 75 cm.

The snake is nocturnal and may be found on warm summer nights as it hunts skinks, small lizards and frogs. When alarmed it may either fling itself about haphazardly or adopt a characteristically defensive attitude by curling itself up in a knot with its head out of sight (hence its name). The toxicity of its venom is only slightly less than that of the red-bellied black snake, and large specimens may be dangerous to people. Smaller specimens could be a threat to children and can kill domestic animals. For example, a 4 kg cat in Alice Springs, the Northern Territory, died a paralytic death 4 hours after being bitten by a 25 cm long curl snake. Bites are reportedly very painful for 30 minutes or so. No information is available on the choice of antivenom but tiger snake antivenom might be helpful.

De Vis' snake

The distribution of this snake (*Denisonia devisii*) is limited to two large adjoining areas in central NSW and Queensland. Superficially, this snake resembles the mainland tiger snake. The late Eric Worrell said people often brought specimens to his reptile park thinking they were either young tiger snakes or even death adders. The snake is squat and is yellow-brown above with irregular dark brown transverse bands. The flat dark head has small white blotches and the lips have marked black and white barring. The appearance of the lips helps the amateur to distinguish this snake from tiger snakes. The death adder has a characteristic worm-like tail, a fact handy for amateur herpetologists attempting identification. The snake grows to some 50 cm long. It is nocturnal in habit and eats frogs and lizards. If angered, the snake will flatten its body and bite at any opportunity. In doing so it will hang on ferociously.

DISTRIBUTION

The average venom output from this snake is 1.9 mg and it has been shown to be neurotoxic but not to cause coagulation defects.

After being bitten, two herpetologists ignored the accident and continued working. Within an hour both had suddenly collapsed. One was said to have been 'knocked out as by a blow' and become unconscious. Both later spontaneously recovered without specific treatment. In one case the bitten area remained painful for days.

No information is available on suitable antivenom but tiger snake antivenom might be helpful.

Grey snake

This snake (*Hemiaspis damelii*) is found in south-eastern Queensland and neighbouring parts of New South Wales. Its maximum length is 90 cm. Nothing is known about this snake's venom or its effects on humans. It caused the death of a dog at Toowoomba, Queensland, and should be treated with respect.

Ornamental snake

This snake (*Denisonia maculata*) has a limited distribution from near Rockhampton to the Dawson River. It is often mistaken for a death adder, from which it can easily be distinguished as it lacks the death adder's characteristic spiny end to its tail. It is a heavily built dark snake with a vertical pupil in its large eye. Its maximum length is 50 cm.

DISTRIBUTION

The ornamental snake is nocturnal and has a nervous disposition. When alarmed it will flatten its body, generally thrash about and strike as soon as its target is within range. The output and properties of the venom have not been investigated. There are no recorded bites from this snake. No information is available on suitable antivenom but tiger snake antivenom might be helpful.

Pale-headed snake

This is a tree-dwelling snake (*Hoplocephalus bitorquatus*) that, like other members of this genus, is popular among snake fanciers. It is found in a broad band running from the Atherton Tableland in northern Queensland to 80 km north of Sydney. It has a patchy distribution and perhaps

may not be found in a
large area near Rock-
hampton. The snake has a
preference for dry areas.

DISTRIBUTION

The flat head is a white
grey colour with black
markings. Some have a
white or yellow spot on
the side of the head. This
is over the cheek, which is puffed out when
alarmed. As a consequence, some people requesting
the identity of this snake have described it as having
large white flaps or ears. (Snakes lack ears and
therefore are deaf.) The body of this snake is
grey and lacks bands. Its average length is less
than 50 cm and the maximum length is 90 cm.

The pale-headed snake feeds mainly on skinks
and its young are born alive. It is as bad tempered
as other members of the genus *Hoplocephalus*. The
venom and venom yield of this snake have not
been studied.

In 1984 a 13-year-old boy was bitten on the foot
by a pale-headed snake near Mount Larcom, about
50 km from Gladstone, Queensland. In the absence
of any signs or symptoms, his envenomation was
considered insignificant until the results of the coagulation profile came to hand. All bleeding and clotting times were 10 times the upper limit of normal
and fibrinogen levels were near zero. His plasma
creatine kinase was double the normal limit.

In view of the gross coagulation disturbance he
was given polyvalent antivenom and the first aid
measures were removed from the bitten leg when
half of the antivenom was infused. Over the next
24 hours his coagulation profile returned to almost
completely normal. The identity of this snake was
later confirmed by the Queensland Museum.

In July 1994 a 24-year-old Queensland man was
envenomed by this snake. The severe coagulation
defect responded over 12 hours following 3000
units of tiger snake antivenom. This case confirmed
earlier cautious assumptions that tiger snake
antivenom was the appropriate antivenom.

Stephen's banded snake

This snake (*Hoplocephalus
stephensi*) is especially
attractive and very much
prized by collectors. It is
sometimes confused with
the bandy-bandy or
ringed snake (*Vermicella
annulata*), which is a far
less offensive snake (see

DISTRIBUTION

below). This snake is found from south-eastern
Queensland to the mountain ranges near Gosford
in NSW. It has a distinct neck and the head is broad
and flat. Characteristically it has broad black transverse bars along the length of its yellow or light
brown body. These dark bands are two to three
times wider than the light coloured interstices. The
tail is quite black. The average length of an adult is
60 cm, and the maximum recorded is 1 metre.

This snake is usually only active at night and
lives in trees, where it feeds on small birds, lizards
and insects. Like the broad-headed snake, it is
easily angered and raises its neck in an S-shape and
strikes like an uncoiling spring.

The average yield of venom from these snakes
is 3 mg. Although the toxicity of this venom in
mice is 50 times less than tiger snake venom, it is
still more toxic than that of the overseas king cobra

(*Ophiophagus hannah*). The venom is powerfully coagulant and neurotoxic.

On 15 January 1985 a 17-year-old male was bitten on the left index finger by a *H. stephensi* that he was trying to catch in the Numinbah Valley. He developed headache, left arm myalgia, left axillary lymphadenopathy and hypofibrinogenaemia. He received antivenom and recovered. No other details are available.

The antivenom of choice is tiger snake antivenom.

White-lipped snake

This snake (*Drysdaelia coronoides*) is found along the eastern third of New South Wales, the southern half of Victoria and nearby South Australia, the Bass Strait islands and Tasmania. A case report has elevated this snake into the league of dangerous snakes. In February 1994 a 34-year-old woman was admitted to a Victorian country hospital after being bitten three times on her left hand by a white-lipped snake. A most peculiar illness developed that appeared only to involve the upper limbs, head and neck. Severe rhabdomyolysis occurred (serum creatine kinase greater than 50,000 IU) with bilateral facial weakness and ptosis. It is not possible to determine whether the single ampoule of tiger snake antivenom given to this woman early in the illness assisted her eventual recovery.

Before this case it had been thought that the venom apparatus of the snake was too small to be a danger to humans. The colour of the snake does not help in identification because it varies from grey, brown to olive-green or shades in between. However, two streaks that run along the side of the head to the neck—one black, the other white—are characteristic. The snake, which grows to a maximum of 50 cm, is occasionally active during the day as it hunts small lizards and frogs.

Yellow-faced whip snake

This (*Demansia psammophis*) is the most important of the five species of whip snake found in Australia. It has a wide distribution in mainland Australia except in the north-western parts. It is a secretive, slender snake, usually pale green above with a belly of the same colour. Characteristically the eye is in the centre of a yellow 'comma', with the tail of the

comma pointing downwards and backwards. No other Australian snake has such a marking. The maximum recorded length of this whip-like snake is 1.4 metres. The snake is diurnal and feeds on small reptiles, especially skinks,

DISTRIBUTION

which it captures after a short chase. The snakes tend to live in a group, and since the female may lay as many as 20 eggs, sometimes a community

clutch of 200 eggs has been found under a stone. Little is known about this snake's venom output or properties.

Bites by this snake produce pain similar to a bee sting but are far more persistent. Local swelling is usual, generally in proportion to the size of the snake. Pain and swelling may persist for several days.

First aid

The pressure–immobilisation type of first aid is applicable to all cases of snakebite in Australia where the bite has occurred on the limbs (see page 186). This accounts for more than 99 per cent of incidences.

For more details on antivenom usage, see page 190.

Note that for bites by the less dangerous snakes, moderate local swelling, tenderness of the regional lymph nodes and/or headache do not warrant antivenom therapy. Rarely with the less dangerous snakes, antivenom might be considered if gross local swelling and pain has occurred, but the real indications would be those that occur after serious snakebite such as vomiting, splitting headache, paralysis and clotting disturbances.

SPIDERS AND OTHER ARACHNIDS

Australian paralysis tick

As the family travelled back from the picnic in the bush, the tiny adult tick crawled deeper into the 14-year-old girl's ear. By the time they reached home it had settled down near her eardrum. Painlessly its mouthparts penetrated the skin and it commenced to feed. Over the next few days its pinhead sized body increased dramatically. As it quietly fed, the toxic saliva escaped into the tissues of the child and were absorbed.

She complained that there was something in her ear, but of more concern to her parents was the confusion and muscle weakness that had developed. When seen by the doctor she could hardly walk and soon became semi-comatosed. Fortunately the doctor spotted the fully distended tick across the tympanic membrane.

The doctor wrote: 'I filled the ear with carbolic oil—one in 40—and the beastie floated up, sting and all, intact. I administered brandy and strychnine freely but the patient gradually sank and died about 18 hours after.'

This case occurred at Mullumbimby, NSW, in 1904. Although the brandy and strychnine would hardly have enhanced the child's chance of survival, this case report neatly illustrates the dangers of the paralysis tick to humans and domestic animals.

At least 20 human deaths have been attributed to the paralysis tick (*Ixodes holocyclus*) in the 20th century, but none have occurred since 1945. Nevertheless, tick paralysis is a common and important disease and is one that practitioners and paramedical staff should be well aware of even if they do not practise near a tick-infested area. With modern transport it is very easy for ticks to be carried by humans or animals to areas where the tick is unheard of.

The Australian paralysis tick *(Ixodes holocyclus)* is the most dangerous tick in the world. It has other names such as bush, scrub, dog or bottle tick. It is found along the eastern coast of Australia, from Cairns in the north right down to Bairnsdale in Victoria. The population of ticks varies considerably with local weather conditions and the terrain.

The lifecycle of the tick involves larval, nymph and adult stages, all of which have to feed on a warm-blooded animal. The bandicoot is its most

DISTRIBUTION

common host but many other animals suffer infestation. Dogs often collect ticks, and this is an important veterinary problem.

The saliva of the tiny adult tick contains a number of components that aid with its feeding. The longer it feeds, the greater the output of the saliva and of the toxin it contains. Normally the tick engorges for a number of days and then falls off, leaving the host unaffected. Should the tick continue to feed for a longer period, more toxin will be absorbed and a patchy paralysis may develop.

The toxin acts presynaptically and relatively slowly, although rough removal of the tick may cause saliva to escape into the tissues, the effects of which become suddenly apparent some hours later.

After being in tick country, every family member, as well as the family dog, should be examined daily for 6 days in case any ticks have become attached. This also includes Mum and Dad.

First aid

The tick or ticks should be removed as soon as possible. The best method of doing this is to lever the tick out using a pair of curved scissors, which should be slid around the shoulders of the tick so that it may be completely removed with its mouth-parts intact. The use of irritating substances such as kerosene or ether are no longer advised because

they will induce the tick to produce more toxin. A check for further ticks is essential, taking special care in areas above the hairline of the scalp and all crevasses of the body.

Mild symptoms will usually subside once the tick has been removed. Because of modern intensive care techniques, antitoxin—which is prepared from the sera of infested dogs—is very rarely required. This is just as well as it never reached the same order of quality as other agents used to treat envenomed humans.

Allergy to tick saliva is a significant problem in tick-infested areas. Sensitised patients can suffer from a range of effects, from gross local swelling to life-threatening anaphylactic reactions. Milder cases respond to the removal of the tick or ticks and administration of antihistamines. The more severe reactions may require adrenaline as well as maintenance of the airways, etc.

If a person has become highly allergic to ticks it is vital that they take care to avoid further contact with these creatures. If the risk of further contact cannot be eliminated it is essential that they have some form of easily injectable adrenaline available and that they and their family be clearly instructed as to its use. At the moment no tick saliva extracts are commercially available for the investigation and immunotherapy of highly allergic individuals.

SPIDERS

Mouse spider

The situation was grim. The 19-month-old girl was critically ill and seemed to be getting worse. She was in the Toowoomba General Hospital, having been bitten by a squat black spider the previous evening near Mt Sylvia. The child had been playing on the kitchen floor of a friend's house when the spider crawled over her right hand and delivered a painful bite. Two fang marks about 0.5 cm apart were clearly evident and the spider was killed and kept.

The little girl had screamed with pain and some 15 minutes later began vomiting copiously. She was taken initially to the Gatton Hospital 35 km away, and arrived there some 40 minutes after the bite occurred. At this stage she was unconscious and her pupils

DISTRIBUTION

were dilated. Muscle spasms were present and at one time mimicked a convulsion. Profuse sweating was present and there was stridor but no cyanosis.

She was transferred to the Toowoomba Hospital, arriving approximately an hour after the bite occurred. On admission she was unconscious but responding to pain and voice, crying uncontrollably and thrashing around in the bed. Her pupils were constricted and unresponsive. She was hypertensive and sweating profusely. Marked inspiratory stridor was present and was associated with tachypnoea and intercostal recession. Her abdomen was distended.

A compression bandage was applied to the envenomed limb. She was given diazapam 1 mg intravenously (IV), maxalon (1 mg IV), hydrocortisone (40 mg IV) and also 500 units of red-back spider venom by intramuscular injection, but there was no apparent improvement in her condition.

Although vomiting and sweating ceased by the following morning, her level of consciousness continued to fluctuate. By this stage a local naturalist had identified the offending spider as a male mouse spider, *Missulena bradleyi*. Advice from CSL was then sought about management.

Let's look at these creatures and then come back to our little patient.

At least six species of mouse spiders live in practically all parts of Australia, but not in Tasmania. Their wide distribution is probably due to the fact that the young spiderlings disperse to wherever the wind takes the tiny gossamer thread that makes them

temporarily airborne. By farewelling their mothers in this fashion they never heavily populate a particular area. Mouse spiders are found in a surprisingly diverse range of environments, from deserts to eucalypt forests, but are not found in the northern rainforests.

The male of one species should be dealt with first since it often attracts the attention of humans. *M. occatoria* is sometimes called the red-headed mouse spider because the region around the male's eyes is bright red, as are its massive fangs. Unlike many large spiders, male mouse spiders may be found wandering around across lawns in broad daylight. The colour of the male is so different to the female that for quite some time they were considered different species.

Mouse spiders vary considerably in size but the leg span of most comfortably covers a 20-cent coin. They are squat, very heavily built spiders with reasonably delicate legs. The head is characteristically different from other large black spiders like funnel-webs as it is divided into two levels, with the rear half a sharp step down from the front half. This is particularly apparent when viewed from the side. The large fangs of most mouse spiders open widely and cross

over in a pincher-like fashion, whereas the fangs of most other trapdoor spiders and funnel-webs lie parallel when they are closed.

Another distinguishing feature of mouse spiders is that the eight minute eyes are spread across the front section of its head, behind the fangs rather than grouped in clumps as with other spiders.

The body colour of male spiders varies from black to dark blue, and some have a yellow patch on part of the abdomen. In one species found in and around Darwin, the abdomen is nearly all yellow.

On the other hand, female mouse spiders are uniformly black from head to tail and are usually larger and more heavily built. Generally they tend to be more sluggish than the males.

Whereas male mouse spiders hike all over the countryside, the female never leaves the vicinity of her rather unusual burrow. Dr Barbara York Main has extensively studied the Western Australian mouse spiders and has found these burrows to be ingeniously designed. First, there are exquisitely engineered double doors on the surface. These are thick and reinforced with soil and have bevelled margins that would impress even the most skilled cabinet maker. Provided it is not too large, the female will polish off any invertebrate from ants to large beetles wandering past this entrance.

The silk-lined main shaft is some 30 cm deep and widens to 4 cm at the bottom where this lady does most of her meditating. At a safe depth the female constructs a little side tunnel as a nursery. To control traffic in either direction, the mother-to-be attaches a vertically hinged door to the nursery. The side of the door facing the nursery is neatly covered with silk, while the side facing the main shaft is left pretty rough.

Little is known about the mating habits of the mouse spider, but it is presumed that the male approaches with considerable caution, preferably after she has just sucked the juices out of a fat beetle. Some 50 eggs are deposited in the chamber in late spring, and in no time at all the young ones have all gone and her house is eerily quiet again.

Apart from scorpions, the female's worst enemies are probably the garden spade and earth-moving equipment.

The fangs of these spiders are particularly large and the spider appears quite menacing when it rears backwards, opening and closing the fangs in a pincer-like movement. Venom droplets are clearly to be seen on the tips of the fangs, and in captivity it is easy to collect this venom from the larger specimens with a pipette.

Only a brief examination has ever been made of mouse spider venom, and the findings were rather worrying. At CSL in 1979, venom was collected from some female *M. occatoria*. The output of venom was equal to, if not greater than, mature Sydney funnel-web spiders and was almost as toxic as the most potent male funnel-web venom.

Some preliminary work determined that the venom causes erratic muscular fasciculations very similar to those caused by funnel-web venom. This brings us back to our mouse spider victim in Toowoomba.

Twelve hours after the bite had occurred, a trial of two vials of funnel-web antivenom was suggested. Fortunately, this was held at this hospital because of the presence in the area of a highly dangerous funnel-web known as the Toowoomba or Darling Downs funnel-web spider (*Hadronyche infensus*).

There were a number of reasons why it was worth trying this antivenom. She was seriously ill and had not responded to the red-back spider anti-venom. Although the work was only preliminary, there were close similarities between the actions of the venoms of the mouse spider and funnel-web spider. The third reason was that neither before nor after this case has funnel-web antivenom been associated with any untoward immediate reactions.

At 10.45 am, after a dose of hydrocortisone, two vials of funnel-web antivenom were given. Halfway through the infusion, her blood pressure normalised. About 90 minutes after the injection there was a distinct improvement in her condition, her level of consciousness improved and she started to spontaneously look around and say 'Daddy'. On the basis of this improvement, she received two further ampoules of antivenom.

Thirty-six hours after the envenomation she was much better, being conscious and able to sit up and point to things. By Day 5 there were no residual neurological problems.

This child's poisoning appears to be clear evidence of the potential danger of mouse spiders, and suggests that funnel-web spider antivenom may play an important role in the management of serious envenomations. There are serious implications of this case since the spider is so widespread while funnel-web antivenom is only kept in the eastern parts of Australia where funnel-webs abound.

From time to time there have been reports of strange syndromes following bites by unidentified spiders. The reports of particular interest are those that develop a syndrome not unlike a funnel-web spider envenomation but have occurred in areas where that spider is not found. It is extremely useful if the offending spider in such cases can be kept for examination by museum authorities. Even if the spider has been virtually ground flat, if it is scraped up and preserved in spirits the experts usually can identify the species and sex of the culprit.

First aid

Prompt application of the pressure–immobilisation type of first aid is strongly recommended after mouse spider bites (see page 186).

As with funnel-web spider bites, quite often the spider will not deliver sufficient venom to cause a significant illness. However, in the light of the case described above, all cases should be observed closely, especially children because of the likelihood of a much higher venom to bodyweight ratio.

The antivenom of choice at present appears to be funnel-web antivenom, and the overall management of the case follows that as described for funnel-web spider envenomations (see page 117).

Should antivenom be required but a serious delay is occurring because of distance, then the re-application of first aid measures should be considered. This is a long shot, but it was found experimentally that the pressure–immobilisation type of first aid appeared to lead to inactivation of funnel-web spider antivenom at the site of injection. This did not occur with other venoms, such as snake venoms, and when the first aid measures were removed, systemic poisoning developed.

SPIDERS

Red-back spider

Each year in Australia some 2000 surprised people are bitten by red-back spiders. At least a quarter of these require antivenom and generally make a rapid recovery. About 17 per cent of cases need extra antivenom.

The red-back spider *(Latrodectus hasselti)* is a quiet little spider that is found in most parts of Australia. Only the female is dangerous to humans; although the male is poisonous, its fangs are too small to penetrate the human skin.

It is possible that the red-back spider only arrived in Australia in the 19th century and steadily spread itself across the country. Whether this is true or not is debatable, but there is no doubt that there are more cases of the syndrome of latrodectism per head of population than in any other country in the world. Furthermore, the seriousness of the illness is generally greater in Australia than is seen

in the USA, such as after bites by the spider's cousin, the black widow spider.

DISTRIBUTION

The red-back spider usually bites a human when its space is being invaded or it is being squashed against a person's skin. It will usually do its best to avoid confrontation and, if disturbed, will generally fall to the ground and pretend to be dead.

However, it is a different matter if it has made its home in old clothing, gloves or boots that the person suddenly decides to use. Country toilets used to be a favourite lurking spot for a red-back and 30 years ago one in five cases involved bites to the buttocks or genitals. As these toilets have been phased out, nips to these regions have dropped to less than 3 per cent.

Cases of red-back spider bite occur throughout the year in Australia but are more common in the warmer months, especially February. The victims have ranged in age from a child who was being breast-fed (both the mother and the infant were bitten and required antivenom) to the very elderly.

The bite is immediately painful and the spider is usually caught in the act. In most cases the spider is easily identified by its bright red stripe, although sometimes it may be orange, pink or even light grey.

The venom has a specific action at the end of nerve fibres. It causes the loss of transmitter substance and produces a peculiar syndrome known as latrodectism, which can continue for many days.

Usually the bitten area is no longer painful an hour or so after the bite, but symptoms emerge elsewhere with pain and areas of sweating developing in other parts of the body. The sweating may be general and profuse or localised and migratory.

The hallmarks of latrodectism are the peculiarly migratory nature of the pain and sweating. Patients generally look miserable and can rarely sleep. Some will be agitated and distressed. Abdominal pain may be dominant, particularly in children. Blood pressure may be moderately elevated and tachycardia may be present, although neither are as severe as after funnel-web spider bites.

In cases not treated early with antivenom, the signs and symptoms increase in severity over 12–24 hours and may then resolve very slowly over the next week. A small percentage of patients suffer bizarre signs and symptoms, such as swelling around the eyes, tingling of the teeth, swelling of the tongue and dysuria. Sometimes, tetanic spasms or an urticarial rash may occur early in the syndrome.

Usually the diagnosis is straightforward because of the prompt finding of the spider and its association with the onset of severe pain. The diagnosis of latrodectism should be always considered in an apyrexic infant who suddenly develops severe pain, regional skin changes and a significant tachycardia.

First aid

Pressure–immobilisation should NOT be used for red-back spider bites. The venom produces its

effects slowly and local pain may become more severe if its movement is restricted. The prompt application of iced water or an ice/water combination is the accepted first aid. The spider should accompany the patient on a careful trip to hospital.

Antivenom should be given if a person has been bitten by a red-back spider and definite and distressing signs and symptoms of envenomation have developed. On the other hand, if the spider has not been positively identified and no signs and symptoms have developed other than some changes at the bite site, antivenom should be withheld for the time being.

The volume of antivenom used is quite small and may be comfortably given by intramuscular injection. If symptoms do not satisfactorily resolve or they increase, additional antivenom should be given. Literature enclosed with the antivenom gives advice on necessary precautions.

Note that the symptoms of red-back spider bites have been found to respond to antivenom therapy days or even weeks after the venom was introduced. This is the only 'venom disease' that shows any response to such delayed treatment.

Scorpion

The doctor's wife called out, 'Why don't you put your Wellington boots on!' As he went out the front door he replied, 'I'll only be a minute and I've got a torch anyway.' A tap had been left running and he wore only a towel and thongs.

He proceeded cautiously because two nights earlier they'd had a blitz on the scorpions and killed half a dozen around the house. On the way back to the house the doctor heard a scuffling sound. Balancing on one foot and holding the scorpion in the torch-light, he beat it to a pulp with the other thong.

He then set off, feeling most pleased with himself until he felt the sensation of a red hot needle pushing into his left great toe. As the searing pain rapidly sped along the toe and into the foot, scorpion number two retreated into the darkness.

Our poor doctor hopped back to the house and collapsed on a bed. It was as though somebody had removed all the skin and the toenail from his toe without anaesthetic. The pain came in waves and the area felt like it was being rubbed down with coarse sandpaper.

This scorpion stinging occurred in West Africa, but the circumstances and immediate effects are similar to scorpion stings in Australia, especially the northern parts.

There are some 650 species of scorpions in the world, but only a few are highly dangerous to humans. Fatal stings are common in Mexico, Trinidad, Brazil and parts of North Africa, the Middle East and India. The most important scorpions belong to the genus *Centruroides*, which is responsible for some 300,000 stings in Mexico each year and causes up to 700 deaths.

Scorpions are found in all parts of Australia and the 29 species belong to six genera. The largest and the most important belong to the genus *Urodacus*. Specimens of *Urodacus* in the Northern Territory may grow to a length of 15 cm.

Scorpions have broadly adapted to either living in the semi-arid central parts of Australia or to the wet southern and northern parts. Only one species, *Cercophonius squama*, is found in Tasmania. This species is also widespread in the southern parts of the mainland. Deaths from Australian scorpions are extremely rare.

DISTRIBUTION

Some of the desert scorpions are great diggers. One was shown to excavate a burrow 1 metre deep in 8 hours. Another specialises in hunting within the burrows of trapdoor spiders like a ferret after rabbits.

Scorpions are among the oldest forms of animal life, having been around for at least 135 million years. They are arachnids, with eight legs and a well developed pair of claws. At the end of its 'tail' is a thorn-like sting or telson that it waves around in a threatening fashion.

The scorpion's head seems to have been squashed flat as though it has been hit by a bus. In this flat region is a mouth and a pair of power-ful jaws. Most scorpions have 6–12 eyes, but their vision is very poor. Some scorpions have no eyes at all.

The 'body' of the scorpion is generally plump and thick-set and usually hugs the ground quite closely like an expensive automobile. The tail section is divided into five segments, with the last bearing both the anus and the venom apparatus.

Scorpions hunt at night and prefer to remain concealed during the day, sometimes in clothing, shoes and the like. Their prey consists of insects, bugs and spiders. Usually their prey is easily dealt with by their claws, but the sting is brought into action if the outcome is in the slightest doubt.

The mating habits of scorpions frequently appear on nature programs because cameramen find them irresistible. When the male finds a female he fancies, he grasps her claws with his own and then they begin a number of backward and forward movements as well as shuffling from side to side. This can go on for an hour or so until the male finds a suitable area of flat ground. While still engaged in the dance, he deposits a capsule of spermatic fluid on the selected spot on the ground. He then nonchalantly manoeuvres the female over this capsule until her genital opening comes into contact with it. The pressure of contact causes the capsule to rupture, and the sperm mass enters her genital tract.

When the young are being born, the mother usually folds her anterior legs under the genital opening so the young do not touch the ground but are instead guided to the nearest leg so that they can climb onto her back and join their siblings. The young stay on the mother's back for several weeks until the first moult. Quite remarkably, they all seem to moult within a few hours of one another. The female is inclined to eat the odd one and so they soon take the hint and move to other pastures.

In Africa the genus *Parabuthus* is the only scorpion that can make a noise. It does this by scraping a specially modified part of its telson over a series of granules on its back. It can also squirt venom up to a metre. This was discovered by a scientist who had a caged specimen that became alarmed when he blew on it from above. He received a direct hit but fortunately was wearing glasses.

Scorpions have two venom glands situated ventrolaterally in the telson. A duct runs from each gland posteriorly to a tiny hole near the tip of the sting. The glands are surrounded by muscles

Pseudoscorpions and earwigs

Pseudoscorpions or chelifers are similar to small scorpions but they lack the telson and associated sting. They have front claws like scorpions, and these have small venom glands. Most are too small to cause any illness. A lady who was nipped by one in the armpit in Kalgoorlie promptly developed a blotchy rash but no other effects.

Earwigs are sometimes mistaken for scorpions. These can deliver a sharp nip but have no venom. Earwigs are more likely to cause mechanical problems, such as when they crawl into a child's ear.

and the scorpion has a fair control of the amount of venom being ejected.

The venom of overseas scorpions has been studied for many years. It is usually collected by immobilising the creature and applying an electrical stimulation to the membrane between the last two abdominal segments (i.e. very near the sting). Drops of venom appear on the tip of the sting and can be collected in a pipette or ampoule.

A variety of neurotoxins and cardio-toxins have been isolated from scorpion venoms. The more important venoms are quite complex and have diverse and specific pharmacological targets. A number have become important research tools for the pharmacologist.

The dangerous overseas scorpions all deliver painful stings and may produce varying systemic effects, including severe cardiovascular disturbances, generalised muscle spasm and paralysis. Excessive salivation and perspiration may occur. Some of the syndromes described are reminiscent of poisoning by a male Sydney funnel-web spider. In others, myocarditis is sometimes described as the likely cause of death. Some venoms are strangely specific and may, for example, cause acute pancreatitis.

Little work has been done on the properties of the scorpion venoms of Australia. The only one investigated was from a species of *Urodacus* found in South Australia and southern parts of Western Australia. The venom was found to contain a variety of substances including 5-hydroxy-tryptamine and histamine.

Even a tiny scorpion can produce a painful sting. The sting may be associated with local swelling and sometimes general symptoms. The pain is usually described as burning and severe, and can persist for a number of hours. Major envenomations may be associated with prostration and fever.

Deaths have followed scorpion stings in Australia. In 1929 at Pemberton in Western Australia, a baby girl was stung by what was believed to be a marbled scorpion *(Lychas marmoreus)*. Many years ago a 3-week-old infant died in Tasmania after receiving scorpion stings on two consecutive days.

Scorpions sometimes wander into houses and get caught up in clothing. On one occasion a young housewife was ironing her son's trousers when a tiny scorpion marched out and stung her on the thumb. The top of her thumb and the proximal joint became intensely painful. She was treated with analgesics and bathed the thumb in warm to hot water. The pain became worse over the next 24 hours and she likened it to a severe toothache.

Now back to our doctor in Africa, who was shaking violently. Having treated many scorpion stings by injecting 1 per cent lignocaine into the site of the sting and seeing the patient striding out smiling and grateful within a minute, he injected the lignocaine into the puncture wound and waited for the magic to work. It didn't, nor did a ring block with lignocaine. Hefty doses of analgesics made the pain just bearable.

The doctor made a couple of observations. One was to always wear shoes at night where there were scorpions about. The other was, just because they worked for others do not expect your treatments to work for you.

Two weeks after the episode he spotted the largest scorpion that he had ever seen scuttle into the torchlight. Revenge was sweet and, despite what everyone else said, he was adamant that it was the one that had bitten him. He was never stung again but treated subsequent scorpion stings with great compassion and diligence.

First aid

Traditionally it is said that scorpion stings should be bathed in warm to hot water to which ammonia has been added. There is no published evidence that this gives relief from pain, and possibly a water/ice pack would be more effective. Anti-histamines would seem to be indicated and appropriate analgesia offered. Opiates might be required for severe pain.

Prevention

In heavily infested areas overseas, great care is taken to try to make dwellings scorpion-proof. Doors are made close fitting, and the more wealthy householders have smooth or tiled walls around their properties as the first line of defence. Such precautions are not necessary in Australia, but since scorpions tend to hide at daybreak it is important to shake bedding and clothing thoroughly in areas where scorpions are common.

SPIDERS

Sydney funnel-web spider

The 9-month-old child screamed as the strong black fangs plunged downwards. Her father dropped his coffee as he ran into the room to find a large black spider firmly clinging to her hand. As a pharmacist, he knew a funnel-web when he saw one. His yells brought his wife running as he tore the spider off with his bare hands.

Their next actions probably saved the child's life. Her mother, an intensive care nurse, quickly applied a firm bandage over the bitten area and forearm while her husband rang for an ambulance. Twenty minutes later the little girl was in hospital.

DISTRIBUTION

The male funnel-web is more delicately built than the female. While female funnel-webs live for perhaps 10 or more years, most males die within 6 months of maturing. The male has a small spur on its second pair of legs, and its little feelers at the front part of its body resemble a thorn. The spurs are pretty important to the male. When mating he uses them to prevent the female's fangs from crashing down and splitting his head open.

The females spend most of their time in their burrows, which can be distinguished from those of other ground-dwelling spiders because they have a number of silk trip lines running across the ground outside the opening. Trapdoor and other spiders don't have trip lines.

Male funnel-webs are fairly sex-mad and spend most nights in summer wandering about in search of females and, to a lesser extent, food. This may account for their short life. Unfortunately males have a tendency to wander into houses, where they will rear up and attempt to envenom any creatures that approach them. Many bites have occurred when the funnel-web has taken temporary refuge in shoes, clothing and bedding.

Dr Mike Gray from the Australian Museum in Sydney advises that during the summer and autumn you should always check clothing and equipment stored in garages and sheds before use, and also check sandpits and swimming pools. He has found that funnel-webs can survive up to 30 hours fully immersed in water, but fortunately will remain sluggish for some time after their removal. Dr Gray advises not to walk around barefoot at night, to wear gloves when gardening and, if camping, use a floored zippered tent if in a funnel-web area. He points out that houses built on ground level concrete slabs are the most at risk and suggests fitting draught strips on outside doors.

Dr Gray is not a proponent of pesticide spraying as he believes it is only a temporary measure; apart from affecting other creatures it may act as a stimulant and increase the wandering activity of funnel-webs!

Tests on the venom show that the male venom is some five times more potent than female venom. In fact, no deaths are known to follow a bite by a female spider. Humans and monkeys have a peculiar susceptibility to the venom, but no domestic animals are known to have died following a

Her pulse rate was over 200, she was salivating and sweating profusely, and was centrally cyanosed. Six ampoules of antivenom were required to reverse the effects of the venom. She made a full recovery.

The Sydney funnel-web spider must be considered the most dangerous spider in the world as it is the only spider that has killed children in less than 2 hours. One 2-year-old died 15 minutes after the bite occurred. By delaying the movement of spider venom, the mother of the 9-month-old may well have prevented her early death.

The Sydney funnel-web (Atrax robustus) is quite a spider. There are a number of other funnel-webs, but from a medical point of view the Sydney one is the king. It is found from Newcastle to Nowra, and as far west as Lithgow. They are large dark spiders with quite massive fangs. Unlike most spiders whose fangs have a pincer-like action, the funnel-web strikes with its fangs like parallel daggers. This means it must first raise its body high before it can strike, delivering a bite not unlike a snake-bite. The fangs can be driven in with considerable force.

One way to distinguish funnel-webs from other large, dark but usually harmless spiders is to look at the spinnerets that stick out from its tail region. With funnel-webs, the last little segment of this spinning apparatus is much longer than the other segments.

funnel-web spider bite and most laboratory animals are highly resistant.

The male spider produces only 0.17 mg of venom on average, but it is extraordinarily potent. Although this amount of venom may kill a human, many people bitten by male funnel-web spiders develop no general effects at all because it has not introduced sufficient venom. Often the spider lunges back and forth with rage, missing its target so that the venom falls harmlessly to the ground.

A person bitten by either the male or female spider may find the experience not only terrifying but usually very painful because of the size of the fangs and the acidity of the venom. Sometimes the fangs are deeply embedded and the spider must be torn off. The local pain lasts for 30 minutes or longer, and usually there is evidence of local sweating and erection of the hair follicles. No local necrosis has been described.

If sufficient venom has been injected and no effective first aid applied, a bite by the male spider will produce systemic symptoms in 10 minutes. First there is usually numbness around the tongue and mouth and spasms of the tongue. This is followed by tachycardia, nausea, vomiting, sweating, salivation and lachrymation. The victim may be very agitated, particularly as severe dyspnoea develops. The mental state may rapidly progress from confusion to irrational behaviour or coma.

The blood pressure is usually markedly elevated and severe vasoconstriction is evident. In severe cases, gross pulmonary oedema may occur.

The main component in the venom, robustoxin, produces a unique and bizarre syndrome by stimulating erratic impulses down nerves throughout the body. In serious cases, both local and general fasciculation of muscles is invariably seen, and it may be prolonged and violent.

Later, the muscle twitching, salivation and sweating subside and a slow but progressive hypotension develops. Studies in monkeys some years ago suggested that the pulmonary oedema may be associated with raised intracranial pressure and associated cerebral hypoxia.

First aid

The pressure–immobilisation type of first aid should be applied following bites by this spider (see page 186). Households located where funnel-web spiders are found should have either crepe bandages or old pantyhose centrally located for use as first aid. Indeed, if a person in the Sydney area is bitten on a limb by any large dark spider, firm pressure over the bitten area with a bandage should be applied immediately.

The limb should be splinted to immobilise it and the patient and spider taken promptly and safely to hospital. In most cases no illness will develop because the spider has not bitten effectively. If possible, the first aid measures should not be removed until the patient is prepared for monitoring in an intensive care situation.

Sometimes it is not possible to apply this type of first aid, for example bites to the trunk. However, it is known that two women who were bitten on the trunk and subsequently died both reached hospital with only mild early symptoms. (These cases occurred before antivenom became available.)

When first aid measures are removed, local or general signs will develop quite rapidly if sufficient venom has been injected. If there is no evidence of local fasciculation or systemic poisoning 4 hours after the first aid has been removed, then the patient may be discharged. If local muscle fasciculation is present, or there is any suggestion of systemic poisoning, the patient may require antivenom, and the sooner the better.

Antivenom

Funnel-web antivenom has been isolated from the serum of hyperimmunised rabbits and consists of immunochemically pure rabbit immunoglobulin (IgG). When the antivenom was tested in monkeys suffering from funnel-web spider venom poisoning, rapid and complete reversal of all signs of poisoning was achieved.

Since it was released late in 1980, the antivenom has been given to at least 100 patients, all of whom have rapidly recovered. No adverse reactions have been reported to date. The last deaths due to funnel-web spider bites occurred in January 1979 and January 1980. The first was of a 30-year-old woman and the other a 2-year-old boy.

If there is clear evidence of systemic envenomation following a bite by a male specimen of *Atrax robustus*, then urgent use of antivenom must be considered.

Skin testing is not recommended with this or any other antivenom. Pretreatment with adrenaline is generally not considered necessary because the venom may have produced a high level of catecholamines.

The dosage of antivenom is the same for a child as an adult. The minimal initial dose for a mild case is two ampoules repeated every 15 minutes if there is no improvement. The antivenom should be given intravenously, and initially very slowly.

SPIDERS

Tree-dwelling funnel-web spider

There was great excitement at CSL. The operator of a sawmill in northern NSW had phoned to say that he had captured a large female tree-dwelling funnel-web spider. This was in the days before funnel-web antivenom was available, and CSL technicians were carefully milking the venom of dozens of Sydney funnel-web spiders each week. However, their collection was lacking examples of tree-dwelling funnel webs, and for years the technicians had been eager to capture one.

The following Friday a large sealed butterbox arrived plastered with ominous warnings about its contents. These warnings, and the fact that something could be heard moving around inside the box, suggested a cautious approach should be adopted.

The decision was made to leave the spider in the box over the weekend in the hope that it would 'quieten down'. When Monday came its activities had increased. Scratching, scraping and gnawing sounds were clearly audible through the thin-walled butterbox.

A large stainless steel tank was obtained and the contents of the box cautiously emptied into it. From the heap of bark and forest rubble emerged one of the largest and toughest spiders you could imagine.

No spider was treated at CSL with greater respect than this lady. Her massive fangs literally dripped venom, and limited studies done on her venom found that it is at least as potent as that of the male Sydney funnel-web spider. The venom also appeared to have similar pharmacological activity. Her heart rate could be counted by the rather revolting pulsations of the large vessel on the upper surface of the abdomen. At no stage did she show any hint of friendship towards humans, and when she finally died of chronic rage her body was preserved. More than 20 years later she is still on display at the Australian Venom Research Unit.

There are two tree-dwelling species of funnel-webs. They both used to be classified with Sydney

DISTRIBUTION

distribution of the genus *Hadronyche*

funnel-web spiders in the genus *Atrax*, but they have now been reclassified under the genus *Hadronyche*. The southern tree-dwelling or paperbark funnel-web, *H. cerberea*, is found in the highland areas of south-eastern NSW. The female very rarely nests in the ground, and the opening to its lair does not have the network of triplines that are charac-teristic of most funnel-webs. Probably only the male of this species is a danger to humans.

The northern tree-dwelling funnel-web *H. formidabilis* is appropriately named. It

Other funnel-web spiders

Several more members of the genus *Hadronyche* are known to be dangerous to humans. Queensland has the Darling Downs or Toowoomba spider (*H. infensa*), and NSW the Blue Mountains funnel-web spider (*H. versuta*). Bites by these spiders have been successfully treated with Sydney funnel-web antivenom. Fortunately the funnel-web spiders found in Victoria, Tasmania and South Australia are not known to have caused any significant human illness.

is a rare spider that usually dwells in thick forest, and it can be found from the Hunter River area in NSW to the Bunya Mountains in Queensland. Both the female and male of this species are a likely threat to human life.

The giant female spider makes her home as high as 30 metres off the ground. Should her home be cut down and she survives the fall to the ground, there is no doubt she would come out to investigate with fangs at the ready.

Case reports indicate that the venom of the male of either species will produce effects similar to those caused by the bite of a Sydney funnel-web spider. The key features are systemic piloerection, sweating, muscle fasciculation, and gross elevation of blood pressure and pulse rate associated with dyspnoea.

A 1927 report of the effects of a bite by a male *H. formidabilis* on a strong and healthy sleeper cutter at Wauchope, NSW, is a graphic guide to the potency of this spider. The spider had crawled into his trousers overnight and he was bitten on the buttock when dress-ing next morning. He knocked the spider off and it fastened to his finger. The bites were extremely painful.

When seen by a doctor 3 hours later he was very ill and suffering from intense vomit-ing, profuse sweating and violent cramps in all muscle groups. He was more or less delirious and was saying that someone was spraying him with something. The doctor included the following description: 'Saliva and other secretions were running so profusely from his mouth that his head had to be kept in a dependent position to facilitate their exit. He was shivering and bathed in profuse perspiration. A military overcoat he was wearing, when lifted, felt as though it had been soaking for a long time in water.'

This man's condition remained critical for hours, and then he slowly recovered. The doctor commented that 'had a child received the same amount of poison, he surely would have died'.

In 1989, a 4-year-old boy was bitten on the chest by a male *H. cerberea* near Wyong in NSW. A critical illness rapidly developed and on admission to hospital his blood pressure was 160/110 and his pulse rate greater than 150 beats per minute. He fully recovered 2 hours later after four ampoules of antivenom. Another severe case occurred in the same district in 1998.

First aid

The application of the pressure–immobilisation type of first aid (see page 186) will retard the movement of these most toxic venoms and may be life-saving.

Clinical experience suggests that the antivenom directed against the venom of the Sydney funnel-web spider is effective in managing bites by either of these spiders. Severe envenomations may need a number of ampoules of antivenom.

Prevention

While the female is in residence way above the ground, the male is generally on the prowl when he is not courting her. A number of bites have occurred after the male has roamed into caravans or tents, particularly after heavy rain. If camping in the midst of this spider's territory it is best to have a zippered tent and make good use of a torch. If visiting 'funnel-web country', even if staying on the tenth floor of a hotel, routinely check shoes and clothing for any unwelcome creature each morning.

SPIDERS

Necrotising spiders

She was three-and-a-half years old and was following her father around the Victorian high school as he was preparing it for the new school year. But she didn't follow him everywhere, electing instead to remain in a store room. He returned and found her examining her bare foot. He could see no sign of a bite but she refused to walk for some minutes before later running around normally.

That night she had nightmares about spiders and vomited extensively at 4 am. The next morning her foot was swollen and she was admitted to hospital looking sick, pale and irritable. She had no temperature but her left foot was now puffy and cyanosed.

That night she became feverish and delirious, and severe diarrhoea developed. She might have died from shock and dehydration if active resuscitation measures had not been taken.

Within 48 hours of the suspected bite, a large area of the foot clearly showed necrosis. The entire thickness of the skin became necrotic and required extensive debridement and skin grafting.

Doctors from all parts of Australia have increasingly reported troublesome lesions that have developed after real or probable spider bites. A major problem facing doctors attempting to diagnose the cause of the lesions is that the offending spider is not usually caught in the act. Gardeners and tradesmen may not notice the penetration of tiny fangs and people are often bitten while asleep in bed. Museum authorities can usually identify a spider by some of its relatively indestructible parts. Even if the offending spider has been squashed and mangled it should be scraped up and stored in spirits.

Usually the speed of onset and other symptoms strongly suggest that a necrotising venom is responsible for the lesions. The effects vary from insignificant to full thickness tissue necrosis involving a wide area. In a number of cases, near complete or complete healing occurs but weeks or months later a near identical lesion redevelops. Occasionally satellite lesions develop long after the initial bite had occurred. Sometimes a dramatic accelerated breakdown of the original lesion is seen. Witnesses have observed almost bizarre acute changes, such as blisters and swelling re-developing in a matter of minutes.

Three species of spiders have been implicated in necrotising arachnidism. These are the common black window spider (*Badumna insignis*), the ubiquitous cupboard or brown house spider (*Steatoda spp.*), and the white-tailed spider (*Lampona cylindrata*).

Brown house spider

Black window spider

The black window spider can usually be found in the corner of windows or in crevasses in fences and trees. Its untidy web has a funnel-like shape and is made of dense, thick, lacy silk. During the day the spider hides out of sight, but at night it may be seen repairing or adding to its web. The body of the spider may be intensely black and is seldom longer than 1.5 cm.

The black window spider can cause quite painful bites and systemic effects, in particular vomiting. A healthy 40-year-old male

DISTRIBUTION

zoologist was bitten on the ankle by a male black window spider that had been trapped in his riding boot. His foot became grossly swollen with ulceration at the bite site. Extensive bruising and discoloration developed in the surrounding area. It was a week before he could hobble around and 3 weeks before healing had occurred. The zoologist felt he was fortunate to have been bitten by the male of this species rather than the larger and presumably more venomous female, which has been implicated in quite serious ulcerations.

Cupboard or brown house spider

The cupboard or brown house spider often resides under lounge suites. In the garden it particularly fancies inverted and empty pot plant containers. Gardeners frequently say it resembles a red-back spider but without the stripe. This is fair enough as it is the red-back's closest relative. (In a recent case its bite caused an illness not unlike that caused by red-back spider

DISTRIBUTION

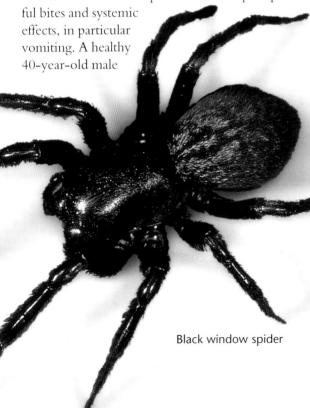
Black window spider

bite. Red-back spider antivenom appeared to effect a cure.) It is a small spider, a little larger than a pea, with a very shiny dark brown or black spherical body. When alarmed it will usually fall to the ground and lie motionless for a minute or so.

The cupboard or brown house spider reportedly causes larger blister formation at the bite site. The bite is usually painless and a slow pruritus may develop. Rather impressive blistering may occur in a short space of time the next day. In time this little spider may be given a higher danger rating.

White-tailed spider

There are a number of species of this type of spider, of which *L. cylindrata* appears particularly common. This native Australian arachnid has a cigar-shaped body less than 1.5 cm long, and both sexes usually have a white or greyish-white spot at the tip of their abdomen. Both the male and the female may be found wandering inside houses, especially at night. The white-tailed spider does not spin a web and tends to hide during daylight.

These spiders have a habit of taking refuge in bedding or clothing that has been left on the floor. As a result, the spider finds itself trapped in a bed with a person or couple when the bedding has been replaced.

DISTRIBUTION

Outside, stacks of bricks make suitable high rise apartments for this spider, while in the garden it lives under peeling bark or dry logs. When disturbed it often remains stationary for a split second or so and then takes off at surprising speed.

Both the male and female white-tailed spider can cause significant lesions. Local, painful blistering and some degree of ulceration follows in 10 per cent of cases. These lesions usually heal within 3 weeks. The occasional presence of scattered lesions indicates the progress of a semi-squashed spider, with the blisters becoming smaller as its venom supply is depleted.

Sometimes a large and extremely painful lesion developing several days after a white-tailed spider bite causes considerable concern because of the possible onset of gangrene.

First aid and medical management

The pressure–immobilisation type of first aid has NO place in the care of these spider bites. If the lesions are initially painful or itchy, some relief may be obtained by the application of an ice/water mixture. Most reactions are minor and merely local. Anti-

histamines are usually prescribed, but it is difficult to establish their efficiency. The sudden development of very painful cutaneous inflammation that spreads rapidly almost invariably leads to the administration of antibiotics. Usually there is no dramatic response to varied antibiotic therapy and no bacteria have been isolated early in the disease from either the skin lesions or the blood cultures. The inflammation is confluent and generally halts of its own accord, leaving a large cyanotic area of threatened viability.

Large, intensely cyanotic lesions that are spreading do not respond to any particular therapy. They may represent a vasospastic condition, and local or general vasodilators might be considered. One practitioner reported a dramatic response to heparin, but it is difficult to understand the mechanism of such a response. Overseas experience with cases of necrotising arachnidism caused by the brown recluse spider suggest that neither heparin nor a high dose of steroids produce significant improvement. Dapsone enjoyed a brief period of popularity and the latest trend in the United States is the use of hyperbaric oxygen therapy.

Biopsy of the lesions is usually unsatisfactory. Clinicians are hesitant to undertake biopsy in the acute stage; later, when the tissue is dead, the results are usually not helpful. On the other hand, when healing is slow, biopsy of the ulcer edge can be very informative. In some cases of spreading painless ulceration *Mycobacterium ulcerans* has been found and appropriate therapy successfully instituted. Fungal infections should also be excluded.

Early excision is often advocated when impressive lesions are developing. Surgical debridement is recommended if there is a large necrotic area. Skin grafting should be delayed for at least 7 days after the onset of the lesion. Earlier grafts will almost invariably fail to take, presumably because of the presence of toxins or toxic byproducts.

A conservative approach should be adopted if the viability of the area is uncertain. Sometimes wide excision of the lesion and neighbouring normal tissue is proposed as a means of limiting further spread. This is to be discouraged as tissue recovery often dramatically coincides with the cessation of venom spread. When the dead epidermis is removed, the subcutaneous fat is often found to be liquefied; such changes may be quite extensive.

SPIDERS

Other Australian Spiders

Spiders are the most widely distributed venomous creatures in Australia. There are more than 2000 named species and probably many more yet to be recognised. Very little is known about the distribution, habits and venom of the vast majority of these spiders. In many cases, identification can only be made by an expert yet there are only two full-time museum-based arachnologists in Australia. This situation sometimes delays the identification of rarer spiders that have caused clinical problems.

Some exciting substances have been isolated from the venoms of some the most common spiders overseas. For example, an interesting calcium channel blocker has been detected in the venom of the relatively innocuous American funnel-web spider, and the pharmaceutical and pesticide industries are pouring resources into the investigation of certain very low molecular weight neurotoxins isolated from orb-web spiders. These easily synthesised little toxins have a high specificity for certain glutamate receptors.

This chapter only considers spiders that have caused significant illness to people. Some do not have common names and it is not possible to give detailed descriptions to allow precise identification. The identification in many cases is difficult and highly specialised, but there are some good field guides available.

Bird-eating spider

These are huge and hairy tropical and subtropical spiders (genus *Selenocosmia*) whose body can measure 7 cm long. These spiders can kill and eat a frog their own size. They are also known as barking or whistling spiders because

DISTRIBUTION

of the strange grumbling sound they can make.

The sheer size and speed of this spider is enough to give one a heart attack. Some years ago Struan took the lid off a large jar containing a fine specimen and in a flash the spider was sitting on his shoulder! Struan went one way and it went the other. Surprisingly, when he put the large jar down on the floor the spider ran straight back into it.

There has been a report of one of these spiders killing a dog. A woman who was bitten suffered severe nausea and vomiting for 6 hours.

Some preliminary work could not demonstrate any toxicity to mice in extracts made from this spider's venom sacs. Further work is required.

Daddy-long-legs

These are shy, clumsy little spiders (family *Pholcidae*) which are incapable of inflicting a significant bite upon a human. Do not believe the contrary.

DISTRIBUTION

Fiddleback spider

From time to time the findings of species of the genus *Loxosceles* have been reported in Australia. Authentic identifications have been made of specimens found in Sydney and Adelaide. Fortunately these spiders

DISTRIBUTION

were not of the highly dangerous American species, *L. reclusa*, which is known as the brown

recluse or fiddle-back spider. The identification of these spiders highlights the importance of our museums and their arachnologists.

Huntsman spider

These large common spiders (family *Heteropodidae*) are also known as giant crab spiders or triantantelopes. They are very flat for their size and the first two pairs of legs are much longer than the

DISTRIBUTION

posterior ones. Their crab-like appearance is enhanced by their ability to run sideways as well as forwards. They build no webs and their flat bodies suit their habitat, which is usually under sheets of bark. They frequently roam through houses and may be seen walking across the ceiling in search of insects. Most people find them

abhorrent and insist they be removed. The spiders have an unpleasant habit of dropping from the ceiling if poked with a broom. Sweeping them out of the house is quite a performance as they often rear up, dance about and attempt to bite. Often these spiders will take up residence in a car and may drop onto the lap of the driver when the sun visor is folded down.

The three genera of this family in Australia are *Delena, Isopoda* and *Neosparassus*. There are at least 60 subspecies.

Bites by this spider usually produce only moderate local pain and the injury is soon forgotten. However, there have been a few cases of excruciating pain barely relieved by opiates and persisting for 24 hours. One species in northern Western Australia is greatly feared by the Aborigines. Its bite produces local swelling, vomiting and a headache. The illness can be so severe that sleep is impossible for several days.

In June 1993 near Derby, Western Australia, a 50-year-old man was bitten by a large huntsman spider when he put on a jacket that had been stored for some time. The immediate reaction was pain and considerable swelling. An hour later he was short of breath, felt unwell and complained of feeling cold. After a few hours he appeared to recover completely. Three days later he suffered a moderate heart attack when trying to catch a cat. It is unlikely that the incidents are related but he and his family could not be convinced otherwise.

On the bright side, little has usually followed the numerous incidents of bites by these spiders in the southern states. In a number of cases infants have received multiple bites. They were usually distressed for 15 minutes or so and some local redness persisted for several days. A number of these bites were on the infant's face. The main danger of huntsmen is in the fright they can give people.

Jumping spider

There are more than 60 genera in Australia of these small and widespread spiders (family Salticidae). They are very common in the tropics, where they are particularly colourful. All species are fascinating to watch as they stalk their prey in broad daylight and then optimistically leap. Like some other hunting spiders they are optically very well equipped.

Both the northern and southern species are known to give a painful bite that may remain swollen and discolored for a week or so.

Leaf-curling spider

This spider (genus *Phonognatha*) often appears in large numbers in late summer. It lives inside a leaf or a snail shell and emerges to feed or when disturbed. It has a plump yellow-brown body with a zig-zagging 'V' down the back. Its legs are a yellow-red to

orange colour. Bites can cause moderate local reactions and sometimes collapse. Preliminary work on its venom at the University of Melbourne has shown that it produces direct activation of beta-adrenoreceptors in isolated rat atria. This could be a useful new pharmaceutical tool.

Orb weaving spider

Some of the most spec-tacular spider webs are spun by the spiders of the genus *Araneus*. These are very common garden spiders that typically make a vertical orb web with a hole in the centre. These are almost invari-ably at face level across garden paths or between trees. The webs are magnificent constructions and characteristically are demolished by the spider as

DISTRIBUTION

the dawn approaches. The spider spends the day-time hiding nearby and then swings into web building again as the sun sets.

These fairly large spiders are often described as having humped shoulders. Bites usually occur when they are accidentally touched as they rest on taps or clotheslines during the daytime. The bite is described as very painful and collapse and pros-tration has occurred, with sudden and apparently complete recovery after about 30 minutes.

The golden orb weaver (genus *Nephila*), which has characteristically banded black and bright yellow legs, often attracts attention because of its impressive yellow web. Fortunately these are usually high above the ground and no bites by this large spider have been reported.

The Christmas or jewel spider (*Gasteracantha minax*) occurs in all states. These pretty, multi-coloured, spiky looking spiders often occur in huge colonies with their webs covering all the vegetation in the area like gossamer. A bite by this spider recently caused a very painful and slow healing lesion on the face of a Victorian woman.

Slender sack spider

There are 11 species of this family (genus *Chiracanthium*) found in Australia. The genus that is found all around the world causes a syndrome in Europe known as chiracanthism. This consists of a vague 2–3 day illness associated sometimes with local pain and ulceration. Such an illness was reported after a bite by the Australian species *C. mordax*. This spider lives in small transparent tubes and is often found in houses. It is a small spider with an almost translucent body growing to a maximum length of 15 mm.

DISTRIBUTION

Trapdoor spider

There are many species of trapdoor spiders (family *Ctenizidae*), which are widely distributed in all parts

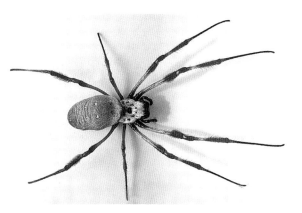

of Australia. They are relatively large, threatening-looking spiders and are often dug up by gardeners. Many don't have a camouflaged lid on the opening of their silk-lined burrow.

Trapdoor spiders are often mistaken for funnel-web spiders, but they can easily be distinguished by their spinnerets. These are the paired outlets for silk that protrude from the rear of the abdomen. In the funnel-web group the terminal spinneret is long and pointed, whereas in trapdoor spiders it is short and blunt. Take care while making this identification.

Bites by any of the trapdoor spiders can be quite painful and cause considerable distress. One Western Australian species *(Aganippe raphiduca)* may cause a severe reaction. The mouse spiders (genus *Missulena*) are trapdoor spiders that may be as dangerous as funnel-web spiders (see page 110).

A bizarre illness was caused by a common Melbourne trapdoor genus *Stanwellia* in April 1994. A woman was cleaning her swimming pool in the bayside Melbourne suburb of Hampton when a spider bit her on the right hand. Within an hour she had developed hemi-anaesthesia involving the entire right side of her body. Apart from a tachycardia and some swelling of the right hand, there were no other signs or symptoms. The family and the doctor were justifiably very concerned, but sensation had started to return 2 hours later and was complete by nightfall. The culprit was officially identified and another venom went on the list of those deserving research.

Wolf spider

There are more than 120 species of these fast-moving hunting spiders (genus *Lycosa*). They are often seen by gardeners, especially when trimming the edges of a lawn. Characteristically, the female drags her egg sac,

which is attached to the spinnerets behind her. When the young emerge they spend their early days riding about on their mother, giving her a strange appearance. Specially developed hairs on her back provide the spiderlings with a good grip. The body of the spider is usually 20 mm in length and has contrasting colours, usually of yellow and brown with some grey. The legs are long and are quite narrow-pointed near the ends.

Although initially suspected as a cause of necrotising arachnidism, no further evidence in recent years has been forthcoming. The spider has been known to cause the death of cats from 10 minutes to 4 hours after the bite. Usually the reaction to a bite is insignificant, but there have been reports of persistent effects including the possible development of a nephrotic syndrome.

First aid and medical management of bites

Usually the bites of these spiders cause no significant problems. It is important to reassure the patient and relatives. Local pain and swelling is usually temporary and may be relieved by ice/water packs. Antihistamines are often prescribed but their effects are difficult to evaluate.

The most common problem is the inability to identify the spider involved, often because it has been destroyed prior to seeking medical aid. Under these conditions all one can do is record a description of the culprit and keep and eye open for the development of a syndrome typical of a bite by one of the more dangerous spiders. When a spider bites a person, if possible collect and preserve the specimen in case an illness subsequently develops. You may discover a new venom disease!

INSECTS AND OTHER ARTHROPODS

Bull ant and jumper ant

DISTRIBUTION

Bull ant

DISTRIBUTION

Jumper ant

A tiny ant caused a most peculiar telephone call to be made from a distant country hospital one Saturday afternoon. On the end of the line was a Melbourne doctor who was in a most distressed state and suddenly stopped talking mid-sentence. Apart from the sound of heavy breathing, there was silence. He had named the hospital he was calling from but it took some time to obtain the telephone number and get back to the hospital. They had never heard of this particular doctor, but when the call was put through to the Emergency Department a nurse there confirmed, 'Yes, the doctor is here, but he's out cold on the trolley.'

The poor doctor had been stung in the bush by a jumper ant and suffered a major general reaction. Somehow he had managed to drive from his camp to the hospital, but collapsed after the phone call. His condition rapidly improved after better airways maintenance and subcutaneous adrenaline.

The doctor had been stung by jumper ants before and his allergic reactions had become more severe with each successive sting. Although he had been warned to always have adrenaline on hand in case of further stings, he went camping without it. He's learned his lesson now.

Ants are highly organised creatures. Every ant has specific duties to do, and their communication systems are most sophisticated. Their defence system is straightforward: get out and sting. In mid-summer, their numbers and activity reach a peak, while in mid-winter they may be fewer, sluggish and hard to provoke.

There are more than 1500 species of ants in Australia, but only a few cause serious illness in humans. Occasionally deaths have occurred following prolonged attacks by huge numbers of ants. One such case involved an infant abandoned by its mother, while the other two were drunks who fell over and rested on ant mounds for too long.

Bull ant

The development of allergy to their venoms makes a number of ants medically important. The main causes of allergy, and of course painful stings, are the jack jumper or jumper ants *(Myrmercia pilosula)* and the bull ant or soldier ant *(M. pyriformis)*. There are a number of sub-species, but for our purposes we will refer merely to jumper ants and bull ants.

Both of these ants are very primitive species. They are among the world's oldest, and are closely related to ants that are known only as fossils. This heritage is seen in their venoms; while most other ants have a simple venom like weak formic acid, the venoms of bull ants and jumper ants are as complicated as bee and wasp venoms.

The precise distribution of these ants is yet to be determined, but unfortunately these ants are found around the most densely populated parts of Australia. The jumper ant is found in a broad band sweeping from southern Queensland to Perth. This ant is particularly common in Tasmania. The bull ant, on the other hand, appears to be mainly found in the south-eastern parts of Australia and Tasmania. As far as is known, it does not inhabit Western Australia.

Jumper ants have a total body length of some 1.5 cm, whereas bull ants are usually 2.5 cm in length and hence may be called 'inchmen'. The nippers, or mandibles, of jumper ants are often a light yellow, whereas those of bull ants are usually dark red or brown.

Both species show little fear of trespassers and are highly aggressive. When its powerful mandibles firmly grasp your skin, the ant curls up its body and thrusts a long, sharp, unbarbed sting into the victim. The retractable sting is situated in the tail and may be used a number of times in quick succession, injecting more venom with each penetration.

In recent years the venom of both ants has been subject to a flurry of research activity. Maria Matuszek, when working at Monash University, confirmed their high histamine content and unearthed a slow acting, but very potent, smooth muscle stimulator. A variety of enzymes and haemolysins have also been identified.

A sting by one of these ants causes immediate pain that may persist for 5 minutes or more. Unlike a bee, an ant can deliver successive stings. There is generally swelling in the area, and aching and itchiness may persist for a few days.

People who are allergic to the ant venom may suffer various degrees of allergic responses. Generally, the reaction may become more severe after further exposure to ant venom. There may be gross local swelling that causes considerable discomfort and takes days to subside. Pruritus may be very distressing. Local blistering may occur.

The general reactions vary from mild to life-threatening. There may be widespread urticaria or oedema of the eyelids or lips. In the more severe reactions there may be bronchospasm, dyspnoea, and potentially dangerous oedema of the pharynx. The most feared reactions are those that result in cardiovascular collapse, hypotension and possibly death.

The allergens have been investigated by Dr Brian Baldo at the Kolling Institute in Sydney. In jumper ant venom, the main allergen has been identified, characterised and parts of it have even been synthesised.

There is currently no commercial source of purified ant venom to test and desensitise allergic patients, as is the case with bee venom allergy (page 141). An attempt to remedy this situation

Avoiding ant stings

Stings often occur when children are walking to and from school or when adults are picking up firewood. Areas around houses should be kept ant-free and well raked so that ants can be spotted more easily.

Ants don't like well watered lawns or gardens. Existing nests can be destroyed with kerosene or an insecticide.

In recent years allergy to ants may have increased because of the larger number of homes being built in natural bush settings along with the declining numbers of the ant's natural enemy, the echidna. Echidnas have been shot and slaughtered on the roads and the survivors have their movements limited by stout fencing.

ground to a halt at about the time CSL Ltd (the former Commonwealth Serum Laboratories) was privatised in 1994. A brief account of how the venom was collected is given here since others will have to cover the same ground in future.

A variety of procedures were investigated but none could provide the sheer quantity of venom required. It was soon apparent that thousands of venom sacs would need to be dissected and the venom subsequently extracted.

The next problems were finding large quantities of ants and capturing them. The first part was easy, as the most ant-infested part of Australia was only 90 minutes drive from CSL in Melbourne. It was rough and inhospitable country, but ant nests abounded everywhere. So did snakes, scorpions and spiders.

The intrepid collectors wore shorts, gumboots, gloves and hats. The gloves and gumboots were regularly sprayed with insect repellent and the furious ants were sucked up using small portable vacuum cleaners. Every 5 minutes or so, the vacuum cleaners would be emptied deftly into plastic bags, which were sealed and placed in dry ice. Despite these precautions, all collectors were stung.

The more delicate part of the operation was carried out at CSL. Using operating microscopes, the ants were individually dissected. This was done by grasping the waist of the thawed ant with a pair of jeweller's forceps, the tip of the sting with another, and then giving a tug. This removes the sting and pearl-shaped venom sac intact. The accumulated venom sacs were then stored at 75°C and later processed to produce an extremely potent venom sac extract. The first major dissection of 12,000 jumper ants produced 539 mg of an attractive fluffy white powder. This is a yield of 42 µg per venom sac. The larger bull ant produced an average 180 µg per venom sac. It is important to know these yields because the dosage used in the immunotherapy of patients is related to the potential venom output of each species.

After spending days collecting ants in the blistering heat, and many weeks dissecting the little brutes, the really hard work began. Assays were to be developed to determine the main types of allergens and how the stability of these could best be studied. Hundreds of vials of in-house reference preparations were dispensed, freeze-dried and stored under a variety of conditions to determine the properties and behaviour of the venom preparations. This was necessary because Federal health authorities required a vast amount of data before they approved the use of these preparations with humans.

It is a shame this project fizzled out in 1994 as there were 300 patients waiting for the end product.

First aid

The ant or ants should be brushed off, and clothing should be removed and shaken. You should also retreat because other ants may be on the attack.

If the pain of the sting is causing distress, apply an ice/water mixture. Cold packs may also give relief if the region becomes particularly itchy.

If the person is known to be highly allergic to bee venom, the pressure–immobilisation type of first aid should be promptly applied to the stung area (see page 186).

For severe general reactions (anaphylaxis) the administration of adrenaline may be life-saving This is the drug of first choice and should be given by intramuscular injection. For an adult the initial intramuscular dose should be 0.25 mL of a 1 in 1000 dilution. The initial dose for a child is 10 µg/kg intramusculary. These doses may have to be repeated in 10 minutes.

Parents and older children should be trained in the administration of adrenaline and should be issued with a form of auto-injector.

Serious reactions may require oxygen and plasma volume expanders. The airways should be maintained and circulation and respiration closely monitored.

Antihistamines may be useful in reducing some of the local reactions and, to a lesser extent, general reactions. Corticosteroids may help in the management of significant local reactions.

INSECTS

Caterpillar

The men had had enough and refused to load any more cement bags. They were working at Meadow Bank in Sydney and were being driven mad by itchy rashes on their forearms, necks and legs. The rashes would flare up again whenever they took more bags out of the old corrugated iron shed. Some sort of flea was thought to be the culprit and a museum expert was called.

DISTRIBUTION

To the satisfaction of the workers he immediately suffered a severe rash, especially on his ears and neck. As he scratched himself he looked around and quickly solved the problem. The building was surrounded by tall gum trees that were infested with a particular caterpillar.

In the interior and the surrounds of the shed were hundreds of pupae and larval skins of mistletoe moths that collectively could release billions of irritating bristles. They certainly did in this case, and work had to cease until the caterpillar population naturally subsided and the building was cleaned up.

There are many caterpillars in Australia that cause human and animal discomfort, but often the culprit is not identified. Let's look at the most important ones, dealing first with some non-venomous ones.

The bagmoth caterpillar and the mistletoe browntail moth

Although many caterpillars produce non-venomous hair or bristles, in Australia these two are the most important. Bristles can penetrate the skin quite deeply and, being heavily barbed, may be difficult to remove. The bristles of the bagmoth caterpillar (*Teara contraria*) cause a patchy and itchy rash that may persist for several days.

The caterpillars of the mistletoe browntail moth (*Euproctis edwardsi*) usually feed only at night and on mistletoes, which frequently grow on eucalypts. They have patches of many fine bristles or hairlets that are easily shed and are particularly irritating. The bristles are also loosely woven into the cocoons before pupation. There may be large numbers shed around the trunks of trees and these may cause unexplained rashes, especially if they are carried by the wind and cause injuries further afield. The delicate bristles penetrate the skin with ease and the barbs allow them to sink deeper. The result is described as a florid maculopapulovesicular dermatitis.

The hairymary caterpillar

This is an important cause of superficial eye injury in Australia. This creature's (*Anthela nicothoe*) bristles are up to 2.5 mm in length and are slender and sharp. The cocoon is also covered with bristles that are easily detached and may become airborne. Most cases occur in late spring or early summer.

The eye symptoms commence suddenly, usually with photophobia and lachrymation. Generally, the severity of the initial symptoms warrant immediate medical attention, usually on the same day. However, sometimes these symptoms are quite mild and the discomfort may be endured for a long period. One not too bright patient actually went 3 months before seeking an examination.

In the early stages, examination of the eye without magnification reveals minimal signs other than some conjunctivitis and occasionally haziness of the cornea. No obvious foreign body is seen and corneal staining with fluorescein may not make the cause obvious without magnification. In fact, unless magnification is used, many cases are diagnosed initially as a non-specific form of kerato-conjunctivitis.

When magnification is used a distinctive pattern of fine linear scratches made by each blink may be seen on the corneal epithelium. Ophthalmologists point out that initially these scratches are vertical but later they tend to be oblique or horizontal. Damage to the corneal epithelium will be greatest where contact is most frequently made. The offending foreign body is twice as likely to be embedded in the upper lid than the lower lid. Sometimes it may deeply penetrate the cornea.

Once spotted, the hair (or hairs) can usually be removed easily. If available, it is best extracted using a pair of fine jeweller's forceps. If these are not at hand it can usually be jiggled out with the use of a fine needle. When removed, symptoms subside rapidly and no further treatment is usually necessary. The extracted hair is usually 1 mm or more in length and microscopic examination will allow its identification by the presence of several dozen extremely delicate barbs.

Venomous caterpillars

Two venomous caterpillars are particularly common in south-eastern parts of Australia. These are the gumleaf skeletoniser (*Uraba lugens*) and Chinese junks (*Doratifera oxleyi*). These both have pointed, but not barbed, bristles that are therefore much easier to remove. Venom is secreted by a gland at the base of each of the tiny hollow bristles. The venom emerging at the tip is known to contain histamine.

The gumleaf skeletoniser feeds avidly on a wide range of eucalypts. It is often mentioned on gardening programs. In early summer the householder complains that the foliage of their prize gum tree seems to have disappeared overnight. Upon investigation they may find themselves the victim of the creature's self-defence mechanism. (It is best to stand back and vigorously hose the foliage down. Use an insecticide as a last resort. The tree usually quickly recovers.)

The mature larvae of the gumleaf skeletoniser are cream coloured with dorsal markings of yellow, brown and pink. Their length is 20–25 mm. They have a double row of clumps of stinging hairs arranged like a series of pincushions along their backs. Immediate pain follows contact with these spines, and large unpleasant weals may occur if many spines have been accidentally pressed against the skin. Fortunately severe reactions are uncommon.

Chinese junks are beautiful little creatures. They look somewhat out of place on a gum tree; being so attractive one might expect them to inhabit a tropical rock pool surrounded by other bizarre and colourful creatures. They are well defended, carrying up to eight tufts of red stinging hairs. These become erect when the slug-shaped creature senses danger. A sting by this little creature typically produces a very painful flat-topped weal.

Fortunately the hairs of venomous caterpillars usually do not attach firmly to the skin and can be easily washed off. The barbed non-venomous hairs can usually be removed by lightly applying transparent adhesive tape to the skin and then stripping it away. (Such tape can then be forwarded to a museum if absolute identification is required.)

Severe stings may require antihistamines and/or pain relief. All significant eye injuries should be treated and assessed by an eye specialist as soon as possible. Failure to detect and remove a deeply embedded bristle may have unfortunate consequences.

Microscopic examination of skin scrapings will easily distinguish between these creatures' bristles or other causes like 'glass fibre itch'. The caterpillar's bristles will be tapered and often barbed but the glass fibres will be smoother and cylindrical.

INSECTS

Centipede

In January 1993, two nursing sisters were holidaying on Fraser Island Village off the Queensland coast. Likewise a long centipede was holidaying in some timber that the nurses brought back from the other side of the Island. When getting up to go to the toilet in the middle of the night one of the nurses trod on the centipede, which bit the top of her foot and swung around and bit other areas, causing severe pain instantly. The two attempted to inactivate the creature but its tough exterior was resisting repeated blows with the heel of a shoe. Finally the centipede was cut in half with a knife, yet it still writhed around in an aggressive fashion. Later it was found to be nearly 14 cm in length.

Over the next 4 hours the victim suffered what was described as 'huge pain'. The pressure–immobilisation type of first aid was applied, but this made the pain much worse. Ice packs were then tried and gave some relief, but the weight of the actual packs themselves on the foot caused considerable distress. In the meantime, the foot was swelling and the patient was sweating. She ate some breakfast, vomited and then refused to eat for the rest of the day. Her temperature was elevated and she had problems keeping down fluids. She was given an injection of stemetil later that day

and settled down. By that stage there was gross swelling and erythaema of the leg up to the knee.

DISTRIBUTION

Over the next few days she rested the leg and the swelling all but went down completely. However, on the flight back to Melbourne the leg swelled up again massively, this time to involve the thigh. It was thought that she might have a deep vein thrombosis but this was not the case. The cause of the swelling was considered to be due directly to the centipede venom. Infection introduced by the centipede at the time of the bite may have contributed to the second episode of gross swelling.

Joined up and pinned to a board, the centipede was brought back to Melbourne as a trophy. Its custodians firmly correct those that believe centipedes are harmless. At the Museum of Victoria, the centipede was identified as the very common *Ethmostigmus rubripes*.

There are more than 3000 species of centipedes described in the world, and they belong to the class Chilopoda, which means claw-footed.

Centipedes enjoy a wide distribution globally and tend to be longer and more venomous in the warmer regions. One of the largest centipedes, *Scolopendera gigantea*, is found in tropical Brazil and may reach a length of 26 cm.

Centipedes are segmentally oriented. The number of body segments varies from 15 to 181, and all but the first and last segments are associated with a pair of walking legs. These legs each have seven segments and are fitted with tiny claws. The number of body segments is always an odd number, so one never can have the 100 legs that give the creature its common name.

Let's start at the front end of the centipede and work backwards. Some centipedes have no eyes, while others have compound eyes like insects. The long antennae arise from the flattened head, and are harmless. The mouth is small with strong jaws, but is barely noticeable because of the creature's large venomous fangs, which are actually modified legs from the first segment. They are quite strong and the venom duct opens near the tip.

The centipede's body is squat and flat, unlike the millipede which is round. Other distinctions are that a millipede has no poison claws and has two pairs of legs per segment. The creature's legs tend to be longer posteriorly, which enables the legs of the animal to cross over for more rapid movement. When scuttling along, the centipede avoids tripping over itself by passing one group of legs moving through the backwards stroke to the inside of a wave of legs making the forward step. The terminal segments of legs have been turned backwards and are elongated. These are used for grasping prey and are not the venom apparatus of the creature, as is often thought.

The colour of centipedes varies enormously. Most of those in the milder regions are reddish brown, but the tropical forms can range in colour from green, red, yellow or blue. Sometimes they even have wild combinations such as yellow bodies and bright blue legs.

Centipedes must have a humid environment because they have difficulty controlling their water balance. Their integument loses moisture easily because it lacks the waxy cuticle of insects and spiders. For this reason they are confined to the moist environment of rotting timber and damp soil, and usually hunt only at night. Unlike millipedes, they are almost entirely carnivorous and will eat practically anything that moves. Some of the tropical species have been known to feed on toads and small snakes. In Western Australia, a 16 cm long centipede was observed to catch and devour a medium sized mouse. Some species are known to rear up and capture insects in flight.

Very little work has been done on centipede venoms. One overseas venom has been shown to cause cardiotoxic effects on isolated heart preparations, as well as causing slow contraction of smooth muscle, probably through the prostaglandin receptor.

Bites by many of the world's centipedes can produce intense local pain, inflammation, oedema and pruritus. In severe cases there may be vomiting, headache and collapse. The regional lymph nodes may become very tender. Blistering and sub-cutaneous haemorrhage may occur. Superficial necrosis has been described overseas, but only rarely reported in Australia. The most consistent observation made about centipede bites every-where is the severe pain, which often relates to the size of the centipede.

There has only been one confirmed death following a centipede sting. The victim was a 7-year-old child who died in the Philippines 29 hours after being bitten on the head by a centipede.

Australian centipedes should be treated with considerable caution, especially the larger specimens found in Northern Australia. For example, in 1973 Dr Ron Southcott described the effect of a probable centipede bite that occurred in Darwin. The victim was bitten near his mouth and shortly afterwards developed swelling of the area and pain extending into the neck. He vomited and became pyrexic. The pain was not relieved by morphine and it took several weeks for the swelling to sub-side and the general malaise to cease.

Bites by the smaller centipedes found in the cooler parts of Australia usually only cause transient local pain. However, in one case in Kew, Victoria, a landscape gardener was bitten on the thumb by a moderately sized centipede. He ignored the bite and some 10 minutes later fell unconscious. He was considered to be pulseless and not breathing by his workmates, who transferred him swiftly to hospital. Twenty-five minutes after the bite he had fully recovered.

Two unusual Australian cases suggest there is a lot more to learn about the effects of centipedes.

A 6-month-old boy was brought to the Royal Children's Hospital in Melbourne with a 12-hour history of lethargy and pallor. The child appeared pale and floppy. His mother had found a centipede encased in his faeces while changing one of his diapers that morning. Both the centipede and faeces had turned blue, suggesting that the centipede had probably been swallowed and passed per rectum and did not merely crawl directly into the diaper.

The centipede was later identified as a hairy centipede *Scutigera morpha*, commonly called a house feather or 'Johnny hairylegs'. No other cause for the child's floppiness could be found. The oral intake had been poor that day with an associated poor suck. There had been no history of recent immunisations or exposure to infectious illnesses. No visible bite marks on the skin or around the mouth or in the mouth could be found.

Examination revealed diminished power of all muscle groups. He was apyrexic. A wide range of investigations were all normal. In hospital the infant remained lethargic and vomited several times but slowly improved over the next 36 hours without any specific treatment. Dr P. Barnett, who reported this case, considered that envenomation probably occurred through the gastrointestinal tract, either following a bite or by direct absorption. It is quite possible that the body of the centipede itself was the source of the toxin that may have produced this unusual illness.

In February 1993 an 11-year-old boy was bitten by what was most probably a centipede near Korumburra, South Gippsland. The bite site was sore for a while but he soon forgot about it. Next morning he was remarkably weak in both legs and one arm and his reflexes were strongly over-reactive. His walking was somewhat uncoordinated and he was admitted to hospital for investigation. His limbs remained weak and floppy overnight, but next morning he suddenly recovered.

All concerned were puzzled about this case, however, when considered alongside the case above it is hard not to suspect centipede venom or some centipede component producing unusual syndromes.

First aid

There is no specific treatment and the pressure–immobilisation type of first aid should NOT be applied because this may increase local pain. Ice/water packs may give some pain relief. Severe pain may require systemic opiates. Tetanus prophylaxis should be updated.

In cases like the nursing sister, a business-like approach should be adopted with effective pain relief, bed rest and probably antibiotic therapy.

Centipedes have occasionally been found in the nose, in the frontal sinuses, the external ear as well as the alimentary tract of humans. Those busy little legs can take them anywhere.

INSECTS

Flea

It is amazing that such a tiny creature can annoy a human so much. Fleas are tiny, laterally flattened, blood-sucking, wingless insects of the order Siphonaptera. They feed on the surface of humans, other mammals and occasionally birds.

The female deposits hundreds of tiny pearly white eggs on the skin of the host animal. The eggs then either fall or are scratched off and hatch into cylindrical, narrow, legless larvae. Kennels, favourite baskets and father's chairs are some of the favourite temporary resting places for an incredible number of hungry little flea maggots. They feed on any dead organic matter, ranging from animal dander, hair, dried blood or compost. After 2 weeks of such activity a cocoon is spun and they begin to pupate.

The pupal life can last from a fortnight to months. The adult fleas will emerge from the cocoons when the temperature and humidity are most suitable.

Now here's the clever part. In an unoccupied and silent building the pupae may lie for a month or so in carpets and crevices. As soon as the resting places are disturbed by the vibrations of people stamping about, the final metamorphosis is induced. As one writer observed, the adult fleas literally jump out of their pupal skins. The same response may occur when a vacant kennel or other preferred sleeping spot of a pet is disturbed.

Worldwide there are more than 1000 species of fleas, 30 of which are native to Australia. These native fleas are very specialised in their feeding habits and tend to leave humans alone. The population of various types of imported fleas in Australia runs into the billions.

DISTRIBUTION

The most common fleas that attack humans are cat fleas (*Ctenocephalides felis*), dog fleas (*C. canis*) and also human fleas (*Pulex irritans*). This latter flea is not seen very much in Australia these days because of better standards of living. These three types of fleas are not species-specific and will feed on whatever is available, within reason. Indeed, in many areas the species infesting dogs is more likely to be the cat flea.

Both cat and dog fleas are the intermediate hosts of the dog tapeworm (*Diphylidium kaninum*). If the animal or human accidentally swallows the infected flea, an adult tapeworm may develop in the new host.

The worst disease spread by fleas is bubonic plague. This dreadful disease may be spread by rat fleas, of which there are two main types: the tropical rat flea (*Xenopsylla cheopis*) and the northern rat flea (*Nosopsyllus fasciatus*). This latter flea, which spends most of its adult life on Norway rats and roof rats, may also spread murine typhus.

Attacks by fleas can cause considerable irritation

engorging with blood. All other fleas in Australia use the equivalent of an ejection seat to leave the scene of their crime! The sticktight flea should be lifted off with a sterile needle, which may be difficult if a marked local reaction has occurred.

Obviously it is important to eliminate the flea population. The aim is to destroy the adult and eliminate suitable breeding places for the larvae. Veterinarians have a variety of effective ways of defleaing cats and dogs. The fleas may not like it but the animals certainly will be healthier. It is important not only to attend to the animal's sleeping quarters but as well to the spot in the garden that your pooch uses regularly for its siesta.

First aid

Most flea bites need little more than a soothing cream. If irritation is significant, antihistamines may help as well as topical steroids if the delayed type of reaction is troublesome. Antibiotic therapy may be indicated if secondary infection has followed the scratching of the bites. See whiplash rove beetles, p.157.

Flea circuses

Fleas can jump 30 cm or more. This makes identification easy but often allows the flea to escape before it can be crushed.

You have probably not seen a flea circus but they do exist. The best fleas for this type of entertainment supposedly come from Russia. They can be trained not only to jump through hoops but to drag along little carts hundreds of times their own weight.

To be a flea trainer requires special patience. A silk thread is tied around the neck of each flea and then an instruction is carried out with the aid of a magnifying glass. Apparently the first thing to train the flea to do is to stop jumping and merely walk. We would prefer it if they were trained not to bite.

and discomfort. Initially the site of the flea bite lesion may show a small, truncate, mildly haemor-rhagic area. The sites of blood sucking are often in clusters as the flea meanders along. Its saliva is irritating, producing a weal within a few minutes, followed almost invariably by pruritus. Generally some itching and swelling persists for the next 24 hours.

Many individuals become sensitised to flea bites and develop a delayed reaction, which is usually evident the next day and may persist for 7 days or longer. Medical treatment may be sought for relief of the very intense pruritus and the associated papular reaction.

The sticktight flea (*Echidnophaga gallinacea*) is primarily a poultry pest but it occasionally attacks humans. It attaches very firmly to the host while

Honey bee

The young tree surgeon was convinced it was the end. Perched high above the ground on a branch, he saw the angry bees swarming towards him. He had been allergic to bee stings and had been told for years that one bee sting would be fatal, so he cast himself off into space. Not having had time to tighten his lifeline, it stretched and barely slowed his fall. He crashed to the ground, covered with bees, and his chainsaw embedded itself in the ground beside his head.

He didn't do too badly considering the 30-metre fall. A couple of broken ribs, and no significant reaction at all to the dozen or so bee stings. He made a smooth recovery.

Had he earlier been referred to an allergist, his bee venom allergy could have been investigated. In his case, it would have been found he was one of the fortunate individuals who lose this life-threatening allergy with the passage of time. If he was still highly allergic, he could have been treated with purified bee venom, which is effective in more than 90 per cent of cases.

Bee-keeping has been carried out for thousands of years, and the common European or Italian bee *(Apis mellifera)* was introduced into Australia many years ago. In Victoria some 80,000 hives produce more than 3000 tonnes of honey each year (or 54 kg per hive). In each hive there are some 50,000 bees and in summer the busy little workers only survive 4–5 weeks. In winter, when life is more leisurely, a worker bee may survive 18 weeks.

Bees are very common

creatures and reactions to them are also very common. Some 10 per cent of persons stung by a bee will have a significant local reaction and one in 200 will suffer a systemic reaction. In one recent summer in Australia, more people died from allergic reactions to bee stings than from snake bites.

DISTRIBUTION

The sting of a bee is an amazing mechanism. The bee's sting is barbed, so once it has been thrust into its target it cannot be withdrawn. The bee frees itself by twisting around, but this leaves the sting and the venom sac behind. Because of the injuries suffered, the bee is doomed to die within a day or so.

Let's look at what the bee has left behind. At the top end is the venom sac, which rhythmically pumps venom down through the complicated sting. The sting consists of a stylet and two beautifully designed barbed lancets grooved into the stylet. These lancets glide over the stylet alternatively, further embedding both the stylet and the lancets. The bee has thus left a self-contained envenomating apparatus that will continue to deliver venom for some minutes. The average output of venom per bee is some 73 µg. It is the most extensively studied venom in the world and has many components. Some are of low molecular weight, such as histamine, which makes up 1 per cent. Four of the higher molecular weight proteins are extremely potent allergens. They are phospholipase A, hyaluronidase, allergen B and allergen C. Some people are highly allergic to only one of these, while others may be sensitive to all four.

Most people find a bee sting immediately painful and it is associated with some local swelling and pruritus. These 'normal' reactions are direct effects produced by the venom components, especially histamine. Stinging of loose tissue, such as around the eyelids or genitals, may cause marked oedema. A sting from a half-swallowed bee may cause gross swelling of the

Investigation and management of bee venom allergy

Before 1975, most skin testing and immuno-therapy of bee sting allergies had been carried out using extracts made from whole bees. After the death from bee sting of a child who had just completed a course of immunotherapy with whole body extract, a Baltimore doctor investigated the use of purified bee venom, which he found was the most suitable material to use for skin testing, serology studies and actual immunotherapy. Following the publication of these findings, the use of whole body extract was rapidly replaced with purified bee venom.

Collecting bee venom in large quantities for research or therapy is quite a stimulating exercise. While it is possible to extract venom from venom sacs one at a time, a rather ingenious device does this far better. It consists of a platform with several dozen fine electrified wires on its upper surface. Below this is a tightly stretched fabric with minute holes in it, and below this is a sheet of glass. The apparatus is introduced gently into a beehive; when a bee lands on two wires, it receives a small electric shock. The bee swears with surprise and instinctively drives the tip of its sting into one of the holes in the fabric. The hole is too small for anything but the tip to penetrate, and so the barb does not get caught. The venom is squirted onto the glass plate from whence it is later collected. The startled bee releases a pheromone that quickly attracts other bees. In no time at all, hundreds of bees are landing, being

stung and taking off, leaving copious quantities of venom behind.

Selected patients benefit from immunotherapy with bee venom. This is usually done over a period of several months, commencing with minute quantities of bee venom and carefully increasing the dose until the patient is tolerating a quantity equivalent to two bee stings. Most allergists then recommend that the patients stay on a maintenance dose of bee venom for a period of at least 12 months. Some allergists use a more intense immunisation procedure known as the 'Rush' method, which requires patients to spend several days in hospital. It has some advantages, particularly when the patient has to be brought in from a remote area.

Patients who develop allergy to bee venom have an elevation of specific IgE antibodies directed at bee venom. These can be quantitated by the RAST test using pure bee venom. Most patients who undergo immunotherapy with bee venom will show a decline in the IgE antibody and the development of an immune or IgG antibody directed at bee venom. This RAST test combined with the clinical history and skin testing with purified bee venom allows the allergist to assess with a fair degree of accuracy the allergic state of the patient.

Bee venom is available as a pharmaceutical benefit. Often doctors can't find it. Look under 'insect'!

Avoiding bee stings

Bees may be attracted by perfumes and after shave lotions. On sunny days, when bees are active, it is best not to wear brightly coloured clothes. It is important that clover on lawns where children play be selectively sprayed, especially if it is near a swimming pool. Finally, NEVER drink out of soft drink cans outside without using a straw. One sip of soft drink, plus a bee, may be fatal in seconds. Sucking ice may reduce the swelling but a tragedy is highly likely.

back of the throat, which can lead to death due to obstruction of the airways.

About 10 per cent of people have a significant local reaction, which can range from a swelling of 5 cm in diameter to swelling of the entire limb. This reaction may take a week or so to subside and may cause significant discomfort.

Systemic reactions occur in 0.4–0.8 per cent of bee stings. The faster these develop, the greater is the danger to the patient. Some systemic reactions are mild and do not endanger the patient's life. These include pruritus, erythaema and generalised urticaria. Angio-oedema of the lips, eyelids or ears may occur.

The serious systemic effects may involve the cardiovascular and/or the respiratory systems. There may include oedema of the upper airways, dyspnoea, bronchospasm or hypotension and collapse.

Knowledge of bee venom allergy has increased in recent years and a lot of previously held views have now been modified. It is agreed that many patients who may have reacted to a sting may have a greater or more serious reaction after a subsequent sting. Patients who have had previous stings and whose allergy has been confirmed by testing have a near 50 per cent chance of reaction to a further sting. In other words, every case must be individually assessed to determine whether the allergy has increased, stayed the same or faded away. A dangerous allergy may fade with the

passage of time, as was the case of the young man in the tree described above.

Fatality is uncommon in children. Unfortunately, some fatal reactions occur in people who have no known prior history of stings. The rate may be as high as 25 per cent. On the other hand, bee stinging is a very common occurrence and it is hard to imagine someone going through childhood and never being stung.

Sometimes individuals receive hundreds of stings and the venom itself may produce a toxic reaction. Adults have survived some thousands of stings, but an infant could well succumb to a smaller number.

First aid

The bee sting (or stings) should be removed as quickly as possible—scrape or pull it off. (It used to be thought that pulling it off would squeeze venom down the sting, but this is not the case.) If the pain of the sting is causing distress, apply an ice/water mixture. If the region becomes particularly itchy, relief may also be obtained with cold packs. If the person is known to be highly allergic to bee venom, the pressure–immobilisation type of first aid should be promptly applied to the stung area (see page 186).

For severe general reactions (anaphylaxis) the administration of adrenaline may be life-saving This is the drug of first choice and should be given by intramuscular injection. For an adult the initial intramuscular dose should be 0.25 mL of a 1 in 1000 dilution. The initial dose for a child is 10 μg/kg intramusculary. These doses may have to be repeated in 10 minutes. Parents and older children should be trained in the administration of adrenaline and should be issued with a form of auto-injector.

Nebulised adrenaline inhalers are also useful in the emergency situation, particularly in reducing the respiratory side of anaphylaxis. Serious reactions may require oxygen, plasma volume expanders etc. The airways should be maintained and circulation and respiration closely monitored.

Antihistamines may also be useful in reducing some of the local reactions and, to a lesser extent, general reactions. Corticosteroids may help in the management of significant local reactions.

House dust mite

When Struan was a little chap he would go to Melbourne and stay with his Uncle Charles, who was one of this country's pioneer allergists and the first to use adreno-corticotrophic hormone (ACTH) in Australia. For a young lad from the country, a few days with Uncle Charles and his wife was something to be keenly awaited. Apart from other things like a tennis court, their house had a fully equipped laboratory incorporated into an old stable. In this laboratory, Charles prepared all sorts of unusual extracts for testing and treating patients, but his main pursuit was investigating the allergens in house dust that made many of his patients' lives quite wretched.

The incidence of house dust allergy seemed to vary from one household to another and the patients' families would provide Charles with the weekly contents of their vacuum cleaners for his research. The mystery of the varying allergenicity of house dust preparations was never solved by Uncle Charles, but a solution was suggested in 1962, the year he died, by a Dutchman named Voorhorst.

Dr Voorhorst of Leiden proposed that a little known mite, *Dermatophagoides pteronyssinus*, might be the source of the allergen in house dust. In 1967, his group published the results of their studies in which they found this mite was present in every one of 154 houses in four Dutch towns, and it comprised 70 per cent of the mites found. In one sample of house dust, there were 490 mites per gram. The numbers varied from house to house and from month to month. In damp houses they were more numerous than in dry houses, and their numbers were highest in late summer. They proposed that this mite be called the house dust mite.

In Japan and Northern America, another closely related mite, *D. farinae,* is far more common in house dust than *D. pteronyssinus*. From an allergenic point of view, both are near identical.

In Australia, the majority of the house dust mites found are the European *D. pteronyssinus*. The other mite does occur and was identified in Australia in 1983, when a study was done on vacuum cleaner dust from a Sydney house. It was found that per gram of dust there were 534 *D. pteronyssinus* as well as 30 *D. farinae*.

The house mite is tiny and cannot be seen with the naked eye. The female is 0.34 mm long and the male only 0.28 mm. They are not parasitic but feed on human skin scales and other such fodder, which may accumulate in house dust or

DISTRIBUTION

blankets, sheepskins and the like. They prefer dampish humid conditions and comfortable temperatures. Every day a human sheds a gram or so of horny scales, which is more than adequate for an army of mites. Since one-third of our life is spent in bed, it is no wonder there is a build up of scales in bed clothing, rugs and on top of wardrobes. The popular habit of using sheepskins under the sheets increases the mite problem significantly.

The folks that like cats or dogs sleeping on their beds will only make the situation worse. Apart from shedding fur and animal scales for consumption by mites, the pets are themselves a cause of significant allergy.

Knowledge of the lifecycle of the house dust mite is helpful in reducing its numbers. It takes about 4 weeks for eggs to develop into an adult at

Prevention

Insecticides or fumigation will only cause a temporary absence of mites, which will be re-establishing their little homes by the time the area is livable again for humans. Considering the above, the positive actions to be taken are as follows:

- Vacuum thoroughly and often, including all flat surfaces.
- Dispose of all rugs, quilts etc. that are not readily washable.
- Dispose of feathered pillows.
- Encase mattresses in plastic covers.
- Treat the bedroom as though it is a hospital ward; the bedding, furniture, ledges etc. should all be washed regularly. Don't forget to wash soft toys.
- If possible, keep the humidity down and use minimal heating.
- Keep pets outside.

There are other important allergens to be found in house dust. Heavy infestations of cockroaches may allow the accumulation of dried allergenic material, in particular their saliva. These cockroach allergens can be potent triggers of childhood asthma.

25°C, but at 20°C it will take 60–110 days. They can survive humidity below 70 per cent provided there is some moisture obtainable from the food available. If the humidity is as low as 50 per cent, half of them will be dead in 4 days and by 11 days all will be extinct.

Dr Voorhorst's findings aroused a flurry of activity among academic and commercial researchers. It coincided with the arrival of the extremely relevant radio-allergo sorbent test (RAST), which could measure levels of the newly discovered specific allergy-related antibody, IgE. This laboratory test and its variations were a great step forward and it has shed light on all sorts of allergies.

The first problem researchers faced was obtaining sufficient quantities of the mites. The early Dutch workers developed a laborious technique of sieving house dust. After various flotation and centrifugation steps they would pick up individual mites with a fine needle from filter paper under a dissecting microscope. To say the least, this required patience.

Culture of the mite in the laboratory was the answer. All sorts of mediums were used such as ground-up cow horn or sweepings from barber shops. Later, sophisticated and potentially non-allergic media were used. Research still continues to perfect the media.

More potent extracts of mite cultures proved 8000 times as active as the standard house dust extracts when used for skin testing. In fact, some patients suffered anaphylactic reactions in the earlier days when such preparations were poorly standardised. Some of these reactions proved fatal.

The next discovery made by the researchers was that the main allergen in the mites was also in their excretions. Further work showed that 95 per cent of the allergen accumulating in mite cultures is associated with faecal particles. The main allergen present, which has been designated Fraction P1, has a molecular weight of 24,000 Daltons and is a glycoprotein. In skin testing, nearly 10 per cent of the population and up to 90 per cent of allergic asthmatics give positive immediate reactions to this allergen. Many patients also react to two other allergens which have the informative names AgX and Ag23. These are also present in both the mite and faecal extracts.

The accumulation of these relatively stable, but minute, mite faecal balls may lead to year-round problems among the allergic because they will be constant or increasing in number while the mite population fluctuates. Any domestic activity such as dusting or shaking of bedclothes will greatly increase the amount of mite antigen in the air. Those pellets and mite bodies that have not been inhaled, and possibly produced rhinitis or asthma attacks, will then settle down again to await the next disturbance.

Sensitivity to house mite allergens is one of the most common problems seen by allergists. The existence of the allergy is usually quite clear by the history, and confirmation can be made by appropriate skin testing and measurement of the patient's specific IgE antibodies by techniques such as RAST.

Before considering immunotherapy with dust mite extracts, it is usual to conduct a vigorous anti-house dust mite campaign in the patient's home. Dryness is an enemy of the mite, so the aim is well ventilated rooms and the elimination of dampness in bedding, carpets and the like. The improvement of some asthmatic patients in hospital may be explained by the absence of domestic allergens. Likewise, staying in an immaculately clean mountain villa will be of benefit to many patients if they only could afford to do it.

Mr Wesley Green, a dust mite expert at Sydney University, believes Australia is the 'dust mite capital' of the world. Mr Green has been researching low toxic solutions that will reduce domestic mite populations. The use of weak tannic acid solutions, including cold tea, appears promising.

INSECTS

March fly

Ouch, you brute! This is the natural response when a large march fly drives its robust mouth parts into your skin. There is no subtlety about its approach, and it doesn't seem surprised or put off if it is whacked with a towel: it comes straight back into the attack, sometimes with dire consequences.

March flies belong to the family Tabanidae and are also called horse flies. They are shaped like a large blowfly with a body length up to 20 mm. March flies have particularly big eyes and are equipped with a large tough proboscis. Other members of the family have similarly enormous eyes, but not all are blood-suckers. Some are relatively small and feed on nectar, and are of no medical importance. Fortunately, none of the Tabanidae in Australia transmit diseases of humans or animals, as they do in Africa and the old world tropics.

March flies are found in most parts of Australia and breed in a variety of situations, ranging from floating vegetation in open swamps to rotting sea-weed or beach sand. At times their numbers can reach plague proportions and make areas of beach unusable by swimmers and sunbathers. Sometimes on an ocean beach there may be one small area inhabited by clouds of march flies, while on each side there is hardly a single one. Protection from prevailing winds is a possible explanation.

DISTRIBUTION

March flies are not merely a beachside problem, and sudden increases in their numbers can cause great concern in some country areas. It is not known why these population explosions occur from time to time.

For most people the bite merely causes immediate but mild discomfort and the annoyance of having to ward off other attacks or move elsewhere. Multiple bites can be very distressing and an injured person or helpless child could suffer severely if attacked.

Unlike some creatures like leeches, the march fly does not rely on a combination of stealth and the use of a local anaesthetic when removing blood from its host. Rather, its tough mouth parts simply tear through the skin and suck up the subepithelial pool of blood that follows the injury. It's not known whether the creature's saliva, which is injected during the penetration, contains an anticoagulant.

It is the introduction of this saliva that causes problems to perhaps 10 per cent of people who are bitten. This unlucky group of victims either suffers marked local changes or general effects that may be life-threatening. The local effects include swelling, which may be gross, and severe pruritus, which may persist for a week or so.

The onset of these local changes can be quite dramatic. The general effects are similar to those seen when hypersensitivity develops to insect venoms. Mild systemic reactions that do not endanger the patient's life include erythaema, pruritus and generalised urticaria. Angio-oedema of the lips, eyelids or ears may occur.

The serious systemic effects may involve the respiratory and/or cardiovascular systems. There may be airways oedema, dyspnoea, bronchospasm or hypotension and collapse.

Near fatalities have been recorded after march fly attacks. In 1982, a 50-year-old man who was fishing at Fraser Island was set upon by march flies and collapsed almost immediately with severe respiratory problems. It was believed that the prompt helicopter rescue organised by his companions may have saved his life.

A march fly attack can have terrifying consequences for people known to be sensitised. Several years ago a young man collapsed and died suddenly while walking on a reef at a Melbourne bayside beach. He had an extraordinary history of severe anaphylactic reactions to bees, ants and possibly mosquitos. A minute or so before he collapsed, he mentioned to a nearby companion that something had bitten him on the shoulder. Later, specific inquiries revealed that many march flies were about on the reef and they would have to be a prime suspect in this young man's death.

Two other points should be made about this case. Nothing diagnostic was found at post mortem. It is sometimes difficult to prove that death was due to anaphylaxis, especially when the precipitating factor is not apparent. A key indication that anaphylaxis has occurred is the elevation of serum tryptase, but this does not rise significantly until some 20–30 minutes after the reaction commences. The rapid death of this young man may not have allowed time for the elevation of this enzyme.

The other point about this fatality is that it may not have occurred had it not been for the foolish behaviour of the life-savers on duty, who had been clowning around at high speed on their rescue craft when the man had collapsed. The quickest way to get the patient to hospital from this beach was by using the rescue craft, but when they went to set off with the patient they found they had run out of petrol and had none in the clubhouse. When the victim finally reached hospital, resuscitation attempts were unsuccessful. The Coroner and club officials were not impressed.

First aid

Usually no treatment is required for the 'normal' sting. The distress of multiple stings may be eased by ice/water packs. Such packs may also give some relief to the local swelling and pruritus that the sensitised patient may develop.

If the bite has occurred on the extremities in a person known to have had a serious general reaction in the past, the prompt application of the pressure–immobilisation type of first aid over the bitten area is recommended (see page xxx).

Should a general reaction occur, then standard first aid for the maintenance of airways, breathing and circulation should be instituted. An injection of intramuscular adrenaline could be life-saving if there is evidence of an obstruction to breathing (laryngeal or bronchial) or cardiovascular insufficiency.

Treatment of allergy

The management of the acute reaction is similar to that described for bee venom allergy (see page 140). Whole body extracts have been shown to be ineffective for managing bee venom allergy, so purified bee venom is now used successfully for both the investigation and immunotherapy of selected patients.

However, it is not realistic to produce march fly saliva for laboratory and clinical use, so whole body extracts are used. CSL ceased the production of whole body extracts from Australian march flies some years ago, but some initial success has been reported using an imported extract made from the equivalent overseas species of *Tabanus*.

INSECTS

Midge and sandfly

The couple had retired to their dream house situated in a sheltered inlet with beautiful views. The bird life on the mud flats was enchanting and constantly changing like the passing clouds. For years they had holidayed in the area in winter and now they looked forward to enjoying it the whole year round. The fishing was still excellent and the husband was looking forward to catching a variety of fish as the seasons changed. He was thrilled with his new power boat and had bought enough fishing tackle to last 20 years.

A year later a 'For Sale' notice was tied to the fence and rattling idly in the wind. Interested parties were asked to contact a local real estate agent or ring the owners, who had moved back to the city 400 km away. The biting midges had won.

Slightly troublesome in past winters, they produced devastating effects on the legs and feet of the wife when the weather warmed up. The poor woman suffered episodes of multiple bites that blistered and often became infected. She led a wretched life, for months staying mostly indoors as she was relentlessly attacked because of the low level of the house and perhaps because they fancied her. When the grandchildren visited, they all suffered as well and were pleased to return home.

DISTRIBUTION

On the other hand, the husband had been brought up in the area many years earlier and was barely affected by the creatures. This couple may not have had to return to the city had more precautions been taken and a little more time allowed for his wife to become 'desensitised' to the local species of midges.

Tourists and other visitors often react more severely to sandflies than do the locals. The reverse may occur when the locals visit the region the tourists have come from. It appears that people become less affected by the local sandflies with the passage of time. A few of course may develop allergies.

True sandflies *(Phlebotomus)* rarely cause any trouble in Australia. However, they certainly do in other parts of the world, particularly in the Middle East. The lives of Australian troops were made miserable at times by reactions to sandfly bites, whereas the locals appeared only mildly affected. In Israel an allergic response to sandfly bites, known as *Harara*, is seen mainly in people who have recently arrived in that country.

What are generally called 'sandflies' in Australia are, in fact, biting midges, so we shall call them either sandflies or midges. There are five genera of blood-sucking midges, the most important belonging to the genus *Culicoides*. This minute creature may be found from the south of Tasmania to New Guinea.

Although they may be found inland, it is mainly in coastal regions that they are a problem to humans. They may occur in huge numbers around coastal lagoons and estuaries and especially on tidal flats where breeding occurs. Mangrove swamps are often synonymous for the presence of a vast biting midge population. In most areas the population is influenced most strongly by the tidal cycle.

The intensity of attacks by *Culicoides* midges varies with the weather conditions. They won't be much of a problem in particularly windy weather, preferring to take shelter in vegetation. Calm conditions suit them best and they usually do their biting around dusk or dawn, but when the populations are high they often bite during the day. Dense populations may drift or fly up to nearly a kilometre from the breeding grounds.

Although biting may occur inside houses in the extreme northern parts of Australia, the intense and therefore important attacks are generally outdoor events. Usually the victim is quite unaware at the time that the bites are occurring. This classically might occur when the visitor from down south is sitting barefoot on a lawn in a beer garden in Cairns.

The effects of *Culicoides* are usually confined to the exposed areas. The little brutes are low flying and so the bites are usually inflicted on the lowest exposed areas, mostly the feet and legs. If feet are well covered the arms and neck may be chosen.

(It is best not to leave a baby out on a tidal flat in the twilight.)

The victim does not have to be stationary. For instance, biting can also occur when walking along a boardwalk through the mangrove swamps at midday. The creatures are so minute that in broad daylight they may hardly be seen or noticed.

An intense itching may develop some 12–24 hours after exposure to the creatures. Often a vesicular reaction occurs that may last for several days. There is a tendency to scratch the lesions, thus rupturing the vesicle and enhancing the chances of bacterial contamination of an already inflamed area. One can imagine how further exposure to midges will worsen the situation.

Some people develop marked allergy to sandfly bites, and pruritus, swelling and blistering may occur quite rapidly after the bite or bites. Quite gross oedema may occur, particularly if softer tissues are involved. For example, the swelling might be quite dramatic if the bite or bites have occurred around the eye. Biting sandflies may well be a cause of 'bung-eye', which has been described as a 'well known Australian condition' in which there is a sudden and enormous swelling of the loose tissues around one eye so the eyelids are soon firmly closed. There is usually little or no pain, with the swelling subsiding over several days.

Sandflies may possibly cause two other types of acute and briefly distressing eye problems. One is an acutely painful eye, the other an acutely itchy eye. Relief of either condition is usually achieved by bathing the eye in fresh water, after which symptoms subside as rapidly as they started.

Precautions

Human skin should not be made available as a feeding ground for millions of sandflies at dawn or dusk. Be liberal with the Aerogard. Clothing and footwear must be adequate if freshly applied repellents are not in use. Positive steps must be made to reduce sandfly bites since at dusk they are almost invisible and the irritation resulting from their saliva may not become evident for some 12 hours or so.

Medical management

Minor bites need just a simple soothing lotion to alleviate the itch. More florid reactions benefit from oral and perhaps local antihistamines. Persistent and distressing pruritus warrants local corticosteroids. Infected lesions should be bathed with diluted antiseptic solutions or covered with antiseptic cream. Antibiotics may be indicated. Regular use of an antiseptic soap, especially on children's legs, may be beneficial during the peak season. Sometimes a chronic condition may develop as a result of repeated exposure, scratching and infection. Reducing the incidence of bites is important in all cases.

The Commonwealth Serum Laboratories (now CSL Ltd) used to produce a whole sandfly body extract for desensitising patients who had developed persistent allergic reactions to sandflies. This and other insect allergen preparations were discontinued for economic reasons some time ago. Some allergists prepare their own extracts from locally collected sandflies. Generally both the allergists and the patients feel that such desensitisation courses have led to the improvement of the condition. On the other hand, the passage of time and direct immunotherapy by the biting creature itself may have influenced the result. Either way, the possibility of desensitisation is an option that can be considered.

INSECTS

Millipede

A 3-year-old girl was brought by her concerned grandmother to a doctor practising on the outskirts of Melbourne. The little girl had six odd ring-shaped lesions on her bottom that had appeared overnight. They were about 1 cm in diameter and remarkably uniform.

Although ringworm was briefly considered, there seemed a strong possibility that the injuries had been inflicted on the child. Later that day the patient was referred to the Child Abuse Centre when a dermatologist expressed the view they were a type of burn, possibly inflicted with a hot wire.

A biopsy was taken by the dermatologist and demonstrated full-thickness epidermal necrosis. There was little inflammation and the absence of coagulation artefacts appeared to exclude thermal burns, but not a chemical burn.

The GP knew the family well but had to tell the caring parents of these developments. They appeared as astounded as he was.

Next day, the matter was resolved by a fascinating turn of events before the bureaucracy got itself into full gear. After talking to their doctor, the mother instigated a full-scale family conference to see if any explanation could be found to account for the appearance of the marks.

DISTRIBUTION

In the discussion, the father recalled flicking a millipede from his shoulder on the way to the shower the morning before. Since the child had been in bed with her parents that night, the three older children were sent out to look for millipedes. Six were found and the father volunteered to have the lot taped to his wrist overnight. Next morning, to the satisfaction of the family, the experiment was seen to be a success.

When the one millipede that was still alive was removed, a circular brown mark was there for all to see. The mother then recalled leaving out unsorted washing from the clothesline the day before the mysterious marks appeared. This was probably the source of the millipedes.

The sensitive and astute handling of the situation by the doctor and the smart detective work by the parents stopped inappropriate and potentially disastrous investigations. Unfounded accusations of child abuse were in the pipeline. It was a close shave for all concerned.

Worldwide there are some 7500 species of these slow and sluggish creatures. Although they are sometimes mistaken for centipedes, they are markedly different. To start off with, they don't have venomous fangs and they don't bite.

Although most gardeners despise them and regard them with suspicion, they do little, if any, harm. In fact, most millipedes coil up into a tight, flat spiral when disturbed. They are antisocial, tend to stink, taste awful and, in general, engage in chemical warfare.

They are basically nocturnal creatures and extremely ancient from an evolutionary point of view. Indeed, they stand out as one of the few animals that have totally declined to participate in any genetic advancement.

They normally eat decaying vegetable matter and are most comfortable in moist conditions. In dry situations, such as in houses, they will die in a day or so.

Millipedes are circular in cross-section and almost all species have a hard casing. Most are only a few centimetres in length but some tropical species reach 30 cm. Each of the millipede's 40 body segments has two pairs of legs; each segment on a centipede has only one pair of legs.

Most segments of the millipede also have a tiny pore on each side that secretes toxins. These pores have a highly descriptive name, repugnatorial foramina. Considering the compounds they make, such as hydrogen cyanide, it is a wonder they don't blow themselves up.

The apparatus usually consists of an inner chamber or reservoir that contains a liquid emulsion of mandelonitrile. When this is squirted into the second compartment it reacts with an enzyme and is dissociated to produce hydrogen cyanide and benzaldehyde.

These two compartments are normally sealed by a valve. When disturbed, the millipede contracts a muscle to open the valve, forcing the contents of one chamber into the other with potentially unpleasant results to the bystander.

More than 30 chemical compounds have been isolated from defensive secretions of millipedes. They range from simple compounds, such as formic acid and acetic acid, to the quinones and

more complex substances. The brown discoloration seen on the skin of victims is due in part to the oxidation of quinones.

The variety and complexity of millipede secretions is reflected in the description in the literature of the smell of millipedes. They have variously been described as being like iodine, chlorine, walnut, garlic, camphor, urine and worse things. No wonder birds seldom eat them. Some birds are aware that the first few segments are gland-free, but it takes delicate beakwork to remove this portion.

The secretions usually ooze from the creature's sides. In some of the larger tropical specimens, fine droplets can be sprayed 60 cm.

Contact with the 12 or so native Australian millipedes or the imported black Portuguese millipede may produce pigmentation of the skin and lesions like mild chemical burns. The pigmentation may persist for many months. Secretions reaching the lips or mouth would be more reactive, but fortunately a child would probably spit the intact creature out. The effects of the secretions on the eye could be serious.

The tropical millipede should be carefully avoided. In 1938, zoologist Eric Burtt reported the effect of a 30 cm black millipede he captured in Tanganyika, Africa.

He had no container capable of holding it so he popped it into his hip pocket, buttoned it up and walked on. In the hour that he took to get home, he felt the millipede moving around in his pocket and became aware that his leg in the neighbourhood of the millipede was becoming a little sore.

While bathing soon afterwards he was surprised the skin had become completely blackened over a large area. Four days later the skin sloughed away, leaving a raw wound. It is not recorded what happened to the millipede. It is probably in a bottle somewhere.

In Papua New Guinea some dangerous millipedes have caused severe ulcerations when children have placed them in their mouths. Blindness has followed a squirt from some specimens. Apparently, many inquisitive village chooks are blinded in one or both eyes.

Dr Ron Southcott of Adelaide spotted a whopper of a millipede near Lae in Papua New Guinea. He cautiously poked it with a stick, but it still sprayed toxin that reached his hand and arms some 60 cm away. Immediate pain occurred, followed by erythaema and papules.

The staining and thickening of the skin lasted about 2 weeks, with the tanned area gradually flaking away. His report does not state whether he washed the secretions off.

We do not advocate self-experimentation with venoms. Apart from the potential dangers, the interpretation of the results may be complicated because of the development of allergies from prior exposure to similar or near-similar toxins.

Mite

The 57-year-old man had a run of bad luck. He had fallen off a ladder, fractured his skull, both arms and one leg. A few weeks later he was complaining bitterly of pruritus, which he said was especially severe in the areas covered by the plaster casts. Initially little attention was paid to him, probably because a patient is unlikely to die suddenly of pruritus.

Eventually closer inspection revealed the presence of small mites. The cast had to be removed, disturbing the home of even more mites. The patient's wife and two daughters, who frequently visited his hospital room, also complained of pruritus. A bit of discussion with the staff revealed that the three previous occupants of that room had complained of pruritus also with mites of similar appearance.

An inspection of the vent in the ceiling over the patient's bed revealed a pigeon nest filled with identical mites to those infecting the patient and his family. The mites were identified as the chicken mite (*Dermanyssus gallinae*).

A flurry of activity then followed. The nest was removed, insecticide was sprayed and the patient was thoroughly washed a few times. His wife and daughters spent a lot of time in the bathroom.

This chicken mite is one of many mites that occasionally attack humans instead of their preferred hosts. In Australia the hands and forearms of poultry workers are the usual sites of attack.

Mites are tiny little arachnids found all over the world. Their head, thorax and abdomen are fused into the one unsegmented body. In their larval stage they have three pairs of legs but, like spiders, they have four pairs in both the nymph

DISTRIBUTION

and adult stage. Their mouth parts are designed for blood-sucking and in general they are parasites.

Three species of mites are obligatory parasites of humans. The most important is the scabies mite (*Sacoptes scabiei*). This annoying creature tends to affect people within crowded, unhygienic conditions, as may occur after some natural disasters or during war time.

At first the presence of the scabies mite is not noticed and they burrow into the outer layers of the skin, often around the wrists, forearms and chest. In severe infestations any part of the body may be involved. Characteristic itching and inflammatory reactions due to hypersensitivity develop 3–4 weeks later.

Further exposure may cause a more rapid reaction. Large patches of erythaema may be distant from the area of burrowing. Burrows are often seen in the webbing between the fingers and around the wrists.

The severe pruritus may cause excessive scratching by the patient and lead to extensive areas of secondary infection. The combination of burrows, pustules and boils may make the skin look like a battle zone.

Genital lesions are common in scabies and excoriated, crusted, itchy papules on genitals or buttocks may be considered pathognomonic.

The two other obligatory parasites of humans belong to the genus *Demodex*. One of these attacks human hair follicles and the other occurs in human sebaceous glands. Usually they occur only in small numbers and cause little damage.

A number of other mites occasionally infest humans in Australia. The starling or tropical fowl mite and the tropical rat mite is usually found around sea ports. People working with hay, grain and even tobacco leaf in Australia have reportedly been attacked by the straw or hay itch mite. Heavy attacks from this mite have caused asthma, headache, vomiting and diarrhoea.

A Queensland scrub itch mite occurs in the rainforests as well as the Atherton Tableland. In South Australia the tea tree itch mite has caused distress to both duck shooters and scrub workers.

Sydney-siders sometimes suffer from grass itch mite in mid-summer. This particular lawn mite favours moist surfaces such as armpits and under tight clothing.

Red spider mites, which feed on plants, also sometimes attack humans. Some mites cause mange in dogs and cats. These in turn can cause a generalised papular dermatitis on their owners. A black soil itch mite in parts of Queensland and northern NSW is best not allowed under tight clothing. And so the list goes on. Anyone for a scratch?

Finally, the existence of a condition called delusory parasitosis is worth mentioning. The patients believe they are infested with little creepies but there is no evidence to support their claim. Usually the patient presents a container containing the remains of the offending creatures. On closer examination these usually are specks of dust, dried blood or a fragment of some harmless household creature. It is said that most of these patients are elderly females and it is possible that any skin lesions that are present are self-induced. Considering the small size of the mites and cases such as the fellow in the plaster casts mentioned above, a diagnosis of imaginary mites should be made most cautiously and after using a strong magnifying glass.

Medical management

When possible, the diagnosis should be confirmed by the positive identification of the mites by a skin scraping. Scrapings are best made at the burrows, especially from the softer skin between the fingers or at the wrists.

Mites do not survive more than 24 hours off a human host and so vigorous insecticidal treatment of bedding, furniture, etc., is not necessary. However, it is a sound procedure to thoroughly launder the patient's clothing, bedcovers, etc., preferably with a hot wash cycle.

A number of scabicides are available, and these are usually applied to the whole body (except the head) and left on for some 14 or more hours as instructed. After this time, the scabicide can be washed off. Although the lesions may continue to be itchy for some days, this does not usually mean the beasties have not been eradicated.

Dr Chris Commens considers that synthetic pyrethroids offer safer therapy because of lower percutaneous absorption. He recommends the use of 5 per cent permethrim cream.

Wasp—Australian native

There are hundreds of species of wasp in Australia, and most are solitary creatures that rarely make contact with humans. They have four wings and usually extraordinarily narrow waists separating the thorax from the abdomen.

Only the female stings, and her unbarbed hollow sting may also serve as an ovipositor. The prey of wasps range from cicadas to large spiders through to common insect pests. Many of the wasps paralyse their prey, introduce their eggs into it and then hide the living incubator in some safe crevice. It is a memorable sight to see a large wasp dragging a huge but paralysed huntsman spider across a suburban lawn. It is something one watches from no closer than a few feet.

Most householders find a solitary wasp popping in and out of a hole in a post or brickwork, and wisely leave it alone. Generally speaking, the larger they are the more painful is the inflicted sting.

Being unbarbed, a wasp can sting a number of times. Humans are unlikely to receive a series of stings over their lifetime and thus hypersensitivity to their venom is very rare.

It is fortunate that the highly dangerous hornets or vespid wasps found in New Guinea do not occur in Australia. One particular brute, *Vespa affinis*, recently caused the death of two boys in the Milne Bay Province of Papua New Guinea. The father and the two sons were returning home on a bush trail when the youngest boy moved off the track to select some betel leaves to chew. Unfortunately he trod on a large wasps' nest near the ground and was stung hundreds of times. When his older brother came to the rescue he also received multiple stings, as did their father. The younger boy became comatose and died that evening, while his older brother died 3 days later, apparently from renal failure.

A number of other deaths have been reported after massive envenomations by these wasps, but there are lighter moments in the literature. One fellow decided to fire his large bore rifle at a hornets' nest from a nearby hill. After the initial impact there was a pause while the surprised hornets gathered their wits together. They then spotted him in the far distance and took off *en masse* after him, and supposedly chased him for 2 km until he threw himself into a creek and nearly drowned himself by excessive submersion. The Australian wasps aren't quite as ferocious as this but certainly may pose a threat to life and health.

DISTRIBUTION

Blue ant or wingless wasp

The female of this common wingless wasp (*Diamma bicolor*) is often found by gardeners who usually don't recognise them as true wasps. They are quite magnificent creatures with metallic blue bodies nearly 3 cm long. They have a large sting and do not hesitate to use it, particularly if she is accidentally picked up. The sting produces immediate and intense pain that may last for hours. Nothing is known about the venom, and allergy to it has not been described probably because it would be most unusual for a person to receive several stings during a lifetime. Anyone who is stung should take special care to avoid a repeat performance.

This wasp is found along the east coast from Brisbane to Adelaide and in Tasmania. It is found high in the Blue Mountains but probably not west of them. Oddly enough it is found on Lord Howe Island (confirmed 1978) and also on Kangaroo Island.

The female wasp is usually found in soft soil around creek beds and is often dug up by gardeners. She hunts by digging a tunnel in the soil and ambushing a large mole cricket nymph in its tunnel. After stinging and paralysing the nymph, she uses her sting as an ovipositor to deposit her eggs in it. The wasp then leaves the poor nymph in her own tunnel at least 50 cm below the surface.

The mating habits of this wingless wasp are different to those of others because of the large size of the female. Normally the winged male drops out of the sky and, while mating, carries the female to a source of nectar. Mating continues while they both feed, after which his chivalry is exemplary. He flies her back and gently deposits her at the original spot on the ground. In the case of the blue ant, the male collects the nectar first and then brings this back to be shared with the female as they mate. The female is quite a good climber and sometimes mating may occur well off the ground.

Social or paper nest wasps

There are perhaps 20 native species of *Polistes* as well as a number of imported members of the genus. These wasps have a slender body and a tiny waist and are dark brown with yellow bands across the abdomen. They are easily distinguished from the imported European and English wasp (genus *Vespula*), which has a much thicker body and waist. *Polistes* is widely distributed in Australia, being quite cosmopolitan as well as thriving in subtropical regions. The most common species are *P. variabilis* and *P. rumilis*. The former is very common in Queensland and the latter is found in all states except Tasmania. The paper nest wasp builds a small, shiny nest out of wood fibre mixed with saliva. The nest is often situated under eaves. It is suspended by a narrow stem and shaped roughly like an inverted cone. From below it can be seen to contain dozens of brood cells shaped like a honeycomb. The base sometimes may be as wide as 23 cm. Any disturbance near the nest may provoke an attack by one or many wasps.

The venom of *Polistes* has been extensively studied in many countries because it is one of the most important causes of significant insect venom allergy. The venoms are complicated, containing some 40 known components including hyaluronidase, phospholipase A and B and some additional highly allergenic proteins that vary slightly from one subspecies to another.

The current medical literature gives an indication of the global activities of this species of wasp. In Japan, evidence suggests this wasp causes more than 20 fatalities per year while reports from as far apart as Houston (Texas) and Spain name it as the major cause of life-threatening insect allergy. In Queensland, Dr Graham Solley found that 61 per cent of patients suffering significant reactions to insect stings were probably due to honey bees and 33 per cent of significant reactions were due to paper wasps.

Dr Solley included a second type of species of paper wasp, *Ropalidia*, which is about one-third the size of *Polistes* and makes a paper-like nest consisting of two linear columns of cells.

Ropalidia's nests are often attached to the underside of trees and shrubs or fences. Usually the victims are stung when mowing lawns or gardening. This dark little wasp also constructs nests under the eaves of houses. Like the *Polistes* nest, it has no entrance or main opening and the individual cells are visible from below.

Provided care is taken, householders can usually inactivate these nests. (It is a different matter with European wasp nests). A can of knock-down insecticide should be used at night when all the wasps are in the nest and likely to be asleep. The best advice is to stand upwind and fire a burst of the insecticide onto the nest and strategically withdraw. Return some 15 minutes later to polish off any near-dead wasps and perhaps fire another shot of insecticide at the nest. The wasps and nest should then be sealed in a plastic bag and disposed of appropriately. If in doubt, call a pest exterminator.

First aid

Application of an ice and water mix to the area of the sting may reduce pain and swelling. If a number of wasps have inflicted stings, particularly in a child, systemic opiates may be required for pain relief and hospitalisation may be essential.

Possibly 10 per cent of people re-stung by paper wasps will develop an allergy and thus have a greater local reaction to a sting, or develop general signs such as urticaria, oropharyngeal oedema, shortness of breath and/or hypotension. People who have suffered an allergic reaction should be referred to an allergist as well as being issued with and instructed how to use an injectable form of adrenalin.

Dr Solley has highlighted the problem of the management of *Polistes* allergy in Australia. He considers the *Polistes* venom extract imported from overseas (and available as a pharmaceutical benefit) may contain allergens differing significantly from those present in the species of *Polistes* causing problems in Queensland. He has no such problem with the imported honey bee venom. The situation is not helped by the unavailability of venom from the other Queensland paper wasp, *Ropalidia*, for testing and possible immunotherapy of patients.

INSECTS

Wasp—European

It was sudden chaos. The doors of the Emergency Department flew open and in stormed the screaming parents carrying their collapsed child and followed by a cloud of angry European wasps.

Five minutes earlier, the child had stumbled across a European wasps' nest. The disturbed wasps had scrambled like fighter pilots and the child had received multiple stings, as had the parents.

The staff at this Melbourne hospital dealt quickly with the situation. While some were active with insecticides, others gave the victims antihistamines, pain killers and steroids. Fortunately none of the family had been stung before by these wasps and no allergic reactions complicated the situation.

It is the development of an allergy to this wasp's venom that poses a far greater danger than the toxic effects from a number of stings. In America, this wasp's (genus *Vespula*) close relative, the yellow-jacket, probably kills more people than all other American venomous creatures combined. The deaths are due to severe allergic reactions.

The European wasp *(V. germanica)* and the

DISTRIBUTION

English wasp *(V. vulgaris)* have been steadily spreading to many parts of Australia in recent years. The European wasp arrived in New Zealand during World War II, probably transported in war materials. By 1959 it was established strongly in Tasmania and by 1970 this wasp had arrived in Melbourne. Subsequently, both it and the English wasp have become firmly ensconced in south-eastern parts of Australia and are steadily increasing their territory.

These creatures are easily identified by their very strong yellow and black coloration. Their aggressive invasion of a family barbecue is characteristic. They'll eat anything from meat to tomato sauce and don't hesitate to help themselves. They appear completely fearless.

Unfortunately in Australia these wasps have neither a natural enemy nor are their numbers limited by the effect of very cold winters (as they may be in Europe). The nests are usually in the ground, and when it freezes most of the workers perish and the lone queen must restart the nest in spring. In many areas in Australia the wasps have survived the winter, and in subsequent years the nests have become increasingly bigger. Instead of reaching a maximum size like a football, some nests have been found that are several metres long and support a wasp population in the millions.

This aggressive beastie is armed with a long, fine sting that is unbarbed, so it may sting a number of times. The venom is complicated, containing pain-producing substances such as histamine as well as a number of very potent allergens.

The sting is more painful than a bee sting, and the local signs and symptoms may persist longer in the non-allergic person. Multiple stings may produce signs of systemic toxicity, particularly in children, who may become shocked when the distress from the severe pain has subsided.

The development of allergy to these wasps undoubtedly will become an increasingly significant problem in Australia. Possibly 10 per cent of people re-exposed to this creature's venom will suffer an allergic reaction. This may involve a greater local reaction to a sting or signs of systemic effects such as a generalised rash, swelling of the eyelids or the tissues of the pharynx, shortness of breath and/or hypotension. As far as is known, an anaphylactic death has not been attributed to this wasp as yet in Australia.

First aid

An application of ice and water to the stung area may reduce the pain and swelling following a sting. If the person is known to be highly allergic, the pressure–immobilisation type of first aid should be applied to the stung area if possible (see page 186).

If a person has suffered an allergic reaction to a wasp sting, and if the practitioner is not familiar with the management of insect venom hyper-sensitivity, then the patient should be referred to an allergist. The extent of the person's allergy can be determined by a skin test and a RAST test, both using purified wasp venom, which is now also available for immunotherapy in selected patients. This is known to have a high degree of success, whereas the previously used whole body extracts have been abandoned.

People who are known to have suffered a

significant allergic reaction to these wasp stings, and appropriate members of the family, should be issued with and instructed how to use an injectable form of adrenaline.

Removing nests

These wasps should be treated with the greatest of respect. They can fly some hundreds of metres from their nest, so take care when eradicating it.

This is best done at night when the wasps are asleep. Many councils have a wasp eradication program and it is best to contact them first.

Biological eradication of the wasp is being attempted by releasing a tiny imported insect that likes to lay its eggs in the larvae of social wasps. At the very best, this might significantly reduce the population of these wasps, but will not eradicate them.

INSECTS

Whiplash rove beetle

In 1954, an astute doctor in Wagga, NSW, noticed something odd going on. After severe floods earlier in the year, several patients presented with strange lesions unlike anything he had seen before. They had developed long, narrow weals, usually some 70 cm long and 1 cm wide. He thought the lesions were like a burn made by contact with the edge of a hot stove.

At first the weal was a purple-red colour, but later became covered with very fine blisters. The area in the vicinity became red and inflamed. The lesions, which usually occurred on the hand or forearm, were very painful but generally healed up 10 or so days later. In no case was there a history of injury.

The doctor's interest in this matter was sharply increased when he himself suffered a typical lesion. A clue came from one patient who commented that he had seen a curious little ant-like creature on his verandah that he had not seen before. It was striking because of the orange colour of its neck and part of the body and its habit of running about with its tail cocked up in the air. The doctor admitted he knew little about insects, but the fact that the creature vaguely looked like a scorpion from a distance marked it out as a potential criminal.

He sent some specimens to the Australian

Museum in Sydney, and they were identified as whiplash rove beetles, whose body fluids are known to cause blistering.

DISTRIBUTION

The doctor decided to research the problem further by conducting some experiments upon himself. He crushed a beetle firmly against the skin over the front of his elbow. Twelve hours later he suffered a typical whiplash injury, which led him to describe the experiment as 'all too successful'.

Undaunted, he proceeded to investigate how the condition of the victim's skin could modify the response. Again using himself, he found that if his skin was thoroughly cleaned with soapy water and petrol, the blisters appeared earlier and the lesions were far more severe. Having determined that the cleaner the potential victim was, the greater the penetration of the toxin, the good doctor gave his body a rest and wrote up his experiences.

Worldwide there are several hundred species of whiplash rove beetles (genus *Paederus*), but only two are found in Australia. They are found throughout Australia, with small and possibly less dangerous specimens found as far south as Melbourne.

The colloquial name for the whiplash rove beetle found in the Mackay district is the Finch Hatton bug. The creature involved is not a bug, but it is a beetle of the genus *Paederus*. The creature certainly makes its mark in this region, with one doctor reporting that he had treated 50 cases in 1 year.

A number of epidemics have occurred in Aboriginal settlements south-west of Darwin. A significant one occurred at Peppimenarti in March 1985. Dozens of people suffered quite severe lesions that itched for weeks afterwards. The local people thought that this blistering dermatitis was due either to the abundant cobwebs in their houses or a white moth frequently seen in the cobwebs.

In fact, it was determined that the open style of housing allowed easy access for rove beetles, which were attracted by the lights left on each night. The cobwebs and the white moths were quite innocent.

Further investigation showed the source of the beetles was a flood plain a kilometre from the settlement. A bit of spraying and putting the lights out earlier reduced the problem until the beetle numbers dwindled naturally.

The Australian species have a body length of 5–10 mm. The tip of the abdomen, wing covers and heads are blue-black, but the prothorax and middle abdomen are bright orange. When disturbed, they characteristically march around with their flexible abdomens raised high over their backs. This posture may be associated with the release of the toxic bodily secretions.

They feed on other small insects and are common near river banks and swamps.

Population explosions may follow because of the increase in their natural prey after floods.

No studies have been done on the toxins of these local beetles, but a toxic alkaloid called pederin has been isolated from overseas members of the genus. This toxin is different in composition from cantharidin, which is extracted from a Spanish blister beetle known as the notorious 'Spanish fly'. This beetle causes extensive blistering among farm workers if crushed on the skin, and if swallowed may cause inflammation of the urinary tract. This is the origin of its unfounded reputation as an aphrodisiac. A candlelight supper is clearly superior to chewing beetles.

No immediate effects have been noted after contact with a rove beetle, be it squashed against the skin or lightly wiped off. Twelve or more hours later, however, erythaema develops over the area of contact. A weal forms within 4 days, as do many small blisters that do not merge. The lesion is now very painful and within 7 days the blisters have broken and exuded fluid. Healing is underway a week or so after contact with the beetle, but marked itchiness often develops and may persist for many days. After healing, pigmentation may be evident for months.

Unfortunately since first contact with the toxic secretions is symptomless, the toxins are easily transferred to other areas. Mirror image or 'kissing lesions' may occur in the cubital fossa (the front of the elbow), for example. Transfer by hand is common.

Overseas, disastrous consequences have followed when the toxins have been transferred by the hand to the eyes.

Severe inflammation may occur, and African children have been blinded by the syndrome 'Nairobi eye'.

First aid

If contact with these beetles has been witnessed, then immediate washing of all areas exposed (or likely to have been exposed) with copious quantities of warm soapy water should prevent the onset of damage.

Unfortunately, the beetle is rarely identified as the cause when the lesions appear. As with a chemical burn, once the lesion is established it will run its course. Steroids or antihistamines do not modify progress. Soothing creams may give some relief and antibiotics may be indicated in some cases. Practitioners should be aware of the existence of this critter, and consult a colleague when faced with an unusual problem, particularly if you are new to the area.

Differential diagnosis

A knowledgeable practitioner can normally diagnose when a whiplash rove beetle has left its mark from the characteristic linear appearance of the weals. In contrast, chemical and thermal burns will not usually produce multiple small blisters, and the early blistering seen in some cases of necrotising arachnidism are usually of varying sizes and often neatly collected together in a disc-like area. Allergic reactions to insect venoms, especially jumper and bull ant venoms, may produce multiple local blisters, but these do not have the characteristic distribution that follows wiping a whiplash rove beetle across the skin.

OTHER CREATURES

Bullrout

The bikies were having a noisy and boozy barbecue on the banks of the Brisbane River. It was a hot afternoon and the water below the weir was dark, cool and tempting. With a merry oath, one 17-year-old took himself into the water. A second later he let out a less merry oath when he suffered stinging pain to his right big toe. Gone was his bravado as he was helped ashen-faced from the water while the pain intensified. The staff in Casualty at the Royal Brisbane Hospital observed he had a tendency to roll around the floor in agony. We will come back to our tattooed friend shortly after we've had a look at the creature he unwittingly kicked.

The bullrout or Kroki (*Notesthes robusta*) is a stinging fish that is also known by other names, such as wasp fish. It has been called Kroki because it produces a peculiar grunting sound, particularly when just caught. Bullrouts are found from the Clyde River in southern New South Wales right up to central Queensland. They inhabit lowland rivers and estuaries, and may be found long distances upstream. These fish particularly like still water under weirs and dams, and thus tend to congregate at some popular picnic spots.

DISTRIBUTION

Bullrouts average some 16 cm length but may reach 35 cm, and are well camouflaged with brown mottling over their dull ochre colour. They lead a fairly boring life, mostly in solitude, and do as little swimming as necessary. In fact, bullrouts are poor swimmers and are not inclined to get out of the way when a human intrudes into their territory. They are difficult to see, particularly when pottering around amid water plants, logs or rocks. When the water is turbid, they cannot even be seen by another bullrout.

The problem is that this little fish literally bristles with highly venomous spines. It has 15 quite long and finely pointed dorsal spines, each of which is associated with a pair of venom sacs. The anal fin has three more poisonous spines, and a few more may be found on the upper jaw. It is presumed that these spines are purely defensive and are to discourage other creatures either socialising or attempting to eat the bullrout.

There are no published studies on the properties of the venom, although there are plenty on the effects of the venom on humans, who are usually stung in mid-summer. When the human treads on or touches the bullrout, the fine spines easily penetrate the skin, sometimes to a depth of several centimetres. If you are really unlucky, a row of spines may penetrate simultaneously. As the spine enters, so does the long venom gland, which ruptures to release venom into the wound. The spines have little problem penetrating light foot-wear, clothing and even wetsuits. Often the creature is not seen, especially in murky water. However, a row of punctures spaced about 1 cm apart, or a neat slit-like puncture occurring in bullrout territory, is generally diagnostic.

A sting produces instantaneous pain. Most published accounts describe the pain as excruciating. The victim is often highly distressed and may even become delirious. The pain steadily increases and commonly spreads to affect the whole limb. Regional lymph nodes may become strikingly tender. Headache and vomiting may occur in severe cases. Fortunately, in most cases the pain has begun to subside by 4 hours and back tracks to the wound area. With severe injuries to the foot it may be days before weight can be borne. Even minor stings are tender to touch for many days.

The stung area usually reveals a slit-like puncture

Avoiding bullrout stings

With care, most bullrout stings can be avoided. If one must wade through their waters, never go barefoot and move along slowly so that the fish has time to move a few inches away from you. Jumping from boats into water barefoot is asking for trouble. Care must be taken when sorting fish or prawns from nets, especially at night. It is best to use thick leather gloves when doing this anyway.

with wound edges discolored. The immediate area is pale and may be slightly oedematous. Sometimes localised sweating may occur. The clinician is usually surprised that such extraordinary pain can be associated with a little slit a mere 2 mm wide.

First aid

Some authors state that the victim may be in danger of drowning and must be promptly removed from the water.

Pain relief is the urgent requirement. Fortunately, bullrout stings often respond to prompt immersion in hot but not scalding water. The first aider should first test the temperature themselves. Relief can sometimes be quite dramatic, but severe pain may come cascading back to the affected area when the limb is removed from the water. The injection of local anaesthetic may give prompt but temporary relief, but in the more severe cases a regional nerve block might be considered using lignocaine or bupivacaine. It may be necessary to give the victim systemic opiates. No antivenom is available.

As mentioned earlier, the pain is usually no longer a significant problem by 5 hours, but one is left with a potentially contaminated wound. Usually it is not necessary to surgically explore the wounds, but prophylactic antibiotics should be considered and tetanus prophylaxis should be updated as required. Occasionally reports come in of the use of potassium permanganate (Condy's crystals). This is a no-no because the chemical causes tissue damage and gives no pain relief.

While the reader skimmed through the above,

our bikie had been quietened down by the hospital staff and persuaded to lower his foot into a bucket of warm water. Within 18 minutes all pain had dramatically disappeared. His bravado now restored, he then refused to stay in hospital, and his doctors recorded that he 'discharged himself joyfully and went off with his leather-clad and chain-adorned mates'. The score: bullrout 1, bikie 0.

OTHER CREATURES

Cane toad

It seemed like a good idea at the time. In 1935, 101 excited cane toads *(Bufo marinus)* were released in a plantation near Bundaberg, Queensland. These poisonous critters had been collected at Hawaii and their job was to knock off the cane beetles that had been wreaking havoc on the sugar industry.

As they shuffled out and blinked in the sunlight, one of the monumental flops of ecological engineering commenced. For starters, the beetles escaped the toads by merely climbing up the sugar cane, so only the dumb ones were eaten. Then the toads, with no significant natural enemies, concentrated on eating and breeding. It is now estimated that in Queensland alone some 200 tonnes of toad flesh is squashed on the bitumen each year.

The cane toad has many other common names, such as the giant toad, Queensland toad and marine toad. They are stocky, heavily built, and extremely warty creatures whose colour varies from a dull green to tan. Both sexes are characterised by large, poisonous parotid glands situated immediately behind the head. The average snout to vent length of the male is 11 cm and the female 12 cm. The largest cane toad recorded was 23 cm long and weighed 1.25 kg.

Cane toads tend to live for a long time. In one laboratory, one lived some 15 years during which time it ate 72,000 cockroaches.

The spread of cane toads appears unstoppable. A survey in 1975 by Dr Jeanette Covacevich of the Queensland Museum found it widespread throughout most parts of Queensland. Ten years later it

DISTRIBUTION

was firmly established in the Northern Territory and moving steadily down the central coast of NSW. If it finds conditions satisfactory, the spread is at a rate of 27 km per year.

Apart from having a rougher skin than frogs, toads differ in that they are clumsier and their leaps are much shorter. Like all members of the family, they blink when they swallow.

Cane toads are one of only two toads that are omnivorous, and they have a voracious appetite. In fact, often bodily distension is the only reason they will stop eating. They will munch up all sorts of creatures, but they won't eat hard-cased adult cane beetles, only the younger, softer ones.

A number of human activities draw cane toads into suburban gardens, such as the attraction of insects to household lights and the availability of other food, including refuse and pet food. Swimming pools are a great attraction and often toad-proof fencing is required.

Cane toads are not fussy eaters. They have been recorded eating the strangest things, such as a lighted cigarette butt, and have even been seen pursuing ping pong balls. Sometimes their greed has proved fatal and they have been found choked to death after partially swallowing young chickens or mynas. They will even eat human faeces, which may lead to the spread of disease.

Toads are fond of bees and, unless the hive is raised well off the ground, they will gather around for a bee-bee-que. They seem unworried by the stings, and a toad may devour 300 bees or more in a day.

Cane toads take breeding very seriously; at times this is nearly a full-time occupation. They may breed twice a year but will reproduce year-round if the temperature and rainfall are suitable.

In most areas of Queensland, breeding starts with the first storms of September. The males reach the breeding sites first and start croaking out their love songs, with as many as a dozen toads per square metre. Mating takes place in the water and may continue for hours. The female can produce 8,000–35,000 eggs, which hatch within 4 days.

Population growth is aided by the fact that the eggs are quite poisonous, and the tadpole develops into a toad in the relatively short time of less than 2 months. The eggs are arranged in a chain-like form, which is different to that of any native Australian frogs. Unlike these frogs, the toad tadpoles only rise to the surface to breathe quite late in their development.

To make matters worse, male toads have the ability to change sex and become fertile females. They have an incipient ovary called a Bidder's organ   that possibly springs into action when there is a large all-male population. Often the trauma of transportation or translocation initiates breeding activity instead of dampening it down.

The skin of frogs and toads abounds with glandular tissue that produces mucus to keep the skin moist, thus assisting gas exchange and evaporative cooling. Some glands produce a variety of toxins; as a general rule, the skin of toads and frogs tends to be poisonous.

The size of the cane toad's parotid glands sets it apart from other frogs and toads. The glands may measure up to 7 cm x 3 cm, and have 50–60 lobules in each gland that discharge to the surface by individual ducts. If you look closely you will see the openings as variably sized dips on the surface.

Handling of the toad may cause the release of the poisonous milky secretion from the parotid gland. Because of the convex surface of the gland, the fluids may be forced out in a variety of directions at once. When severely stressed, the toad may squirt these secretions out in a fine spray, reportedly as far as 2 metres. The usual distance, however, is no more than 40 cm.

The output of this secretion can be massive. For example, a toad weighing 254 grams produced 710 mg of fresh secretion. Usually about 500 mg

Uses of toads

The Chinese have used toad toxins and skin extracts to treat cardiac failure and other matters. Some practitioners of Chinese medicine have claimed toad brews have 'a high cure rate' for lung cancer, tuberculosis and other diseases. This codswallop has led to some strong comments in the press by the interested parties. No one doubts the existence of pharmacological effects, but to modern eyes it is unstandardised gunshot therapy. It is different if you intend to use it as a poison, such as using toad skin extracts for coating the tips of arrows, or making a witches' brew.

However, *Bufo marinus* is good for some things. Toads were used for a simple human pregnancy test, and for years sat around uncomplaining in laboratories. They were temporarily better off than the 100,000 per year used for experimental and dissection purposes in secondary schools and universities each year. Innisfail Apex Club in North Queensland made enough money from the sale of cane toads to build a nursing home known locally as 'Toad Hall'.

Finally, there is always someone that benefits from a plague. A Townsville taxidermist, Mr John Kruger, discovered that stuffed cane toads were a hit with souvenir-hunting tourists, mainly as book-ends.

of venom (dried weight) can be expressed from the glands of a mature toad. Unlike snakes, the toad takes weeks to accumulate new reserves of secretions.

For more than 100 years, biochemists have had a wonderful time studying toxins extracted both from the parotid glands and the skin of toads. The main compounds, the bufogenins and the bufo-toxins, are steroid compounds with many effects including cardiotoxicity. The action of some components is not dissimilar to that of digitalis. Some of the bufogenins are potent local anaesthetics. In the skin of the cane toad alone, eight structurally different bufogenins have been isolated. A variety of catecholamines are also present in the secretions.

Overseas, human fatalities have followed the ingestion of cane toads and no doubt some deliberate poisonings have occurred. In Peru, a number of deaths followed the eating of a soup that had been made from boiled toad eggs.

If the toxin makes contact with the eye, sharp pain and intense irritation develops. One victim who was hit in the eye when he struck a toad with a pick described that it was as if someone was lighting matches under the eyeball. He was blinded for 5 hours.

On the skin, the toxin produces unpleasant sensations of numbness and tingling, and the hands feel stiff and extremely dry.

Hallucinogenic effects may be produced by the smoking of dried toad skin, a procedure that must be considered highly dangerous because of the associated effects on cardiac function.

The primary function of the toad venom is defence, and the glands are positioned so that the predator will either be hit in the eyes or the mucus membranes of the mouth. The toll on domestic animals is very high; each year at least 50 dogs die in Hawaii alone after eating or molesting toads.

Animals that absorb the toxin may die within 15 minutes of contact with the toad. The usual symptoms are profuse salivation, prostration, cardioarrhythmia and convulsions.

The toll on domestic fauna is enormous and is increasing. Amongst regular victims are western native cats, goannas, crows, kookaburras and even Tasmanian devils. The effects on Australian snakes have been particularly severe, and certain snakes have completely disappeared in some areas of high toad infestation.

A snake or goanna swallowing a cane toad has only a slim chance of surviving. One snake, the common keelback, is the only Australian species of animal that can regularly eat mature cane toads without apparent effect. Chooks can eat very young cane toads.

At present there is no effective biological control nor is there one in sight. The spread of toads is only limited by prolonged cool temperatures and, to a lesser extent, dryness. In Australia there has been no successful large-scale eradication.

As a general rule, contact with toads should be avoided, especially if a person has a known cardiac disease. Round-up and destruction of cane toads should be encouraged. Apparently a humane way to kill them is to place them in a deep freeze overnight.

First aid

If the skin of man or animal has been exposed to the toad toxin, the area should be washed well with fresh water. If the toxin has been swallowed and the victim is conscious, vomiting should be encouraged, and washing of the mucus membranes of the mouth carried out.

There is no specific therapy for toad poisoning. In studies carried out in experimentally poisoned dogs, Hawaiian researchers determined that the use of propanol hydrochloride could prove highly successful if the cardiac effects were not too advanced. The dose they recommended was 5 mg per kg bodyweight, and had to be repeated in 20 minutes if necessary. These workers did not consider atropine, antihistamines or steroids to be indicated.

A few guidelines are available regarding human poisonings. If significant hypertension develops, it should be treated with both alpha and beta blockers. Arrhythmia should be treated on merit, taking care not to cause depression of myocardial contractibility.

OTHER CREATURES

Crocodile

Crocodile attacks are rare, but they certainly produce headlines. From 1975 to 1988 there were 13 fatal attacks in northern parts of Australia. Two of these were in Western Australia, five were in the Northern Territory and the remaining six in Queensland. Most occurred within 50 km of the sea.

There are some dramatic stories of survival. The most impressive involved a Macquarie University lecturer, Val Plumwood, who in 1985 was making a lone canoeing expedition down the East Alligator River in the Northern Territory. As she paddled gently through a paperbark swamp she saw what she thought was a floating log. On closer inspection she realised it was a crocodile.

Val could not back off in time and the animal started a battering assault on the canoe as she tried to paddle away. She made for the edge of the swamp and reached up to grasp some overhanging branches when the crocodile seized her left thigh and pulled her into the water. Fortunately it was shallow, and her head came to the surface as the crocodile spun her around. She grasped a mangrove stem and held tight, trying not to struggle. The crocodile decided to change its grip and she swam away quickly, reached a paperbark, and started to climb it. The crocodile grabbed her again, but as she was spun she managed to grasp a mangrove. Again she

DISTRIBUTION

escaped when the crocodile tried to change its grip, and with it watching she slowly clawed her way up the mud bank. After bandaging her torn thighs with strips of clothing, she somehow managed to struggle through the rain and thick scrub to reach a Park Ranger's station. Four hours later she was rescued, and after emergency surgery at Darwin Hospital made a good recovery.

Later that year, in a tributary of the Daintree River in far north Queensland, a 43-year-old woman was less lucky. She was standing in knee-deep water a few metres from a crocodile warning sign. There was a swirl of water and she disappeared completely. Three weeks later, an autopsy on a trapped 5.6 metre crocodile revealed what were believed to be her fingernails, toenails and some of her bones.

In 1992, Drs Allan Mekisic and Jonathon Wardill reviewed crocodile attacks in the Northern Territory for the 10-year period to June 1991. Sixteen attacks were reported and four of these were fatal. Most occurred when the victims were swimming or wading in shallow water and half of them were affected by alcohol. Most attacks occurred at dusk or at night.

Death in fatal attacks was caused by transection of the torso or decapitation. The survivors suffered injuries varying from minor lacerations and puncture wounds to major abdominal, chest and limb trauma. The authors found that wound infection occurred in six of the 11 survivors, one of which developed a life-threatening infection in a crushing injury to a thigh.

Crocodiles and alligators are sometimes confused. Apart from in zoos, there are no alligators in Australia as they are found only in China and the south-eastern parts of the USA.

Alligators are less of a danger to humans and are more sluggish. They have broader snouts than crocodiles and the fourth tooth of the lower jaw is not visible when the mouth is closed, as is the case with crocodiles.

The freshwater or Johnstone's crocodile (*Crocodylus johnstoni*) is named after a certain Sub-Inspector Johnstone, who collected the first museum specimen from the Herbert River in Queensland. This shy creature never attacks people although there have been a number of cases of serious injuries when wounded specimens have been handled. It is found in most lagoons, rivers and freshwater billabongs located north of a line running between Broome on the west coast to Townsville in the east. It is very rarely found in salty water or in waters inhabited by the extremely dangerous estuarine crocodile.

The freshwater crocodile has a much narrower snout than the latter, and has some 60 very fine sharp teeth. At maturity, the male may weigh 70 kg and average 3 metres in length. The female may measure 2 metres and reach 35 kg.

A characteristic feature of this crocodile is the presence of four large scales on the posterior of the neck. The upper surface of these creatures is brown while the ventral surface is whitish. They feed on frogs, crayfish, fish, water rats, goannas and even the young of their own kind.

These crocodiles mate in the dry season and

usually a dozen eggs, similar in size to hens' eggs, are laid in a hole in the ground. They are covered in sand and usually hatch 2 months later before the water rises to flood the area. The mother keeps an eye on the nest, and when the little ones hatch they are some 25 cm in length and make cute sounds like a little puppy.

Fortunately for this crocodile, its skin makes poor quality leather that wears out quickly. It can also supposedly run at 45 km/hour.

The estuarine crocodile *(Crocodilus porosus)* is also known as the saltwater crocodile. It is found from the Fitzroy River in the west to a little north of Gladstone in the east. This crocodile also inhabits South-East Asia and some Pacific Islands such as the Solomons and Fiji.

The first described specimen came from India. The largest ever described was collected in Bengal in 1840, and was said to be 10 metres long with a girth of 4 metres. In 1930, one only slightly shorter was trapped in the Pioneer River near Mackay in Queensland. Nowadays the average length of a large adult is 4 metres. A crocodile may live for 70 years and, like all reptiles, continues to grow throughout its lifetime.

The back of this crocodile varies from very dark brown to a mottled yellow/brown combination. Its belly may be white or a yellow creamy colour.

Crocodiles are very powerful and clever creatures. They are direct descendants of the dinosaurs and are cold-blooded. Their body temperature is kept reasonably constant by basking in the sun and staying in the water on cool nights. Cooling can be maximised by holding the mouth wide open to expose the highly vascular throat tissues.

They devour a wide range of prey, from fish and water rats to birds, smaller crocodiles, snakes and wallabies. In fact, they will eat almost anything. They do not prefer decomposed meat; the old theory that the creature kept its prey untouched in underwater lairs until it had rotted is quite untrue.

This crocodile has usually 17 teeth on each side of the upper jaw, and 15 on each side below. These conical teeth are regularly replaced.

The estuarine crocodile cannot chew; rather, small prey is either crushed and swallowed whole or shaken so it breaks into appropriately sized pieces. Because they have no lips, the creature's mouth does not seal tightly and therefore eating and swallowing cannot be done under the surface without some intake of water.

With larger prey, the crocodile does its infamous 'death roll'. It awaits its prey submerged, with only its nostrils and watchful eyes poking above the surface of the water. When its prey comes to

Catching crocodiles

Eric Jolliffe, the famous Australian cartoonist, has a special interest in crocodiles and has described the cunning way that Aborigines can catch even the largest specimens. They construct a very large paperbark raft, and a hole is made in the centre of it through which a line is passed. This is fastened to a detachable harpoon that in turn is fitted to the end of a long pole.

The hunters hop on the raft, and one slaps the surface of the water with the flat side of the paddle. The others all watch for the telltale bubbles coming to the surface from the crocodile below. The pole is used to ascertain the size and position of the crocodile, and the spear is suddenly driven home. The great strength of the crocodile is of little help to it, and because the line runs through the centre of the raft, the worst the crocodile can do is to give the hunters above a rough ride. When it eventually becomes exhausted, the crocodile is dragged up to be killed by spear and waddy.

If a stream has to be crossed, the Aborigines will splash around and make a lot of noise to attract the crocodiles, but then race further downstream to cross in safety. It is said even dingoes have been seen to use this trick. If a particularly dangerous stretch of water must be crossed, the Aborigines would send the youngest first and finally the old people. They were aware that crocodiles always picked the last to cross, be it animal or man, since they would be the weakest and the most vulnerable.

the water to drink, its head and neck may be grasped like a flash by the enormously strong jaws, and with a twisting of its body the poor animal is thrown off its balance. The crocodile may roll over a number of times with lightning speed, spinning the poor animal into the water as it does so. Its neck may be broken by the first stage of this manoeuvre, but usually death is due to prey being held firmly underwater until all struggling has ceased. Large chunks are then wrenched off the prey by a combination of powerful jaw work and head shaking.

The crocodile can eat the lot: bones, hoofs, horns inclusive. It even swallows pebbles and rocks, which aid digestion by helping to mash the food in its stomach. These rocks also increase the specific gravity of the crocodiles, which allows them to approach neutral buoyancy in the water. Most of the eating is done in the hotter months of October to December.

For years, scientists were mystified how this creature could survive comfortably in either fresh-water or saltwater. Many marine animals have a salt-secreting organ, but none could be found in the crocodile. Eventually it was discovered that salt was shed through the crocodile's tongue. The creature has muscles that close both its nostrils and its throat; by using this, the salt can be easily washed away. These muscles also come into use when a prey is being drowned as it prevents water reaching the crocodile's lungs.

Crocodiles stalk their prey and at times can move with great speed, certainly faster than most humans. The crocodile can crawl or it can raise its body and run. The third option is to wriggle and slide; it can do all of these with sudden and explosive speed. It can also leap high out of the water, and a swipe from its powerful tail can knock any creature down. Thus both ends of the crocodile are dangerous.

Crocodiles are generally territorial. If another male wishes to cross his territory, it must raise its head to expose its neck in submission or prepare for battle. Before the crocodile throws itself at the intruder it may give a warning by breathing out loudly or sometimes growling.

The breeding season of estuarine crocodiles is much longer than that of the freshwater species. Mating takes place several times between

November and May, and the female will lay 40–80 eggs on firm dry soil. The eggs, which are hard-shelled and measure up to 8 cm in length, are incubated in a mound of leaves 40 cm deep and 2 metres across. The female keeps a very close eye on the nest, maintains it in neat condition and protects it from wild pigs and other predators. The father remains close at hand.

The eggs usually hatch 3 months later and the newborn average 33 cm in length. Prior to hatching, the young crocodiles can be heard yelping, and this apparently coordinates hatching at the one time and also signals the mother to help expose the shells.

Movement of each egg's inner membrane causes part of the shell to flake off, and the little creature uses a tiny egg tooth on the tip of its snout to rip open the membrane. This egg tooth falls off a day or so later. The mother can assist if necessary with her own teeth. This is done with great care.

All the hatchlings from the one nest share the same sex, which is most probably determined by the incubation temperature. Many of the eggs fail to hatch. The young, which all have a fine set of teeth, join the mother in the water for the first few days, after which each goes its own way.

It was not until 1971 that Western Australia became the first state to give legal protection to crocodiles. In 1972, the Federal Government prohibited the export of crocodile products, having imposed restrictions on crocodile shooting in the Northern Territory in the previous year. In 1974, Queensland finally declared the creatures to be protected.

Before these moves, crocodiles had almost been wiped out in some areas. Only the remoteness of some places, and the cunning of these animals, had allowed their survival. A combination of spotlight shooting, power boats and light aircraft caused a massive slaughter.

Even the freshwater crocodile came heavily under attack. Tanneries had developed techniques for making use of their skins and specimens of all sizes were caught in nets. Thousands were stuffed and sold as tourists' souvenirs.

Now there are many crocodile farms set up specifically for the supply of crocodile meat and the revived skin export trade. The breeding rate in these farms is very successful and the survival rate of the young is very high. The survival of the estuarine crocodile is now guaranteed.

In the Northern Territory three such farms exist to which large and dangerous crocodiles may be taken for breeding purposes. Because of the homing instinct of these crocodiles, they have to be kept on farms. In the past, some that have been removed more than 100 km from their breeding grounds have turned up there again within a few weeks.

In populated areas such as Darwin Harbour, traps are laid permanently because of the resurgence of the crocodile population.

Crocodile meat is considered a delicacy by many and is now available in specialty butchers through-out Australia.

First aid

First aid and medical treatment is similar to that described for shark attack (see page 47). Infection of injuries would appear to be an even greater likelihood than in the case of a shark attack.

The advice given to those that are attacked is to retaliate. Six of the victims reviewed by Mekisic and Wardill escaped by fighting back. Three of them were released following a tug of war with the crocodile, and two escaped when a friend went to their help. The other three escaped by gouging the crocodile in the eyes or nostrils.

To avoid attacks, do not swim in crocodile-infested waters or clean fish or camp nearby. Small boats are not safe. Take notice of warning signs!

OTHER CREATURES

Dingo

'A dingo stole my baby!' Few Australians would not recognise these famous words, which created a storm of controversy in 1980 when Lindy Chamberlain explained the disappearance of her daughter Azaria in the Northern Territory.

What the many doubters of her testimony did not realise is that significant dingo attacks were recorded long before the Azaria Chamberlain case. In pioneering days, hungry dingoes were known to attack children and adults. In 1845, a 12-year-old girl who hid in the bush overnight, fleeing parental punishment, was believed to have been killed by dingoes. Her gnawed bones were discovered the next day.

In 1932, Adelaide University professor of pathology, Sir John Clelland, published details of two cases of injuries caused by dingoes. In one, a farmer found his cow trying to beat off a dingo persistently returning to her newborn calf. As he picked up the calf the dingo sprang at him and

knocked him over. He was badly hurt before he could beat it off. In the other case, a child left sleeping under a tree was heard to cry and was rescued from a dingo as it dragged the child away.

There have been reports of dingoes relentlessly stalking injured or stranded stockmen. In 1978, a young policeman was stranded in the Simpson Desert when his vehicle broke down. For most of the 50 km walk back to his base he was followed and harassed by a dingo pack. A number of times they rushed in to snap at his heels or jump on him. He maintained steady progress, keeping them at bay by swinging a large tree branch and lighting matches. The next morning a tour bus came around the corner and he waved it down. The dingoes watched his departure solemnly from near the edge of the road.

Did a dingo take baby Azaria Chamberlain from her tent near Ayers Rock (Uluru National Park) in August 1980? The investigators found no motive, witnesses or body. There had been recent attacks by dingoes in that area. And carrying off a baby would not be a problem for a dingo. In complete silence a dingo can kill a 13 kg wallaby and carry it off briskly for at least 1 km without resting.

The dingo (*Canis familiaris*) is the oldest pure-bred dog in the world. It is a fascinating animal with a fine set of sharp teeth.

The dingo is a subspecies of the domestic dog and is able to interbreed with them. However, dingoes were isolated from other dogs for 5000 years or so before the arrival of Europeans and their dogs.

The Aborigines named these creatures the 'warrigal' and gave the more trainable European dogs the derogatory name 'dingo', which may have led to some confusion for a time.

The fossil record of dingoes in Australia studied to date are little more than 3000 years old. Scientists believe they probably descended from the Asiatic wolf and were brought from the north, presumably by sea within the past 10,000 years.

The numbers and distribution of dingoes in Australia have fluctuated. Dingo populations increased dramatically when Europeans introduced sheep, rabbits and foxes to Australia. At times at least 50 per cent of newborn lambs and calves were destroyed. When the settlers built dams and other watering places, the dingoes found these very convenient. They like a reasonable walking distance between food and water and were grateful for their new amenities.

Although breeding with runaway domestic dogs may have reduced the number of pure-bred dingoes, the species is in no danger of extinction even though thousands are killed each year.

Dingoes differ from domestic dogs in that the female comes on heat only once a year, not twice. Dingoes do not bark, but yelp or howl. They communicate over long distances by this some-what dismal vocalisation.

Another difference from most other dogs is that the dingo's thick triangular ears are permanently erect, which is a primitive trait. A pure-bred dingo

can be distinguished from domestic dogs because it has no eyelashes.

The dingo has heavy splayed feet that are usually white, and its short bushy tail is generally white-tipped. The skull of the dingo is broader than that of other dogs and its tooth formation is characteristic.

Interbreeding in an animal may be easily picked by loss of breadth in the animal's skull, its smaller feet, longer tail and the absence of rigid ears.

In hot areas, dingoes' coats are smooth and short, the fur becoming thicker in the south.

Although most dingoes are creamy to reddish yellow, other colours can occur. Early settlers reported white piebald and sometimes black dingoes and albinos. These variations in fur colour have led to the belief that pure-bred dingoes are rare. This is not the case; although there has been much interbreeding, purebred dingoes are still found in many parts of Australia.

Dingo pups are born 9 weeks after mating, with five pups in the litter on average. By 5 months they are weaned and have become used to chewing up wallabies and other creatures that the parent has brought back to the breeding den. The same den is used each year by the female, but the dingo family will have many other dens it uses in the course of the year.

The dingo parents have an excellent education plan for their children. They are taken out to observe hunting and killing techniques, while also becoming familiar with their territory and safe areas. Apart from early family hunting expeditions, most prey capture is done in solitude, hunting in silence like wolves.

There is nothing cute about dingoes when they start using their strong teeth to tear the flesh away from its prey. Sometimes bullocks have been attacked, successive slabs being torn off the animal until they resemble a walking skeleton.

There is no doubt they enjoy killing and maiming. Frequently dozens of sheep will be attacked just for the sport. However, when large numbers of animals are killed and not eaten, the villains are more likely to be feral domestic dogs or hybrids.

When targeting a kangaroo, dingoes may work in relays until the kangaroo collapses from sheer exhaustion. Sometimes the kangaroo will get the better of a dingo in a fight and disembowel it with its hind legs, but usually even a full-grown kangaroo may be quickly dispatched by these killing machines.

Aborigines considered baked dingo pup a great delicacy and their love of it probably helped control dingo numbers. The appearance of the Seven Sisters Constellation at sunrise was a time of great rejoicing for the Aborigines because it coincided with the arrival of the dingo puppies.

Occasionally orphaned pups were suckled by the Aboriginal women and, although later they were only fair as 'hunting dogs', they fulfilled two useful roles: bed warmers in winter and as portable food supplies!

Farmers and governments have spent millions of dollars trying to reduce the dingo population. The 8000 km dingo fence from Queensland to eastern South Australia is the world's longest fence. Third generation dingo hunters use methods ranging from shooting and trapping to poisonous baits.

In most areas dingoes are declared noxious animals, obliging land owners to kill all dingoes on their land. They are protected in National Parks which, combined with other refuges and the cleverness of the creature, will ensure the survival of the species.

When dingoes become 'tame' and to some extent dependent on tourists and campers for food, serious problems can develop. Recently *Australian Doctor* reported that Dr Dennis Costigan, who practises on Fraser Island, called for the local eradication of dingoes because increasing numbers of hungry dogs and rising tourist numbers in a confined space posed special dangers. The dingoes' food supply had diminished on the island as rubbish tips were closed and brumby foals became uncommon with the removal of wild horses. Dr Costigan said packs of hungry dingoes had herded children into the water like wallabies.

Positive measures must be enforced to minimise contact between these unpredictable canines and tourists. Incidents of dingo pestering or attacks should be immediately reported to local authorities.

First Aid

Dingo bites should be treated as potentially contaminated. Tetanus prophylaxis should be updated.
DON'T FEED THE DINGOES!

OTHER CREATURES

Frog

Deep in the jungle, the Colombian Indian was extracting poison from a small but beautifully coloured frog, *Dendrobates tinctorius*, by making it sweat profusely. The wretched little frog had been impaled on a sharp thin stick running from its mouth to its thigh, and this spit was turned slowly over a fire. As the sweat of poison drops appeared, the Indian scraped them carefully into a little vessel.

After processing several frogs, the container was full of sticky dark liquid. It would later be used to poison the tips of his blow pipe darts to cause rapid paralysis.

For thousands of years, the Colombian Indians have routinely used this toxin for catching prey such as monkeys. Because the potency of the brew varied from time to time they had developed probably the first bioassay. Each batch could be classified as a 'one tree', a 'two tree' or a 'three tree' brew depending on how many trees the monkey had leaped to before it crashed to the floor of the jungle.

The Amazonian Indians use skin extracts from the same frog for dyeing the feathers of parrots. Having caught the parrot, they pull green feathers out and rub the frog secretion into the feather sockets. The new feathers grow out yellow or blue and the parrots are known as *contrafeitos*. An interesting hobby but not much fun for the parrot.

Frogs are fascinating creatures. They are amphibians, which are vertebrates lying in the evolutionary scale between fishes and reptiles. They are the first true land vertebrates, having hopped out from the oceans in the early Devonian period a mere 300 million years ago.

The arrival of frogs and their relatives heralded

a number of evolutionary firsts, such as the development of an anti-diuretic hormone to help control water balance, and the ability to sing. Prior to their arrival on land, the only animal sounds to be heard were made by insects. Frogs certainly like to sing, especially prior to rain, and are thus regarded as weather indicators in many parts of the world.

Frogs, like toads, belong to the order Anura. Toads are distinguished from frogs by having much rougher skin due to glandular tubercules. They also have shorter back legs, are clumsier than frogs, and can't leap as far.

The frog's skin is smooth, soft and moist, and well supplied with blood vessels. Gas exchange through the skin is very important as the lungs are usually small. Numerous glands in the skin produce fluid and sometimes poisons. The pigment cells present in the inner skin of the frog may contract and expand to cause colour changes for camouflage.

Frogs have highly specialised skeletons that allow them to jump long distances. The backbone is shortened and many vertebrae are fused together. The limb girdles are firmly attached to the backbone. A lot of their anatomy, like muscles and the digestive system, are similar to that of the higher animals, and thus generations of students have dissected millions of frogs and toads.

Thousands of French chefs around the world routinely dissect frogs and remove the potentially poisonous skin before cooking the frogs' legs. The largest known frog in the world is *Hyla infrafrenata*, which is found in New Guinea and grows to a maximum body length of 14cm. Heaven knows how long its legs are.

We should all be grateful to the food-snatching tongue that frogs use to catch insects. The tongue is fixed in the front but is free behind. A sticky tip combined with a trigger-like action gives an insect a one-way trip. No amphibians can chew as there is no bone between the eye and the mouth. Thus the eye is pushed against the roof of the mouth, helping push the food further

backwards but also causing the frogs to blink when they swallow.

A number of European frogs such as *Rana viridis* have unpleasant odours and produce a burning sensation if they are handled. The American pickerel frog is of the same genus and its skin secretions can produce similar effects.

The most famous poisonous frogs belong to the genus *Dendrobates*. These occur in Central America and the northern parts of South America. They are small, fast-moving creatures with intense brilliant colours. Some have beautiful longitudinal golden stripes while others have orange or red spots.

Extraordinarily toxic alkaloids have been isolated from these frogs. The compounds have been named batrachotoxins, which are among the most potent naturally occurring non-protein toxins. They selectively increase the movement of sodium ions by altering the permeability of the outer membranes of nerve and muscle cells. This causes an irreversible electrical depolarisation, producing fibrillation, arrhythmias and heart failure. In nervous tissue, batrachotoxin prevents the normal closing of the sodium channels, resulting in a massive influx of that ion.

These substances have proved remarkable tools in pharmacological research. To date, no way has been found to reverse their effects, although some other toxins may interfere with their actions.

In Central America, frogs of the genus *Phyllobates* produce a toxin that specifically affects the transport of calcium ions. The toxin, pumiliotoxin D, is extraordinarily poisonous to humans and animals. It facilitates the release of calcium ions from storage sites in muscle cells when they are electrically stimulated, thus increasing the power of muscular contraction. The toxin also appears to delay the return of the calcium ions to the storage site. This prolongs the contraction of both heart and skeletal muscles. There may be clinical applications for this class of alkaloid in the future.

This genus of frogs really goes for an amazing range of colours. Some have red bodies and bright blue legs, while one species in Costa Rica is the only purely black and white frog described.

In the Amazon there is one large tree frog of the genus *Hyla* that is sometimes called the India rubber frog because its skin secretions are so abundant they can be worked into pellets. Contact with the skin secretions causes inflammation of the skin and a violent headache.

One ardent frog collector captured one of these when it dropped 10 metres from the sky at his feet. It had been rejected by a bird that was carrying it off. He popped it in the cage with other types of frogs he had imprisoned earlier. Later in the day he found all the other frogs dead and stuck together. As if losing his collection was not bad enough, he developed a smarting rash on his hand and forearm.

There are many species of frogs in Australia but the most famous is the Australian gastric brooding frog, *Rheobatrachus silus*. This frog was discovered in 1972 in south-east Queensland and a second species was discovered in Eungella National Park, west of Mackay, in 1984. This tiny Queensland frog gives birth to its young through its mouth. When this was written up in 1973, the British scientific journal *Nature* found it too much to believe and declined to accept the paper. After Professor Michael Tyler managed to breed the frogs in captivity in Adelaide, all doubts evaporated. When Professor Tyler filmed the birth, the youngsters were spewed up to 60 cm away from the mother.

The female gastric frog swallows her fertilised eggs and keeps them inside her stomach for up to 8 weeks. She eats nothing during this time while her young grow on the food contained in the yolk sac.

This frog actually switches its stomach off after the eggs have been swallowed. The production of hydrochloric acid stops and the muscles of the stomach fade away to become a thin transparent membrane. The fact that an animal can shut of its secretions of acid at will and subsequently restore it is of great interest to those working on peptic ulcer research.

As the babies grow, the mother sinks so that only the tips of her fingers and her nose peeps above the water line.

Unfortunately the habitats of Australian frogs are rapidly being diminished. Professor Tyler and other zoologists believe that if this continues, the gastric frog is due for extinction in the next decade or so.

A number of Australian frogs have been found to be quite poisonous to humans and animals. Systematic research has found a variety of toxic substances, the most alarming being the finding in 1992 that the red-back frog *(Pseudophryne coriacea)* has a pumiliotoxin B-like alkaloid. This very attractive frog inhabits forests in south-east Queensland and the coastal areas of northern New South Wales. At least eight other species of this frog are found in all states of Australia other than the Northern Territory. There are no published reports of this creature poisoning people.

However, there are several reports of poisoning by plump little frogs of the genus *Heleioporus*. This has been found in all states except South Australia and Tasmania. In Western Australia there are two interesting reports of the effects of this frog. One man who picked up a recently killed specimen accidentally transferred some of its slime to his eye. He developed an immediate intense burning sensation and had an irritable and weeping eye that was very painful. Although pain was relieved by bathing the eye, it was some 24 hours before the inflammation settled.

The second interesting case occurred when slime from the frog accidentally contaminated an antacid tablet. Shortly after chewing the tablet, the victim's lips became swollen and he became acutely short of breath. For half an hour or so he lay slumped in his car, apparently with a very slow pulse rate. This man, who was a university zoologist, then made a spontaneous and complete recovery. Subsequently all his colleagues took greater precautions when handling frogs.

Dr Julian White of Adelaide recently described a marked reaction in a 5-year-old boy who handled the trilling frog, *Neobatrachus centralis*. Dr White warns of the dangers of frog collecting in general, and suggests that the practise of kissing frogs by princesses should be discouraged.

First aid

Skin that has made contact with toad secretions should be washed well.

Ingestion of material may produce an alkaloid-type poisoning requiring careful monitoring.

Handling of frogs should be avoided.

Leech

Most people find leeches revolting. After all, it's bad enough to have contact with this creepy-crawly, but to suck your blood as well is poor taste. What's worse is that the bleeding wound left after the leech is removed may take days to heal.

There are hundreds of types of leeches (class Hirudinea) found in the world. They characteristically have a sucker at each end of their body, and the posterior sucker is larger and cup-like. Leeches move by alternately fastening these suckers as their bodies expand and contract, and can advance by almost their entire body length in this fashion. Leeches can swim at a fair pace as well.

Leeches come in all shapes and sizes, from a few millimetres long to 45 cm (the giant Amazon leech). Their bodies, which can stretch and distend enormously, always have 34 segments, although these may be hard to discern. Leeches have both male and female reproductive organs, but generally engage in cross-fertilisation.

Many species of leeches feed on the blood of humans and other vertebrates. The mouth, which is situated in the front sucker, is equipped with a set of tiny teeth that can make a painless incision into the host. It floods the wound with an anticoagulant named

hirudin, and its powerful pharynx allows swift aspiration of blood. The creature's saliva also contains a local anaesthetic and vasodilator that makes its vampire-like activities safer and more efficient. When full, the leech will normally detach itself and drop from its host.

DISTRIBUTION

Blood-sucking leeches generally feed for up to 30 minutes after attaching themselves, and their body may engorge by a factor of 10. They usually then fall off and digest their meal. However, these beasties sometimes enter a body orifice and find themselves trapped there. Thus it's best to avoid them wherever possible.

Leeches have been medically significant throughout the ages. For example,

Allergy to leeches

Although leeches may be irritating and severe infestation could cause significant blood loss, the development of allergy to leeches is the most important clinical problem. This allergy develops in a similar fashion to other salivary (e.g. tick) or venom (e.g. bee) allergies. Management of the acute allergies is similar (adrenaline and care of airways, breathing and circulation).

Immunotherapy of leech allergy is not widely available, so strict avoidance is the only choice for most allergic people.

it is estimated that 12 million leeches slurped up some 363,000 litres of French blood from compliant patients in 1825.

One of the most ancient operations in surgery is the removal of blood. Leeches were used to deliberately extract this precious fluid from humans as way back as the Trojan wars of 1200 BC. Only occasionally would it do the patient any good, but overall it probably caused less harm than some other forms of medical intervention and hocus pocus practised over the years. Blood-letting was also satisfying for both the doctor and patient as something was clearly seen to be done. Naturally, in most cases only 'bad blood' was supposedly removed.

Blood-letting with leeches was big business in France early in the 19th century. It was the rage in many countries and the most suitably used leech *(Hirudo medicinalis)* was listed in the pharmacopoeia and regularly dispensed by pharmacists. A huge industry existed, with leeches shunted from one country to another to meet fluctuating demands.

In Australia, a most suitable freshwater leech *(Hirudo australis)* was found in the Murray River and its tributaries. It was reported in 1869 that an enthusiastic entrepreneur shipped a cargo of leeches *(H. quinguestriata)* to England to make his fortune. However, he struck a dip in demand for leeches and all but four specimens (which went to the British Museum) were apparently thrown into the Thames River.

In Australia, the leech industry still was worth a few bob at the turn of the 20th century. The large Melbourne wholesaler Rocke, Tompsitt & Co. provided leeches in lots of 25 as required. These were collected from the Murray River by pegging the skin of a freshly killed sheep to the bottom of the river with the wool side uppermost. This was a unique Australian method for trapping fine alluvial gold in the wool, and the leeches were a bonus.

In 1913, leeches were being supplied to all states by Felton & Grimwade at a wholesale price of 35 shillings per hundred.

Many pharmacists sought their own supplies. Some were from boys who would wade bare legged in the swamps around Sydney and Melbourne in summer. Larger quantities were collected by professionals who had their secret methods and collecting sites. One Aboriginal collector who could supply 300 leeches at a time claimed that leeches would not bite Aboriginal people.

Pharmacists regularly discovered additional hazards when they went hunting in swamps for their own supplies. They found the threat of venomous snakes so serious that they abandoned summer collections and wisely contacted suppliers such as Felton & Grimwade.

Leeches were used to exsanguinate all and sundry. By the turn of the 20th century, their use for illnesses such as pleurisy and meningitis had faded but they were still the treatment of choice for swollen black eyes and other subcutaneous bruising. One writer stated that their most common use was for the treatment of bruises obtained during sporting events, and that there was much demand for leeches to treat black eyes following the closing of hotels on Saturday nights.

By the 1930s, leeches had all but dropped out of the bright young doctor's armament, but not quite. Believe it or not, a 1931 book, *Recent Advances in Cardiology*, gave guarded approval for the use of leeches in treating liver engorgement in acute cardiac failure. The authors added the interesting rider that 'the relief is not related to the amount of blood which is removed, and that the patient welcomes the application of the leech.' An interesting conclusion.

Leeches are back in vogue these days. Plastic surgeons sometimes use them to remove haematomas from under grafts, and a modified leech protein may soon be as important as heparin as an anticoagulant.

Since 1884 it has been known that the saliva of the common medicinal leech *H. medicinalis* had anticoagulant properties. Now a synthetic hirudin has been produced by genetic engineering and has undergone clinical trials. It seems likely that these synthetic hirudins will replace heparin to a large extent because they are better antithrombotic drugs. They have a number of advantages over heparin, including no direct effects on platelets.

Protection from leeches

Leeches cannot penetrate clothing, so ensure that there are no gaps between your trousers, socks and boots. Plentiful application of insect repellents helps, but may have to be repeated. Don't forget that leeches are good swimmers and can overtake a slowly moving person. They attach rapidly, but usually don't start to bite for 30 seconds.

Leech removal

No attempt should be made to pull the leech off as this may leave a ragged bleeding injury. There are a number of ways the leech can be encouraged to pack up its teeth and go home. They include the application of salt, or carefully touching its body with a hot object such as the hot tip of a snuffed out match. Some people have successfully used detergent or toothpaste. Carefully slicing the leech in half with a knife also does the trick. Take care with the knife!

Special problems may occur when the leech has firmly attached itself in awkward anatomical sites such as the eye or the urethral meatus of the male. A careful plan of attack and dexterity may be required. Attacking the leech with the heated end of a paperclip or fine scissors may do the trick.

OTHER CREATURES

Magpie, cassowary and other birds

Magpie

Most Australian children will have been harassed by magpies. Indeed, both authors have experienced the dangers of magpies first hand! Struan attributes much of his baldness to multiple attacks some 50 years ago. And Guy was regularly bailed up by a magpie guarding the path between the clubhouse and courts 7 and 8 at the local tennis club.

On the other hand tame magpies can be a constant source of joy and hilarity. When Struan was growing up, a local wood merchant who had chopped down trees containing magpie nests would offer the young to his customers, including Struan's family. Sometimes his sister would practise the piano at 7 am with a magpie's curious little head sticking out of her school jumper. And once this pet magpie accompanied Struan's father while he planted a long row of tiny bulbs. As he rested and mopped his perspiring brow he noticed that the magpie had followed him along, deftly extricating each bulb!

Magpies hear through cute little holes in the sides of their heads, and they like this region tickled. This should only be attempted if the magpie is very tame.

Although the colour of magpies varies somewhat in Australia, they all belong to the one species, *Gymnorhina tibicen*. The birds are widely distributed in Australia and live in social groups of 12 or so.

In south-western Australia these 'families' may number 20 or more. They occupy a large area of about 20 hectares, which provides them with seasonal food throughout the year.

Magpies are generally ground feeders, living mainly off insects and worms. Their nest is built in

Other birds

Over the years a variety of injuries have been attributed to various other birds. Cleland reported in 1912 that a wedge-tailed eagle (*Aquila audax*) attacked and injured a boy near Bathurst, NSW, breaking his leg. Most reported attacks on children by this eagle, which can have a wing span of up to 2.7 metres, do not withstand closer scrutiny.

An authenticated attack did occur near Albany many years ago. Fortunately, the eagle was driven off before much harm could be done to the 6-year-old boy involved.

Incidentally, there is one report from Norway in 1932 of an eagle carrying off a small girl. This episode, which the experts described as fairly convincing, had a fortunate ending when the girl was dropped unharmed about 2 km away.

Butcher birds (genus *Cracticus*) have carried out some impressive attacks in the vicinity of their nests. It was recorded that one man, who threw his cap at an attacking butcher bird, had his head cut in many places. The hooked beak of this bird can more easily break the skin than can the beak of the magpie.

It is pleasing to report that our emu (*Dromaius novaehollandiae*) has a fairly clean report card. One little boy who received superficial injuries in an attack had been playing with a ball at the time. It was believed that the attacking emu thought the child was interfering with an egg.

tall trees and is usually made from sticks or grasses, but sometimes they incorporate man-made materials, especially shiny items such as cutlery. One nest in Western Australia was found to contain 243 pieces of electrical wire off-cuts.

Up to six eggs are laid, but usually only three survive. The female incubates the eggs and the young hatch after about 3 weeks. The youngsters remain dependent upon the parents and relatives all summer. They are particularly demanding children and, even when quite large, they follow their parents around for hours demanding titbits they could well pick up themselves.

Magpies are extremely territorial and adopt the attitude that aggression is the best form of defence. During spring and early summer they show some of the most aggressive behaviour towards humans that is seen in the bird world. Their aerobatics are magnificent, but the suddenness of the sharp-beaked swooping attacks combined with the whirring of the wings make the experience terrifying. Not only parents attack. Non-breeding adults also join in to keep the feeding area free of potential predators. The aim is to make the feeding area safer for when the vulnerable young start their ground feeding.

The most serious injuries from magpie attacks are eye injuries. Traumatic cataract was first reported by Sir John Cleland in *The Medical Journal of Australia* in 1932.

Dr Bradley Horsburgh and his colleagues reported six severe ocular injuries in the same journal on 7 December 1992. Each patient suffered a penetrating eye injury ranging in degree from moderate to extremely severe. All but one of the victims were children, two of whom were attacked while riding their bicycles. Although diagnosis of corneal lacerations with iris prolapse prompted early attention in the severe case, some delay in seeking treatment followed the minor injuries. This could have had disastrous consequences.

The importance of early diagnosis of penetrating eye injury cannot be overstressed. Such injuries should be suspected when there has been a blow to the eye. Persisting discomfort or redness of the eye warrants urgent ophthalmic consultation. Remember that evacuation by air in unpressurised aircraft has the potential to worsen such penetrating eye injuries.

Domestic animals are sometimes injured. In South Australia a magpie attacked a horse that was being ridden. Despite the rider beating at the bird with a stick, both the horse's eyes were severely damaged and it had to be destroyed.

Magpies are fully protected by the law and only when particularly aggressive and unacceptable behaviour is occurring will police or wildlife officers neutralise the threat. The best way to do this is to trap the bird and pluck out certain feathers on one wing so its food-collecting flying is not impaired but it can no longer engage in the brilliant aerobatics required for high-speed attacks.

During the breeding season it is best to avoid the magpies' territories, but if there is no option it is best to wear a stout hat and carry a stick or umbrella. Wildlife authorities advise not to duck as the magpie attacks. They also advise the potential victim to look straight at the attacking magpie and keep on walking in a steady fashion. This sounds great in theory.

Leaving a few scraps out for the magpies will usually promote more cordial relations between bird and human. One magpie taps on Struan's study window when it feels neglected. Its reward is special mince. Likewise Guy's mother enjoys the company of two magpies at breakfast time.

Cassowary

The cassowary is a huge flightless bird that can and does kill humans. The species found in Australia (*Casuarius casuarius*) inhabits the rainforests north of Townsville, Queensland. The female is larger than the male and may weigh up to 60 kg, which makes it the heaviest Australian bird. Either sex may stand some 2 metres high with its head crowned by a bony outcrop called a casque. This bit of its anatomy is used to divide and open its way through the tropical vegetation. The cassowary's head and neck are brilliantly coloured, as is its throat wattle. These splendid colours are in contrast with the dull appearance of most other flightless birds, like emus.

As the rainforests diminish, cassowaries are forced to have more contact with humans. Their diet includes insects, the flesh of small dead animals and, especially, fruit on the tropical rainforest floor. Some tourist areas encourage their visits by leaving scraps, whereas fruit plantation owners see them as thieves.

The inner two toes of the cassowary are equipped with dagger-like claws that may reach 12 cm in length. When going on the offence the bird leaps off the ground, kicking out with both feet. The combination of its height, strength and weaponry can produce terrible injuries. Apart from humans and dogs, the cassowary has no natural enemies and so it very rarely has to use its feet for

anything other than walking, scratching the ground and grooming.

Except during the breeding season, it lives a solitary existence. The cassowary is a fast runner but usually prefers to stand its ground and eye off any intruders. Initially, it may make a low rumbling noise in warning. If further approached it will hiss while holding itself at its maximum height with feathers erect. Generally, if the intruder does not retreat the bird will, stamping irritably as it goes.

A cornered cassowary or, worse, one that is wounded or being threatened by dogs may attack furiously. Unprovoked cassowary attack is most unlikely, so these creatures should never be made to feel threatened or cornered. In Papua New Guinea there are an additional two species of cassowary that have been widely hunted and have often injured or killed the hunters.

First aid

See first aid for shark bites, page 47.

OTHER CREATURES

Platypus

The fisherman was a brave man. Having suffered shrapnel wounds in Vietnam, he knew all about severe pain. He even had a Victoria Cross to prove it.

He spotted the small platypus resting on a log in the middle of the river. It remained stationary, even when he waded right up to it. Thinking it was either sick or injured, he gently picked it up by the back of the neck as one might a kitten. Supporting it underneath, he placed it back in the water.

In a sudden flurry of motion, the platypus came to life and drove the two spurs on the inside of its rear legs deep into the fisherman's hand. The pain was instantaneous, and soon became so severe that the patient became incoherent. The platypus was detached with difficulty and the victim had to travel some 100 km over rough roads for medical help.

The victim took more than 4 hours to reach the doctor's surgery, during which time he had severe unremitting pain worsened by the bumpy trip. On examination his hand was swollen and pale but circulation appeared normal. He was given 15 mg of morphine intravenously, with little evidence of pain relief. Additional morphine was required before pain was reduced to a tolerable level. Pain relief by lowering the injured hand into warm water was attempted, but this was not possible because the patient could not tolerate moving his hand below heart level. When ice was applied to the hand, the pain greatly increased. (Some days later cold packs were found to be effective in reducing pain and tenderness, but this returned as soon as the area was permitted to warm.)

DISTRIBUTION

More than 5 hours after the sting, the patient was given a full right wrist block with bupivacaine. This gave significant relief. However, he required an infusion of morphine for more than 48 hours for pain relief. If the infusion was reduced, the patient began to complain of severe generalised muscle and skin pain.

Two weeks after being stung, the patient still had pain and tenderness in the right hand. It was months before near full function returned.

The platypus *(Ornithorhynchus anatinus)* is such a strange creature that the first specimen received at the British Museum in 1799 was regarded with extreme suspicion. The Museum staff were aware of previous hoaxes, such as the sale of 'Eastern Mermaids' to European adventurers by the 'artful Chinese'. These mermaids consisted of the front part of a monkey skilfully sewn onto the rear half of a fish. It is not surprising, therefore, that this first museum specimen still bears the marks made with scissors when the staff attempted to lever off the bill.

The platypus is a furry creature with a bill like a duck, webbed feet with claws and a paddle-like tail. The female lays eggs and suckles her young, and the male is equipped with two venomous spurs.

Platypuses, which are now completely protected, are relatively common in the unpolluted streams

and rivers in eastern Australia. They are found in icy mountain streams at altitudes as high as 1500 metres to warm coastal rivers. Their distribution extends from near Cooktown down the eastern parts of Australia through NSW, Victoria and Tasmania. In South Australia they are found only in the extreme south-east, except for introduced specimens that have thrived on Kangaroo Island.

The male platypus may grow as long as 63 cm and weigh 3 kg. One-third of its length comprises the beaver-like tail. The female is two-thirds the length of the male. She can be distinguished from the male by a reddish tint to the fur in her mammary area. Both sexes have a core temperature of only 32°C.

The beak appears to resemble a duck's bill, but is different in structure and function and really should be called a muzzle. The bill is very soft and flexible and is covered with extremely sensitive blue/grey skin. In 1986 it was discovered that there are remarkable electroreceptors in the bill of the platypus. These receptors allow the platypus to detect moving prey by the minute electrical activity of the prey's muscles. The platypus can then home in like a flash on any worm or yabbie that moves. Research workers found that, in captivity, a tiny battery could be located by the platypus in seconds. The existence of these senses probably

explains the rhythmic side-to-side movement the platypus shows when it is hunting. This probably helps it determine the exact position and size of the prey. A worm would have no chance.

Platypuses generally feed at night, but sometimes do so near dawn and dusk. They can dive for up to 5 minutes at a time but soon drown if caught in fishermen's nets. They have a voracious appetite; when kept in captivity, keeping up a supply of food for them may be a problem.

Except when mating, the platypus leads a solitary life. Both sexes excavate individual burrows that may be extraordinarily long. Usually they are 5–10 metres in length but the main passage may be as long as 55 metres from the creek or river.

The breeding season is in spring, and the female makes a special chamber at the end of her burrow. After preparing a nest of grass and leaves, she blocks the tunnel in several places with earth and then lays up to three eggs, which she then incubates. The eggs are ellipsoidal, measuring 14 x 18 mm in size. They have tough yet flexible shells and are always joined together. The eggs hatch about 12 days later.

The female suckles the young via special mammary patches on the abdomen. By 16 weeks they are weaned from the milk and become semi-aquatic. They are mature adults by 2.5 years and may live 16 or more years.

The male platypus is the only mammal in the world with a functioning venom apparatus. (The male echidna has a tiny venom apparatus, but this is of doubtful importance.) On the inside of each thigh of the male platypus is a kidney-shaped venom gland. The duct from each gland enters a moveable hollow spur that is attached to the inner hind leg close to the ankle. The spurs are curved, conical and measure about 15 mm.

To poison a victim, the spurs are raised at right angles to the legs. The victim is then squeezed between the creature's legs and the spurs driven in deeply. A fisherman gripped by the arm or leg by a platypus will find that the creature is quite strong and may be difficult to disengage.

Not much is known about platypus venom. Early work showed that it was quite toxic to experimental animals and could cause local haemorrhage and swelling. The venom is known to be very complicated, but only recently has some become available for research. Four major proteins have been isolated, one of which has a variety of actions including increasing the amount of sodium excreted in the urine. It will take some time to sort out this fascinating venom.

The normal purpose of the platypus' venomous spurs is to discourage other males from invading its territory. Some biologists have suggested that the apparatus may also subdue the female during mating. Human envenomation is largely avoidable, but was probably much more common in the days when platypuses could be legally trapped for their furs.

Obviously it is best never to handle a platypus unless it is really essential. If it must be picked up, the safest way to do this is to lift it from above the tip of the tail. If a platypus is accidentally hooked, wrap it in a bag or coat and cut the hook in half with pliers. If a platypus is caught in a net, cut it free while it is wrapped as above.

First aid

If still attached, remove the platypus! Try to avoid being envenomated. Assist the victim to dry land. If bleeding is profuse, apply a pressure dressing. Of top priority is pain relief, and this is probably only achieved by opiates or local anaesthetic. Although not effective in the case of the fisherman, it may be worth trying ice packs or warm water. The pressure–immobilisation type of first aid should NOT be used as restricting the movement of venom would only increase the local pain.

Clinical management

Significant envenomations should be treated in hospital, where infusion of narcotics will be required. Corticosteroids may possibly be helpful but evidence to date is inconclusive. Since the wounds are potentially contaminated, antibiotics may be required and tetanus prophylaxis should be updated. Significant cases will require days of hospitalisation and it may be months before full function to the envenomated area is restored.

Tasmanian tiger

On 28 January 1995, *The Age* newspaper reported that Charlie Beasley, a national park ranger, had sighted a Tasmanian tiger (*Thylacinus cynocephalus*) 3 days earlier in the island's north-east. Charlie said he watched the sandy-coloured animal in light inland forest for about 2 minutes. He described it as 'about half the size of a fully matured German shepherd dog, it had stripes over its body from about half way down and the tail was curved like a kangaroo's'. This sounds pretty like a thylacine, which is from the Greek word for the pouch that both sexes of the species had (or perhaps have).

Let's hope further sightings occur. Although officially extinct since 1936, anyone familiar with the Tasmanian wilderness will bet there are tigers still quietly padding around. After all, they were (or are) fascinating creatures.

The late David Fleay, a zoologist and writer, was the last known human to have been bitten by a thylacine. This happened in 1936 at the Hobart Zoo where the last captive thylacine was held. Fleay had set up his camera on a tripod in the centre of the creature's cage. It appeared to ignore him completely and casually paced around the perimeter at a fairly constant rate. Fleay bent over the camera and took a series of photographs at near regular intervals. When the subject failed to make its next expected appearance, Fleay went to straighten up and investigate but the critter beat him to the punch and gave him a brisk nip on his bottom! Luckily the injury was minor as the powerful jaws of this beast could have rendered him almost bottomless. Among the photographs was one

Thylacine clones

In 1999 *Australasian Science* magazine reported plans to clone the thylacine from a specimen preserved in alcohol at the Australian Museum. The Director of the museum, Professor Mike Archer, told Guy Nolch that the clone would be 'incubated' in the pouch of its closest relative, the Tasmanian devil. While scientists have debated whether the pickled tiger's DNA will be too badly damaged to clone from, we await with anticipation the results of feasibility studies.

of the creature finishing a yawn, nicely demonstrating its gaping jaws, which can open almost to a straight line. This last captive thylacine died a few months later.

In November 1945, Fleay led a search for a pair of thylacines from which he hoped to breed. This was an official expedition supported by a number of societies as well as the late Sir Keith Murdoch. The search was centred around the Loddon Range and extended some 22 km in all directions. A definite sighting had occurred within this area 2 years earlier.

The circumstances of the sighting were unusual. A certain Mick Tiffin was cross-cutting a trunk of a giant tree for firewood and as the last section fell he was frightened out of his wits when the thylacine jumped out from the cavity in which it had been resting. It uttered a husky cry and bounded into the scrub. After talking to Tiffin and inspecting the site, Fleay was certain the creature was a young thylacine.

Despite setting many caged traps that could catch a thylacine unharmed, the expedition failed in its prime objective. There were some successes though. They heard the creature, they found definite tracks and some droppings, and one escaped, leaving behind only tracks and a tuft of hair.

Until some 3000 years ago, the Tasmanian tiger or marsupial wolf was widely, but sparsely, distributed over mainland Australia. It is likely that competition from the more efficient dingo led to its disappearance from mainland Australia.

There is no fossil evidence of dingoes in Australia prior to 10,000 BC, which is about the time rising sea waters separated Tasmania from the mainland. The presence of Bass Strait thus accounts for the absence of dingoes in Tasmania. Fortunately there are no foxes there either.

The Tasmanian tiger grew to more than a metre long. Fleay described its general contours as wolf-like but pointed out that its tail is a characteristic marsupial appendage, tapering from a broad base. It had 15–20 dark-brown dorsal bands extending to the mid-point of its flanks, which is why it was compared with a true tiger.

Tasmanian tigers tended to hunt in pairs and usually at night. Even when they were plentiful in the early days of white settlement they were rarely seen. They had great strength and stamina and could outrun any creature to exhaustion. The hunted was relentlessly followed into icy lakes and across rivers. Once caught, the prey's throat would be ripped out and usually blood and rich organs such as the heart and liver eaten first.

The Tasmanian tiger thrived with the arrival of sheep. Apart from being a pushover to catch, sheep were a nice change in diet after 100,000 years of eating the same old marsupials. They were to regret this predilection for sheep.

Sadly, very little scientific research has been done on the thylacine. We know that their sheltered dens were established in caves or under impenetrably thick vegetation. Sometimes hollow logs or trees were used. The female had litters of up to four that were nursed in her pouch for about 5 months. The pouch opened backwards rather than forwards, as with most marsupials. This is clever as it would perhaps prevent the young from getting a face full of dirt if they stuck their head out when Mum was in hot pursuit of that night's dinner. It is believed they would stay with their parents for at least 1 year learning the tricks of the trade.

Fleay described the sound of its 'creaking bark' as neither like a cat nor a dog. He recalled how one night, as they sat beside the fire, 'there came from an adjacent high hillside, a most extraordinary cry. It suggested the brief sharp creak of a door and was quite unlike any cry of a mammal or bird I have ever heard.'

Although the thylacine is known as a fastidious

eater, bushmen knew that it had a special fondness for bacon. Oldtimers told of the creature's habit of thieving bacon that was left around camps and of licking out frying pans. In earlier times, live specimens had been caught in box traps using bacon. Fleay's 1945 expedition had no luck with bacon or a variety of other seemingly attractive baits. The one time the thylacine entered the special trap, it had been lured in by a small Bennett wallaby. Two nights later the visitor, or one of its kind, returned near the traps and was identified by its classic footprints and droppings of the type that oldtime bushmen had described.

Fleay described the creature's footprints as un-dog-like, superficially resembling an imprint of a wombat's front foot. The thylacine's forepaw is typically round and some 7 cm in diameter. Five long clawed digits, well indented, are spaced and visible, not being obscured by prominent pads (as in the case of the dog). The two main cushioned pads, one large and the other small, leave no strong impression and form a rough crescent at the base of the digits around the palm.

It seems thylacines only attacked people when they were defending their young, cornered or held in captivity. Zoo keepers found them to be almost as bad tempered as those fat little bundles of teeth and piggy eyes, the Tasmanian devils (*Sarcophilus harrisii*); both have bone-crunching jaws. (Incidentally a possible reason why remnants of dead tigers have not been found is the eating habits of these little devils.)

Before the arrival of Aboriginal people, the thylacines ruled supreme at the head of the food chain (except in areas where crocodiles were found). Competition with people for food was uneven because the former had the advantage of both weapons and fire. Dingoes worsened the odds for mainland thylacines.

The white settlers in Tasmania were not raising their sheep to feed the thylacines. Systematic shooting and indiscriminate trapping took an enormous toll on their numbers. Early in the 20th century the extermination process reached its peak with as many as 5000 thylacines destroyed.

One theory advanced from time to time is that thylacines may have been decimated by some infectious disease. The gloomy suggestion that perhaps a virus may have been carried into the deepest recesses of forests and polished off all non-immune thylacines must be given some credence.

In 1930 the last known wild thylacine was shot at Mawbanna in Tasmania's north-west.

Photographs show it was a magnificently long and lean animal that was surprisingly run down by the sheep farmer's small dog. This grand finale was unusual because dogs almost invariably would avoid an encounter with a Tasmanian tiger; on picking up its scent they would retreat in haste, their tail between their legs. Horses also became very nervous in the vicinity of this creature.

Is the thylacine extinct? The answer would be yes were it not for the vast areas of barely penetrable and heavily forested areas in Tasmania. The countless unexplored hectares would remain an ideal habitat for this cautious and skilful hunter.

In 1966 zoologists made an exciting study on the north-west coast a few kilometres away from where the last thylacine was shot in 1930. They found a lair inside an old boiler from a wrecked ship, and concluded that it had been used by a female thylacine and her pups. For many years this north-western part of Tasmania has been the area of most thylacine sightings, the most recent sighting in January 1995 being an exception.

The nice thing about thylacines is that no one can prove they do not exist. Unlike fairies at the bottom of the garden and the Loch Ness monster, we know they did exist because men have shot them.

First aid and medical management

If someone is bitten by a thylacine, please refrain from retaliating in case some injury is done to the animal. Make soothing sounds and offer it bacon scraps, your lunch or anything else it might fancy. If the wound is bleeding profusely, apply pressure. The injuries should be treated as potentially contaminated. Tetanus prophylaxis should be updated. The victim and witnesses should secure television rights for their story as soon as possible.

First aid

The pressure–immobilisation technique was developed from research into first aid for snakebite. The technique replaced the older, dangerous types of first aid in Australia and a number of other countries. The technique also immobilises other types of venom and is the standard first aid method for all bites and stings in Australia except for:

- bites by red-back spiders and Australian paralysis ticks: and
- stings by jellyfish, stinging fish, platypuses, ants, bees and wasps.

The pressure–immobilisation technique

Venom is usually deposited subcutaneously, and its systemic spread largely depends on its absorption via the lymphatic system or small blood vessels. Lymph production is markedly reduced by immobilising the limb, and its central movement is easily retarded by a constrictive bandage at pressures less than either arterial or venous pressure.

Thus the application of pressure to the bitten area, combined with immobilisation of the limb, effectively delays the central movement of venom. Firm crepe bandages are ideal for this purpose, and panty hose are satisfactory. These should be applied at the same pressure as to a sprained ankle, and the entire limb should be splinted. This effective first aid is simple and easily taught. In practice, strips of clothing and a splint made of any rigid object can be used in most cases.

There are a number of advantages of this method. First, the crepe bandages are comfortable and do not damage the limb, and may be left on for hours if necessary. Second, if a snakebite victim reaches hospital desperately ill because of inadequate first aid, bandaging of the leg will slow further venom absorption and allow the doctor to deal with the venom already in the blood stream. Third, since

at least 95 per cent of snakebites occur on the arms or legs, first aid is applicable to most cases.

Valid first aid measures may be summarised as follows:

1. Immediately apply a firm bandage over the bitten limb and the length of the limb if possible.
2. Immobilise the affected limb. Keep the victim still.
3. Reassure the victim and transport him or her safely and without panic to the nearest hospital.
4. Do not incise or excise the bitten area.
5. Do not wash the bitten area so that hospital staff can later identify the venom and thus determine which antivenom to use (the venom will not be absorbed anyway).
6. If possible, alert the hospital because urgent treatment may be required when the victim arrives, especially as deterioration may occur when the restrictive bandage is released.

When the victim is admitted to hospital with the first aid measures in place, it is best they are not disturbed until the doctor has assembled the appropriate antivenom and drugs that may be needed when the dressings and splints are removed. If a swab of the bitten area is required for venom detection, the dressing over the bite should be quickly cut away and fresh bandages applied after the swab is taken.

If the victim collapses after the release of the first aid measures, the bandages may be temporarily replaced to retard further venom movement while the circulating venom is neutralised with antivenom.

However, as a general rule, the first aid to the bitten limb of snakebite victims should usually be abandoned soon after the patient's admission to hospital. Unfortunately, often patients may be admitted and left in bed for many hours with the first aid measures undisturbed.

The pressure–immobilisation technique—FOR LEG BITES

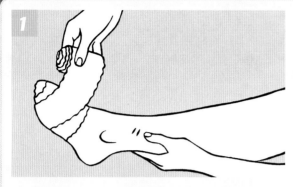

Starting from the toes put a broad firm bandage around the bitten area. Don't take off any clothes like jeans but cut the seams if they can't be pushed out of the way, and keep the leg as still as possible while you are bandaging.

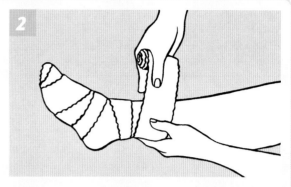

Make the bandage as tight as for a sprained ankle.

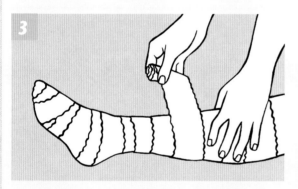

Bangage as much of the leg as possible, especially the toes.

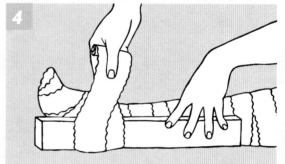

Put a splint beside the bandage and bind that to the leg to help keep the leg still.

Once the patient has reached medical care, it is no longer appropriate to retard venom movement.

Exceptions to the pressure–immobilisation technique

Ants, bees and wasps
The pressure–immobilisation technique should only be used if the victim is highly allergic to ant, bee and wasp stings. The technique will retard the movement of the venom while the patient is taken to medical care. If breathing and/or the heart stops, give cardio-pulmonary resuscitation and get medical help.

For non-allergic people, though, the pressure–immobilisation technique may prolong the pain of the sting. Instead, remove the insect and, in the case of a bee, the sting and attached venom sac from the wound as quickly as possible and apply a plastic bag containing iced water.

Australian paralysis ticks
The tick or ticks should be gently removed as soon as possible. Curved scissors are ideal to lever the tick out. Do not squeeze the tick, or use kerosene or other irritants, as the tick may release more toxin. If the patient is feeling ill and the bite was to a limb, apply the pressure–immobilisation technique after the tick has been removed.

Red-back spiders
Restrictive bandages should not be applied because this venom moves slowly and any attempt to retard

The pressure–immobilisation technique— FOR HAND OR ARM BITES

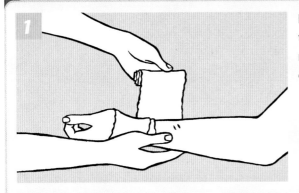

Put a broad firm bandage around the bitten area up to the elbow. Start from the fingers and bandage as much of the arm as possible. Make sure the victim can still bend the elbow.

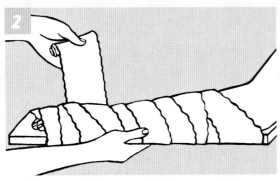

Put a splint under the arm and bind it to the arm.

Put the arm in a sling.

its spread further increases pain. While no first aid is required, the victim should seek medical help immediately, taking the spider in a jar for identification. Pain can be reduced by applying a plastic bag containing iced water, but be careful not to freeze the skin.

Box jellyfish
Before trying to remove any tentacles adhering to the skin, pour vinegar or dilute acetic acid—but never spirits or other types of alcohol—over the tentacles to inactivate them. You must inactivate the tentacles first or else your efforts will simply trigger off more stinging capsules.

Take the victim to a hospital for treatment with box jellyfish antivenom. If breathing and/or the heart stops give cardiopulmonary resuscitation and summon medical help.

Irukandji and jimble
Apply vinegar or dilute acetic acid to the stung area and see a doctor if the reaction is severe.

Bluebottle and sea blubber
Do not use vinegar to remove tentacles. Instead, apply a plastic bag filled with iced water to the stung area.

Platypus
Ice and water may provide some pain relief, but most patients will need to see a doctor to administer painkillers.

Stinging fish
Pain relief is most effectively controlled by a medical practitioner as local anaesthetic and/or opiates may be needed in severe cases.

If no medical help is available, bathe the wound in hot water—but not hot enough to scald the skin. This will increase local blood flow and thus disperse the venom.

Antivenom will be needed for severe stonefish stings.

Cardiopulmonary resuscitation

Cardiopulmonary resuscitation should be attempted if a victim's breathing and/or heart is failing.

Place the victim flat on his or her back on a hard surface. Tilt the head back so that the chin is pointing up. Look, listen and feel for signs that the victim is breathing.

If the victim is not breathing, begin mouth-to-mouth resuscitation with five slow breaths to make the chest rise and fall.

Check for a pulse in the neck. If a pulse is absent, begin external cardiac compression. Depress the lower half of the sternum one-third of the depth of the chest at a rate of 100/min (five times in 3 seconds).

Cardiopulmonary resuscitation in basic life support

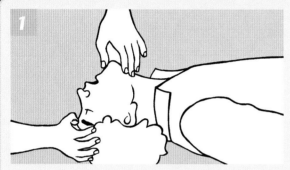

Send for help. Place the victim flat on the back on a hard surface. Lift up the jaw. Look, listen and feel for breathing.
- Look at the chest.
- Listen for breathing sounds.
- Feel for breath.

If the victim is not breathing, begin expired air resuscitation (mouth-to-mouth or nose breathing) —5 slow breaths to make the chest rise and fall, then ...

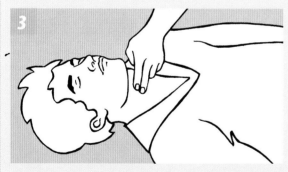

Check the pulse in the neck. If the pulse is absent, begin external cardiac compression. Depress the lower half of the sternum (breast bone) one-third the depth of the chest at a rate of 100/minute (5 times in 3 seconds).

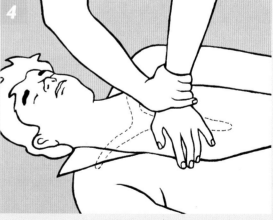

Combine external cardiac compression and expired air resuscitation in a ratio of 5:1 (5 compressions then 1 breath in 5 seconds) for babies and children, but in a ratio of 15:2 for adults (15 compressions then 2 breaths in 15 seconds) where there are one or two rescuers. Continue uninterupted until trained assistance arrives.

Combine external cardiac compression and mouth-to-mouth resuscitation in a ratio of 5:1 (five compressions followed by one breath every 5 seconds) for babies and children, and a ratio of 15:2 (15 compressions followed by two breaths every 15 seconds) for adults. Continue this uninterrupted until medical help arrives.

Doctors' guide to antivenom usage

Envenomations tend to be unexpected events, and a massive envenomation by an Australian snake will rapidly produce a critical illness requiring swift and decisive treatment. As a consequence, information on antivenoms is often requested as a matter of great urgency. In retrospect, many cases of envenomation would have been better handled had those attending the patient been better informed. Fortunately, in most cases antivenoms are not required and in a vast majority of the others antivenom treatment is highly successful.

Antivenoms are the only specific therapy available to reverse the effects of the potentially fatal Australian animal toxins. More than 600 Australians receive antivenoms each year, and without this therapy perhaps 40 might die, hundreds would need prolonged hospitalisation and many would be left with sequelae. Thus the economic benefits alone far outweigh the relatively minuscule cost of antivenom research.

This chapter will hopefully assist in the prompt and effective administration of antivenom and thus the reversal or prevention of the effects of venoms. The information is regularly sought by doctors, pharmacists and paramedics.

Indications for antivenom

Usually it is quite clear whether or not antivenom is required at a particular time. In the case of spider and snakebite, any evidence of significant systemic spread of venom is an indication for antivenom, and the sooner it is given the better. Indications may take the form of signs and symptoms and/or positive laboratory tests. Modest regional lymphadenopathy alone is not a definite indication for antivenom.

In the case of marine injuries due to stonefish or box jellyfish, significant local effects alone may warrant antivenom therapy.

After bites by either snakes or spiders, the presence of fang marks alone is not an indication for antivenom therapy. The clinician must have evidence that the creature has introduced sufficient venom into the victim to warrant specific treatment.

Selection of antivenom

The accompanying guide to antivenom use in Australia (see page 194) indicates the appropriate antivenoms that may have to be used. In the case

Expert help

Details of the management of some of the uncommon complications of say, snakebite, are beyond the scope of this book. The reader is referred to the sources of further information on page 200. Remember also that instructions on usage accompany each unit of antivenom. Medical practitioners and veterinarians can seek expert advice of the Australian Venom Research Unit directly on (03) 9483 8204 or via the Poison Information Centres (13 1126 Australia-wide). The Unit provides a 24-hour service.

of snakebite, Venom Detection Kits (VDK) often reduce the need to use combined antivenoms or large volume polyvalent antivenom when the identity of the offending snake is not known.

If the identity of the type of offending creature is unknown then skilful diagnostic work may be required to successfully select the correct antivenom. The usual problem is to decide if the critter was a snake, a spider or neither. Snake VDKs are very useful, as is the fact that clotting disturbances are unlikely after spider bites. Usually red-back and funnel-web spider bites produce illnesses that are easily diagnosed. If the possibility of tick paralysis is considered, the offending animal or animals can easily be found in almost all cases.

Box jellyfish and stonefish stings are usually self-evident, but injuries by unidentified marine creatures can muddy the diagnostic waters. If the patient is suffering and there is a fair chance the antivenom may be helpful, then give it.

Route of administration

The intravenous (IV) route should be used in all seriously ill victims. Snake antivenoms are always given by this route because of the volume involved and the slow absorption if injected intramuscularly (IM). The IV route has been used in all 100 or so patients that have received the funnel-web antivenom since it became available in 1980. This record reflects the speed of onset of the envenomation and the need for rapid therapy. On the other hand, red-back spider antivenom is usually given IM because it is of small volume and the illness is slow developing.

Antivenom should not be injected around the injured area or into wounds.

Indications for further antivenom

Should the clinical response be poor or actually worsen, then more antivenom is indicated. Sometimes there will be an improvement over the first hour or so after antivenom and then deterioration occurs as more venom is absorbed from the bitten area. The amount of injected venom is always unknown and it is best to be on the safe side and to give extra antivenom if there is any doubt. In the case of a persistent coagulopathy after snakebite, additional antivenom should be given before infusion of fresh frozen plasma is considered.

Delayed administration of antivenom

As a general rule there is little point in antivenom administration 3 days after the envenomation occurred. The earlier antivenom is given the more effective it will be and fewer ampoules will usually be required.

Red-back spider antivenom is the exception to the above rule. A surprising finding is that red-back spider envenomations have responded to initial antivenom therapy as late as 2 weeks after the bite occurred. There is some evidence that benefit has been obtained by even later antivenom administration.

Administration of antivenoms

As described below, antivenoms are currently raised in animals and are associated with adverse reactions that at times have been fatal. Since 1976, specific recommendations to minimise reactions to antivenom have been enclosed with all CSL antivenoms. When these recommendations have been closely followed, the incidence of immediate life-threatening reactions has been markedly reduced. (The reader may consult the relevant leaflets or further reading on page 200.)

The following is a summary:
- Antivenoms should only be administered by physicians and in a situation where resuscitation facilities are on hand and tested. (The exception is the very rare remote area rescue operation.)
- Loaded syringes with adrenaline (1 mg in 1 mL), antihistamine and steroids should be at hand.
- Oxygen and appropriate airways and suction apparatus must be tested and ready for immediate use. Prior skin testing or conjunctival sensitivity testing is not recommended. Such tests are unreliable and delay specific treatment.
- Antivenoms that are to be infused IV should be diluted in 1:10 Hartmann's solution.
- Before IV antivenom, most patients should

receive subcutaneous (SC) adrenaline (0.25 mg for an adult and 0.01 mg/kg for a child). Appropriate doses of antihistamines may also be given. Patients could be told that the adrenaline may make them feel 'jumpy' for a few minutes. (*Note*: the use of IV adrenaline has never been recommended as pre-medication. Hypertensive episodes induced by IV adrenaline may lead to cerebral haemorrhage in snakebite victims.)

- Five minutes after the adrenaline premedication, the infusion of diluted antivenom can cautiously begin. After a few minutes it may be increased.
- Should a reaction occur, the infusion should be temporarily stopped and the premedication repeated. Usually any such reactions are quite mild and should not delay the recommencement of the life-saving infusion. If the infusion is reaction-free, as it usually is, premedication is not required before the administration of additional ampoules of antivenom.

Delayed serum sickness

Delayed serum sickness is surprisingly rare after the use of Australian antivenoms. Perhaps 1 per cent of those receiving the small volume red-back spider antivenom suffer this illness, which usually responds dramatically to prompt steroid therapy. On the other hand, at least 10 per cent of people receiving polyvalent snake antivenom succumb to this immunological response to the challenge of the foreign protein. Experience over the past 20 years suggests that if patients receiving the larger volume antivenoms are commenced on a short course (4–5 days) of corticosteroids, the incidence and severity of this illness is markedly reduced. Prednisolone 50 mg (adult dose) is recommended each day for 5 days after the administration of antivenoms.

Volumes of antivenoms

Each ampoule of antivenom is designed to neutralise the average output of venom from a particular creature. For example, an ampoule of tiger snake antivenom contains 3000 units of antivenom activity in 7 mL of a 17 per cent protein solution. This will neutralise the average output of a tiger snake, which is about 30 mg of venom. Polyvalent snake antivenom, on the other hand, has to neutralise the average output of the five important types of Australian snakes and its volume is usually about 40 mL. This is the largest volume antivenom in the world, and is also the most expensive. Some of the other antivenoms are relatively minuscule in comparison. For example, the red-back spider antivenom is 1.0 mL and stonefish antivenom is 2.0 mL.

Cost of antivenoms

Antivenoms have steadily risen in price over the years. For many years hospitals ordered quantities and types of antivenom that were considered necessary for them to stock. They would then be reimbursed by the Commonwealth Government. A few years ago this system changed and hospitals had to pay for antivenoms from their own budgets. There was an immediate 50 per cent fall in the sale of antivenoms. Some hospitals ceased to hold any antivenoms while others modified the number and range of antivenoms they held. The shelf life of antivenoms is 3 years and stocks dwindled as ampoules reached their expiration dates. This reduction in the availability of antivenom resulted in suboptimal management of some patients. (Incidentally, expired snake antivenoms are usually welcomed by veterinarians provided they have been stored correctly [see below] because the cost of antivenoms is unaffordable for many pet owners, particularly if multiple doses are required.)

Red-back antivenom is available as a pharmaceutical benefit. Surprisingly only a handful of prescriptions are processed each year and hundreds of vials are bought directly by hospitals.

Manufacture of antivenoms

Most antivenoms involve the immunisation of horses. After plasma is harvested, a complicated purification procedure results in a product consisting only of modified antibody components. The only antivenoms that are not of equine origin are box jellyfish antivenom (sheep), tick antitoxin (dog) and funnel-web antivenom (rabbit).

Storage of antivenoms

Antivenoms should be stored at 2–8°C and protected from light. Liquid antivenoms should not be frozen.

Incorrect storage of antivenoms

Two storage problems frequently arise. One is when antivenoms are exposed to ambient temperatures for lengthy periods. This may follow the temporary breakdown of a refrigerator or when they are accidentally left out after a fridge has been defrosted. A few hours at moderate room temperature may do no harm but exposure to higher temperatures will accelerate loss of antivenom activity.

The other problem is the accidental freezing of antivenoms. This will lower their activity and possibly make them unsafe for IV use. Sometimes a situation has arisen where such antivenoms have had to be used. The advice has been to use in-line filters and larger quantities.

Incorrectly stored antivenoms have to be replaced but situations may warrant a bending of the rules. If an antivenom has been stored incorrectly but is crystal clear, it should be reasonably safe to use. The same may apply to expired antivenoms in an emergency.

Quantity of antivenom to be held by hospitals

Metropolitan and regional centres should hold adequate antivenom to cover two serious cases of envenomation by the major snakes found in that state (i.e. four ampoules of each monovalent antivenom). Except in southern Victoria and Tasmania, four ampoules of polyvalent antivenom should be held for the treatment of cases in which the snake has not been positively identified. In Victoria, polyvalent antivenom is not required for local snakes and a combination of tiger snake antivenom and brown snake antivenom can be employed when the identity of the snake has not been determined. In Tasmania only tiger snake antivenom is required.

Small centres and single-doctor hospitals, as a general rule, should hold sufficient antivenom to treat one serious case of snakebite. The decision is up to the local practitioner as to whether two ampoules of polyvalent antivenom should be held or two ampoules of each of the appropriate monovalent antivenoms. If a small centre treats a significant number of snakebites each year, the quantity of antivenoms should be increased. Alternatively, if snakebite is rare in the area and a large hospital can be reached within 30 minutes, then it is probably inappropriate to stock polyvalent antivenoms.

FIRST AID

Guide to antivenom use in Australia

LAND SNAKES

Creature	Antivenom of choice	Initial dose (units)
Bandy-bandy or ringed snake (*Vermicella annulata*)	Tiger snake?	3000
Bardick (*Echiopsis curta*)	Very unlikely antivenom required Death adder first choice?	6000
Black whip snake (*Demansia atra*)	Tiger snake	3000
Black-bellied swamp or marsh snake (*Hemiaspis signata*)	Tiger snake?	3000
Blue-bellied or spotted black snake (*Pseudechis guttatus*)	Tiger snake*	3000
Broad-headed snake (*Hoplocephalus bungaroides*)	Tiger snake	3000
Brown snake, the common eastern (*Pseudonaja textilis*)	Brown snake	1000
Brown-headed snake (*Glyphodon tristis*)	Preliminary work suggests no existing Australian antivenom gives protection	
Chappell Island tiger snake (see tiger snakes)		
Clarence River or rough-scaled snake (*Tropidechis carinatus*)	Tiger snake	3000
Collared brown snake (*Pseudonaja modesta*)	Brown snake	1000
Collett's snake (*Pseudechis colletti*)	Tiger snake*	3000
Copperhead (*Austrelaps superbus*)	Tiger snake	3000
Death adder (*Acanthophis antarcticus, A. praelongus* and *A. pyrrhus*)	Death adder	6000
De Vis' banded snake (*Denisonia devisii*)	Tiger snake?	3000
Dugite (*Pseudonaja affinis*)	Brown snake	1000 (2000?)
Fierce, small-scaled snake or western Taipan (*Oxyuranus microlepidotus*)	Taipan	12,000
Grey snake (*Hemiaspis damelli*)	Tiger snake?	3000
Gwardar (*Pseudonaja nuchalis*)	Brown snake	1000 (2000?)

Creature	Antivenom of choice	Initial dose (units)
Ingram's brown snake (*Pseudonaja ingrami*)	Brown snake	1000
King brown or mulga snake (*Pseudechis australis*)	Black snake	18,000
Pale-headed snake (*Hoplocephalus bitorquatus*)	Tiger snake	3000
Red-bellied black snake (*Pseudechis porphyriacus*)	Tiger snake*	3000
Rough-scaled snake (see Clarence River snake)		
Small-eyed snake (*Cryptophis nigrescens*)	Tiger snake	3000
Speckled brown snake (*Pseudonaja guttata*)	Brown snake	1000
Stephen's banded snake (*Hoplocephalus stephensi*)	Tiger snake	3000
Taipan (*Oxyuranus scutellatus*)	Taipan	12,000
Tiger snakes:		
Chappell Island tiger snake (*Notechis ater serventyi*)	Tiger snake	12,000
Eastern or mainland tiger snake (*Notechis scutatus*)	Tiger snake	3000
Tasmanian tiger snake (*Notechis ater*)	Tiger snake	6000
Western Australian tiger snake (*Notechis ater occidentalis*)	Tiger snake	3000
All other tiger snakes	Tiger snake	3000
Western taipan (see Fierce snake)		
Whip snakes (see Black whip snake and Yellow-faced whip snake)		
Yellow-faced whip snake (*Demansia psammophis*)	Tiger snake	3000

*Tiger snake antivenom is preferrable to the larger volume black snake antivenom.

A STATE-BY-STATE GUIDE TO ANTIVENOM SELECTION WHEN THE IDENTITY OF THE OFFENDING SNAKE IS UNCERTAIN**

State	Antivenom of choice	Initial dose (units)
Tasmania	Tiger snake	6000
Victoria	Tiger snake	3000
	AND brown snake	1000
All other states	Polyvalent	1 ampoule

**Venom Detection Kits have improved the situation but sometimes time factors and/or negative or confusing findings necessitate selection on a state basis.

SEA SNAKES

CSL Ltd sea snake antivenom is raised by immunising horses with both beaked sea snake (*Enhydrina schistosa*) venom and also mainland tiger snake (*Notechis scutatus*) venom. The inclusion of the latter venom gives considerable paraspecificity. The resultant antivenom is known to neutralise the sea snake venoms listed below and most probably others not yet tested. If sea snake antivenom is not available, tiger snake antivenom may be used as an alternative.

Creature	Antivenom of choice	Initial dose (units)
Blue-banded sea snake (*Hydrophis cyanocinctus*)	Sea snake	1000
Disteria major (Major's sea snake)	Sea snake	1000
Elegant sea snake (*Hydrophis elegans*)	Sea snake	1000
Hardwick's sea snake (*Lapenis hardwickii*)	Sea snake	1000
Olive-brown sea snake (*Aipysurus laevis*)	Sea snake	1000
Sea krait (*Laticauda semifasciata*)	Sea snake	1000
Stoke's sea snake (*Astrotia stokesii*)	Sea snake	1000

SPIDERS AND TICKS

In recent years, knowledge of the distribution and classification of funnel-web spiders has expanded dramatically but the neutralising ability of the antivenom has not been explored further since its release in 1980. A systematic assessment of its effectiveness against all available funnel-web spider venoms is long overdue. Fortunately no significant envenomations have followed bites by the generally smaller funnel-web spiders found in Victoria, eastern Tasmania and rarely in South Australia. However, the clinical course of some funnel-web bites in New South Wales suggests that the ability of the antivenom to neutralise the particular venom involved may not be optimal.

Creature	Antivenom of choice	Initial dose (units)
Red-back spider (*Latrodectus hasselti*)	Red-back spider	500
Northern tree funnel-web (*Hadronyche formidabilis*)	Funnel-web	250
Sydney funnel-web spider (*Atrax robustus*)	Funnel-web	250
Toowoomba or Darling Downs funnel-web (*H. infensa*)	Funnel-web	250
Mouse spiders (Genus *Missulena*)	Funnel-web	250
Australian paralysis tick (*Ixodes holocyclus*)	Tick antitoxin (Only to be used in cases of significant paralysis)	1 ampoule

MARINE ANTIVENOMS (OTHER THAN SEA SNAKES)

Creature	Antivenom of choice	Initial dose (units)
Box jellyfish or sea wasp (*Chironex fleckeri*)	Box jellyfish	20,000
Chiropsalmus quadrigatus (no common name)	Box jellyfish	20,000
Stonefish:		
Estuarine stonefish (*Synanceia trachynis*)	Stonefish	1 ampoule
Reef stonefish (*S. verrucosa*)	Stonefish	1 ampoule
Indian stonefish (*S. horrida*) (Believed not found in Australian waters)	Stonefish antivenom probably effective	1 ampoule

ANTIVENOMS AWAITING DEVELOPMENT

Antivenoms would be most useful in the management of envenomations by the following creatures:

- some common spiders, especially the white-tailed spider (*Lampona cylindrata*) and the black house spider (*Badumna insignis*);
- the platypus (*Ornithorhynchus anatinus*);
- venomous cone shells (especially *Conus geographus* and *C. textile*);
- jellyfish, especially the Irukandji (*Carukia barnesi*); and
- common blue-ringed octopus (*Hapalochlaena maculosa*) and the tropical blue-ringed octopus (*H. lunulata*)

ALLERGY TO ANTS

Hundreds of people in Australia suffer anaphylactic reactions following stings by jumper or jack-jumper ants (*Myrmecia pilosula*) and/or bull ants (*M. pyriformis*). Doctors frequently request advice on treatment and ask if antivenom is available. An antivenom would not be an appropriate treatment. As with other venom allergies, patients should be issued with an injectable form of adrenaline and instructed in its use. Unlike the case with bee venom allergy, no purified Australian ant venom is available for immunotherapy of these patients to reduce their allergic status. A project that was proceeding satisfactorily towards such a preparation at CSL Ltd ceased in 1994 when Commonwealth funding was not renewed.

Glossary

Anamnestic reaction: the body recalls previous exposure to a substance.
Anaphylaxis: sudden and life-threatening allergic reaction.
Angio-oedema: swelling in tissues due to fluid escaping from small blood vessels.
Apyrexia: no fever.
Arrhythmia: abnormal heart beat
Aspiration: the act of inhaling a foreign substance or removal of substances from a cavity.

Bilateral upgoing plantars: abnormal reflex reaction of the big toes.
Bronchorrhoea: excessive production of mucus from the lungs.
Bronchospasm: abnormal contraction of the smooth muscle of the lung (e.g. asthma).

Catecholamine: group of compounds which includes adrenaline.
Clonic movement: rapid successive contraction and relaxation of muscles.
Coagulopathy: disorder of blood clotting.
Consumptive coagulopathy: coagulopathy in which a blood clotting component, fibrinogen, is consumed.
CSL: Commonwealth Serum Laboratories
Cyanosis: bluish discolouration of the skin.

Debridement: removal of dead tissues or foreign material from wounds.
Defibrinate: breakdown of fibrin, a clotting protein in the blood.
Desquamation: shedding of skin.
Digitalis: drug derived from the purple foxglove, beneficial to the heart.
Diplopia: double vision.
Diuresis: passing large amounts of urine.
Dyspnoea: difficult breathing.
Dysuria: painful or difficult urination.

Erythaema: abnormal redness of the skin caused by inflammation.

Fasciculation: twitching of muscles visible through the skin.
Fibrinogen: blood protein which forms clots when converted to fibrin.
Fundi: the rear of the interior of the eyes.

Gastric dilation: distended stomach.

Haematuria: presence of blood in the urine.
Haemodialysis: removal of waste products from the blood by causing them to diffuse across a membrane.

Haemolysis: destruction of red blood cells.
Haemorrhage: bleeding.
Hepato-pancreas: liver-pancreas
Hygroscopic: attracting moisture.
Hypertension: high blood pressure.
Hyperventilation: abnormally rapid or deep breathing, over-breathing.
Hypervolaemia: abnormal increase in volume of circulating blood.
Hypotension: low blood pressure.
Hypoxia: insufficient oxygen in the tissues.

Ichthyotoxicosis: poisoning caused by eating fish.
IgE: immunoglobulin (antibody) associated with the development of allergy.
IgG: immunoglobulin (antibody) associated with the development of an immune response
Immunotherapy: broad term, covers immunisation, desensitisation with allergens, immunosuppression, etc.
Infarct: death of tissue due to lack of oxygen (e.g. myocardial infarct = heart attack).
Integument: covering (e.g. skin).
Intercostal recession: abnormal drawing in of the tissues between the ribs during breathing.

Lachrymation: production of tears.
Lavage: irrigation or washing out of an organ.
LD$_{50}$: dose that is lethal for 50 per cent of the test subjects. A measure of toxicity.
Lymphadenopathy: inflammation of the lymph nodes.

Myalgia: pain in muscle or muscles.
Myocarditis: inflammation of the muscular walls of the heart.
Myoglobin: oxygen-transporting pigment of muscle.
Myoglobinaemia: the presence of myoglobin in the blood.
Myoglobinuria: the presence of myoglobin in the urine.
Myolysis: breakdown of muscle tissue.

Necrosis: death of tissue or organ.
Nematocyst: minute stinging structure containing venom and an inverted thread.
Nephrotic syndrome: a kidney disease.
Neurotoxin: a toxin that poisons or destroys nerve tissue.
Normotension: normal blood pressure.

Oedema: presence of abnormal amounts of fluid in tissue.
Opisthotonus: type of spasm in which the head and heels are bent backwards whilst the body is bowed forward.

Ovipositor: organ at the end of the abdomen through which eggs are deposited.

Papules: small, pointed elevations of the skin

Parenteral: taken into the body by a route other than the digestive tract.

Pathognomonic: sign or symptom on which a diagnosis can be made.

Pharynx: back of mouth.

Photophobia: intolerance of light.

Piloerection: erection of the hair (goose flesh).

Platelets: tiny structures in the blood which are involved in coagulation.

Polyvalent: able to neutralise a number of different venoms.

Postsynaptic: distal to a synapse (e.g. the muscle-side of the junction between a nerve and its muscle).

Presynaptic: proximal to a synapse.

Procoagulant: tending to cause clotting of the blood.

Prostration: extreme physical weakness, collapse.

Prothrombin: one of the factors involved in blood clotting.

Pruritis: itching.

Ptosis: lowering of the upper eyelid.

Pyrexia: fever.

RAST: radioallergosorbent test (measures level of IgE in serum).

Renal: of the kidney.

Rhabdomyolysis: breakdown of muscle.

Serosanguinous fluid: mixture of serum and blood.

Stridor: a loud sound made on breathing associated with large airways obstruction.

Synapse: a junction between cells across which signals are transmitted (e.g. nerve and muscle cells).

Systemic effects: affecting the whole body (not just local).

Tachycardia: heart rate over 100/minute.

Tachypnoea: rapid breathing.

Tetanic spasm: sustained uncontrolled muscle contractions as seen in tetanus.

Thrombocytopaenia: fall in the number of platelets.

Thromboplastin time: laboratory coagulation test.

Tubular necrosis: death of kidney tubules.

Urticaria: allergic skin condition with itchy weals (hives).

Vasoconstriction: constriction of blood vessels.

Vasodilation: dilation of blood vessels.

Vasospasticity: spasm of blood vessels.

Vesicles/vesicular: small blisters.

Voluntary muscle: muscle that can be contracted at will.

Weal: small itching or burning swelling on the skin.

Further Reading

Cogger, H. G. (1996) *Reptiles and Amphibians of Australia*. Frenchs Forest, NSW: Reed Books.

Covacevich, J., Davie, P. and Pearn, J. (eds) (1987) *Toxic Plants and Animals: A Guide for Australia*. Brisbane: Queensland Museum.

Edmonds, C. (1989) *Dangerous Marine Creatures*. Frenchs Forest, NSW: Reed Books.

Gow, G. F. (1993) *Graeme Gow's Complete Guide to Australian Snakes*. Sydney: Cornstalk Publishing.

Hawdon, G. and Winkel, K. D. (1997) Venomous marine creatures. *Australian Family Physician* **26**: 1369–74.

Hawdon, G. and Winkel, K. D. (1997) Spider bite: a rational approach. *Australian Family Physician* **26**: 1380–85.

Hawdon, G. and Winkel, K. D. (1997) Could this be snake bite? *Australian Family Physician* **26**: 1386–91.

Mascord, R. (1983) *Australian Spiders in Colour*. Sydney: A. H. & A. W. Reed.

Mirtschin, P. and Davis, R. (1992) *Snakes of Australia: Dangerous and Harmless*. Melbourne: Hill of Content.

Shine, R. (1998) *Australian Snakes: A Natural History*. Australia: Reed Books.

Sutherland, S. K. and Tibballs, J. (in press) *Australian Animal Toxins. The Creatures, their Toxins and Care of the Poisoned Patient*. Melbourne: Oxford University Press.

Sutherland, S. K. and King, K. (1991) *Management of Snakebite in Australia*. Royal Flying Doctor Service of Australia Monograph Series No. 1.

Underhill, D. (1987) *Australia's Dangerous Creatures*. Sydney: Readers' Digest.

Weigel, J. (1990) *Guide to the Snakes of South-East Australia*. Gosford, NSW: Australian Reptile Park.

Williamson, J. A., Fenner, P. J., Burnett, J. W. and Rifkin, J. F. (eds) (1996) *Venomous and Poisonous Marine Animals: A Medical and Biological Handbook*. Sydney: University of New South Wales Press.

Index

A Venomous Life

The Autobiography of

PROFESSOR STRUAN SUTHERLAND

A Venomous Life ...

... 'rolls effortlessly along on Sutherland's droll humour.'
ADRIAN MCGREGOR, *THE AUSTRALIAN*

... 'an entrancing life related by a natural story-teller ... it really is very funny.'
TERRY BROWN, *THE HERALD SUN*

... 'a gem of a book ... required reading for anyone contemplating a career in research.'
MICHAEL WOODHEAD, *AUSTRALIAN DOCTOR*

Published in paperback by Hyland House
ISBN 1 864470 26 7   RRP $29.95
Available from good bookshops anywhere

HYLAND HOUSE